LOGGING BY RAIL

Robert D. Turner

LOGGING BY RAIL

The British Columbia Story

PUBLISHED BY

Sono Nis Press

VICTORIA, BRITISH COLUMBIA

Canadian Cataloguing in Publication Data

Turner, Robert D., 1947-
  Logging by rail

  Includes bibliographical references.
  ISBN 1-55039-018-X
  ISBN 1-55039-065-1

  1. Logging railroads—British Columbia—
History. I. Title.
TF27.B8T87 1989   385′.54′09711   C89-091490-7

FIRST PRINTING: OCTOBER 1990
SECOND PRINTING: FEBRUARY 1991
THIRD PRINTING: JUNE 1995
FOURTH PRINTING: SEPTEMBER 1997

Financially assisted by the Ministry of Municipal Affairs,
Recreation and Culture through the British Columbia
Heritage Trust and British Columbia Lotteries. Also, the
Canada Council Block Grant Program.

JACKET AND FRONTISPIECE ILLUSTRATION: Hillcrest Lumber
Company's Climax No. 9 works a heavy train of logs in the
Cowichan Valley on Vancouver Island.—ROBERT D. TURNER

BACK OF JACKET: The last logging railroad. Canadian Forest
Products diesel locomotives lead a long train to Beaver
Cove on Vancouver Island.—ROBERT D. TURNER

This book was designed at Morriss Printing by Bev Leech.

Published by
SONO NIS PRESS
1725 Blanshard Street, Victoria, B.C., Canada V8W 2J8

PRINTED IN CANADA BY FRIESENS

http://www.islandnet.com/~sononis/
sono.nis@islandnet.com

To Gerry Wellburn

Logger, lumberman, historian, collector, friend and founder
of the British Columbia Forest Museum. More than
anyone else in British Columbia, Gerry saw the importance of
preserving forest history for future generations.

Gerry Wellburn admires a magnificent stand of old-growth Douglas-fir in the Cowichan Valley on Vancouver Island, in 1957.
— GAR LUNNEY PHOTO, NFB, GERRY WELLBURN COLLECTION

PREFACE

My first experience with logging locomotives was as a small boy visiting Ladysmith on a hot summer afternoon in the early 1950s. There, before me, were five steam locomotives and all of them were so very different. Two — both big ones which turned out to be 2-8-2s Nos. 11 and 16 — had steam up and I was told that on Monday morning they would be working again. These were machines to capture the imagination! How on earth did the No. 12, which I later learned was a Shay, actually work? And why did they all have such large smoke stacks? These contraptions, I found out, were spark arresters to help prevent forest fires. Libraries held few clues to understanding these unique pieces of railroad equipment.

Another decade brought enough mobility for me to return to Ladysmith and to visit the Nanaimo Lakes, Chemainus, Crofton, and Mesachie Lake where I had learned there were other steam locomotives still running. Comox Logging had begun using a diesel which, as it turned out, had certain charms of its own. Some years later, I had a chance to ride on this diesel's last run out to the Nanaimo Lakes, an enlightening and deafening experience that will not be forgotten. Gradually, the story of railroad logging came together for me, particularly as I was able to travel further afield in B.C., including visits to the long-abandoned Aero Camp on the Queen Charlottes and the former sites of other operations on Vancouver Island and the Mainland, all quiet now but with a lingering aura of history. At the same time, I learned more about the magnificent forests of British Columbia, their history, geography and ecology. Both the logging railroads and the old-growth forests have become a part of our history. Many details and stories came from searching old records, visiting remote parts of the province and interviewing old-timers, some of whom spent a lifetime in the woods. My aim in this book is to share some of these discoveries and insights, and record them, both for those who are familiar with logging and railroading and for those who are not. These little seen industrial lines are an important part of the transportation history of British Columbia.

This book focuses on the story of railroad logging, the equipment used and the people who used it on a day-to-day basis. The technology itself is fascinating, and the men who worked and maintained the machinery have made a tremendous contribution to the development of British Columbia. I have emphasized the operation of the railroads and the changing patterns of their use, not the individual corporate histories or the broader issues of forest policy and management.

In the span of little more than a lifetime, logging railroads have come and all but gone from British Columbia. The story of the logging railroads begins in an earlier era when the cutting of the old-growth forest was unquestioned; the giant trees were a convenient and important resource and a hindrance to agriculture and settlement. In the 1920s, when railroad logging was at its heyday, few people had any doubts about the use of our forests; to most British Columbians the forests seemed endless and reforestation was not a concern. The story ends in an era of conflicting, sometimes seemingly irreconcilable interests and judgements over the future of our forests. It is an inescapable fact that logging railroad technology, coupled with steam yarding and loading equipment, greatly changed the landscape of British Columbia. Logging in the steam era was both very destructive and highly wasteful. It is a background to this story that is pervasive and one from which we should learn.

One of the great pleasures of exploring history is to meet many kind and interesting people. Many individuals have contributed to this book and my sincere thanks go to: Jean Alsop, Maynard Atkinson, Tom Beaton, the late Fred Bell, Eric Bernard, R. Ken Bradley, Herbert L. Broadbelt, the late Bob Brown, John Buchanan, George Byrnell, the late B. A. "Spike" Carson, Frank Carter, Maurice Chandler, the late Cam Chouinard, the late Tom Coates, Ken Cringan, Mike Cross, Arnold Edwards, May Ellingsen, Albert Farrow, Del Fowler, Fran Fowler, Norman Gidney, Wilmer Gold, Bill Green, Sam Hardy, Elaine Hebda, Owen Hennigar, Richard Herrling, Jim Hope, Mark Horne, Jack Howe, John Illman, Walter Infanti, Richard V. James, Bill and Dorothy Johnstone, Alan Kollman, Peter Locke, Bradley Lockner, the late John Lockner, George Lutz, the late Pete McGovern, Tom MacPherson, Alec Matkoski, Ken Merilees, Warren E. Miller, Tom Murphy, the late Cedric Myers, Jack Payne, the late Onni Parta, the late Albert H. Paull, Bill Presley, Doug Richter, Gordon Robertson, Bill Robinson, Jessie Robson, the late Ted Robson, Charles A. Rogers, Jr., Geoff Rowe, Ken Rutherford, David Scholes, Douglas C. Smith, Fred Smith, Steve Stark, the late Bob Strang, Jessie Sweatnam, Sonny Tolman, Stan Unsworth, Barry and Lou Volkers, Bert Ward, Bob Whetham, Elmer Winton, Wilbur C. Whittaker, Jim Wolverton, Harry Wright, Brian Young and Ken Young. Unfortunately the passage of time has broken contact with some of these friends but my thanks are nonetheless sincere. I hope too that I have not overlooked anyone. Unfortunately, in many collections, the names of some photographers, amateur and professional, are not known and hence their photographs cannot be fully acknowledged.

British Columbia has been fortunate in having a number of excellent commercial photographers who worked in the woods and camps and did so much to record the history of this vast province. These include: Jack Cash, Cam Chouinard, Leonard Frank, Wilmer Gold, Otto Landauer, W. F. Montgomery, and A. A. Paull. As I study their photos and venture to similar locations with my modern photographic gear I never cease to appreciate their work, artistry and perseverance. I have been fortunate to meet or correspond with several of these fine photographers. In particular, the late Otto F. Landauer, of Leonard Frank Photos, himself a very accomplished industrial photographer, went out of his way to be helpful in providing fine original prints of his own and Leonard Frank's work.

Institutions have also helped enormously by making their valued collections accessible and for allowing permission to use the materials in their care. These institutions include: Alberni Valley Museum, Port Alberni; British Columbia Archives and Records Service (BCARS), formerly the Provincial Archives of British Columbia, Victoria; British Columbia Forest Museum, Duncan; British Columbia Forest Service, Victoria; British Columbia Legislative Library, Victoria; Campbell River and District Museum and Archives, Campbell River; Canadian Pacific Corporate Archives, Montreal; David Thompson Library, Nelson; Fernie Historical Society; Fort Steele Heritage Park; Kaatza Station Museum, Lake Cowichan; Kelowna Museum; Ladysmith Railway Historical Society; Nanaimo Centennial Museum; National Archives of Canada (NAC), Ottawa; Nelson Museum; Nicola Valley Museum-Archives, Merritt; Penticton Museum (the R. N. Atkinson Museum); Railway Negative Exchange, Moraga, CA; Royal British Columbia Museum (RBCM), Victoria; Sooke Region Museum and Archives; University of British Columbia Library, Special Collections, Vancouver; City of Vancouver Archives (CVA); Vancouver Public Library (VPL); the City of Victoria Archives; and Vintage Visuals, Calgary.

The staff in the corporate archives and the men and women in many field offices and logging operations of the forest companies (and of their predecessor corporations) have always been helpful in answering questions or in making material available. My thanks go to: B.C. Forest Products Ltd. and Crown Forest Industries (both now part of Fletcher Challenge Canada Ltd.); Canadian Forest Products Ltd. (Canfor Corporation); Hillcrest Lumber Company; MacMillan Bloedel (the MacMillan Bloedel material is now with UBC Library's Special Collections); and Western Forest Industries, for their assistance.

Special thanks are due to my friends and colleagues Peter Corley-Smith and Dave Parker for reading the manuscript and aiding the project in many ways. Bob Griffin provided many leads to information, insights and sources. Elwood White generously provided many of his superb photos from the 1950s. Dave Wilkie and Patrick O. Hind both read the manuscript and made helpful suggestions. Dave Wilkie also shared many of his beautiful photos. I am also especially grateful to Robert E. (Bob) Swanson, former Chief Inspector of Railways in British Columbia. He made a tremendous personal contribution to the development and maintenance of safe, practical logging equipment in British Columbia and to the preservation of steam equipment, and shared with me many interesting stories and insights on railroad logging history.

Gerry Wellburn, to whom this book is dedicated, has provided great support and encouragement. He has spent many hours with me at the Forest Museum or in other locations recalling the history of the forest industry, providing a depth and personality to the story with each recollection. Gerry also made available his notes, photos and other material for my research. Much of this important collection is now in the care of the Royal British Columbia Museum.

A project as extensive as this becomes a family exercise. Special thanks go to my brother Bill and mother Isobel. My wife Nancy brought patience, professionalism and botanical knowledge to this project as a sympathetic editor, scholarly consultant and best friend, which has been invaluable. Our daughters Sarah, Molly and Katie have given great encouragement and understanding.

Finally my friends at Sono Nis Press and the Morriss Printing Company, in particular Dick Morriss, Patricia Sloan and Bev Leech, were always helpful and encouraging. As usual, they made the transformation of my manuscript, maps and photographs into a book a very interesting and pleasurable process.

In the early days of British Columbia's forest industry, bulls and horses skidded the logs to the coast or nearest waterway. — GERRY WELLBURN COLLECTION

PROLOGUE

To early explorers, settlers and loggers, the vast stands of Douglas-fir, Cedar, Spruce and Hemlock must have seemed endless. For many hundreds of miles, they stretched from shorelines to the alpine meadows of the mountains — uncountable millions of trees, many of them giants of eight, ten, or even 15 feet (2.5 to 4.5 metres) in diameter, trees containing a wealth of lumber that were to prove far greater in value than all the gold from all the great gold rushes of British Columbia and the Klondike. Surely the trees would never be exhausted. But today, after just 100 years of mechanized logging, the old-growth stands have all but vanished from large parts of the province.

The forces and processes that contributed to this enormous change to the face of British Columbia — sometimes the total, permanent removal of the forests — are many. Often, logging was thought of as only the first stage in land development leading to settlement and farming. In fact, much of British Columbia's best farm lands were once covered by some of the province's most productive forests. In the Fraser Valley of the Lower Mainland, and the Comox Valley and other parts of Vancouver Island, farmers moved in as the loggers finished. In 1918, the Canadian Commission of Conservation in its report *Forests of British Columbia* noted:

Clearing the land on the coast, where the forests are so heavy and the stumps so large, is a serious handicap to settlement, costing from $100 to $300 per acre. When operations are conducted on a large scale, and machinery is used to haul out the stumps, it can be done much cheaper. Development of the agricultural resources of the province is one of its most imperative needs.... A large increase in the rural population would materially assist in solving the labour problem, especially in the lumber industry.[1]

Even when the forests were regarded as a renewable resource, this conservationist attitude was tempered with the overriding belief that forests and other natural resources had no value in themselves, but only if they could be used by people to generate wealth:

All the efforts of the Dominion must be devoted to production and economy. The vast resources of Canada, to which the term "illimitable" has been so frequently applied, because of lack of knowledge, must be turned to some useful purpose. Untilled fields, buried minerals or standing forests are of no value except for the wealth which, through industry, can be produced therefrom.... Too frequently the forests are considered... [to be]... non reproducible, such as minerals. Beyond question, the best interests of the province, and the Dominion as a whole, demand that this vast area of non-agricultural land be devoted to the systematic production of successive crops of timber.[2]

The value of the forests as wildlife habitats, and as vital reserves for biological and cultural diversity, was scarcely thought of by anyone. Unfortunately, detailed knowledge of forest ecology and the implementation of policies and programs to ensure the long-term production of forest crops lagged decades behind the pace of logging and would have little impact on forest policy until the steam era in the woods was in decline.

The first logging by the early white explorers and settlers was very limited. A few spars to repair ships were cut or land was cleared to make room for farming and to provide wood for structures. Gradually, a small, locally based sawmilling industry developed but by the 1860s and 1870s, there was a growing market for lumber both within British Columbia and for export. Camps were established in prime forest lands to supply the increasing need for saw-logs.

Geologist and naturalist George M. Dawson, of the Geological Survey of Canada, described one of these early logging camps, and the forests themselves, in his diary, dated December 3, 1875:

Decided to return to New Westminster today & so obliged to make a visit to logging camp. Weather fortunately finer. Started at 8 a.m.... on the tug "Jerk" [a makeshift, scow-type side-wheeler powered by a threshing machine engine with a locomotive steam boiler] & got to camp about 9.20. "Camp" rather a permanent affair. A large stable erected for the oxen & Mules, & houses for the men. These on the bank above the shore. Lumbering roads radiating back into the woods in all directions for several miles. Roads well made, & wide, bankes often cut through & ravines bridged to get greater uniformity of grade. Cross pieces imbedded in the road at intervals, & notched in the centre. Oxen tackled to log, which rests on the Cross pieces, man going before with brush & smearing them with dog-fish oil to make the logs run easily. Trees when felled first deprived of bark by chopping. Then sawn up into lengths by hand saw.

Truly magnificent woods. Chiefly of Douglas-fir, but also gigantic cedars, & undergrowth of vine maple &c. Lichens & moss hanging yards long from the lower branches, & long straight clean trunks of the Douglas-firs stretching up fifty or a hundred feet without a branch. The age of the larger pines is very great often I think over 400 or 500 years...[3]

The forest described by George Dawson was typical of the almost unbroken stands which covered much of the lower slopes and valleys all along the British Columbia coast west of the Coast and Cascade mountain ranges. It is classed by modern forest ecologists within the Coastal Western Hemlock Biogeoclimatic Zone, having abundant rainfall and mild temperatures. Large, old-growth Douglas-fir (*Pseudotsuga menziesii*) is characteristic of the drier parts of this zone, but western hemlock (*Tsuga heterophylla*) and amabilis fir (*Abies amabilis*) dominate the areas of medium rainfall. These species, western red-cedar (*Thuja plicata*) and Sitka spruce (*Picea sitchensis*) are found in the moister sites, and, on very wet parts of the west coast, these trees attain tremendous sizes. Red alder (*Alnus rubra*) is a predominant deciduous species, and cottonwood (*Populus balsamifera* ssp. *trichocarpa*), and bigleaf maple (*Acer macrophyllum*) are also common in many parts of this zone, although they do not occur on the Queen Charlotte Islands. Understory shrubs, including salal, several types of blueberries and huckleberries, salmonberry, thimbleberry, wild rose, and devil's club form a dense, almost impenetrable thicket throughout much of this zone, as anyone who has tried to walk through it can attest. Large areas of this lowland forest type, more than any other, was later to be logged using railroads.

The coastal forests of the mild, relatively drier region of the southeast coast of Vancouver Island and the adjacent Gulf Islands, in the rainshadow of the Olympic and Vancouver Island ranges, are classed in the Coastal Douglas-fir Zone. Virtually all of these forests on Vancouver Island were logged by railroad. Douglas-fir is the predominant tree in this zone, with garry oak (*Quercus garryana*) and arbutus, or Pacific madrone (*Arbutus menziesii*) growing on drier sites. Western red-cedar is typical of the wetter sites. Grand fir (*Abies grandis*) also occurs in this zone, and salal and Oregon-grape are common understory shrubs. The Coastal Douglas-fir Zone, sometimes said to have a Mediterranean climate, became some of the most productive agricultural land in British Columbia after it was logged off.

At higher elevations along the Pacific Coast, generally out of reach of the logging railway systems, is the Mountain Hemlock Zone, with mountain hemlock and amabilis fir as dominant trees, and varying amounts of yellow cedar (*Chamaecyparis nootkatensis*). In the upper reaches of this subalpine zone, where the snow pack is heavy, the trees are stunted and clumped, interspersed with meadows. Lower down, the forests are more productive, but the growing season is short and regeneration is slow.

In the interior of the province are several other major forest zones. One that featured in railroad logging was the Interior Cedar—Hemlock Zone, in the lower and middle elevations of the Kootenays, a region often called the Interior Wet Belt. This zone contains the widest variety of coniferous trees of any forest zone in the province. Western red-cedar, western hemlock, and Douglas-fir grow here, as well as western larch (*Larix occidentalis*), western white pine (*Pinus monticola*), lodgepole pine (*Pinus contorta*), Engelmann spruce (*Picea engelmannii*), and subalpine fir (*Abies lasiocarpa*). Cottonwood (*Populus balsamifera*), trembling aspen (*Populus tremuloides*), and birch (*Betula* spp.) are common deciduous species.

Also well penetrated by logging railroads was the Interior Douglas-fir Zone, found at mid-elevations in the dry southern Interior. Stands of Douglas-fir (an interior variety) are dominant, and ponderosa pine (*Pinus ponderosa*) and lodgepole pine are characteristic successional species, after fires or logging. Below the

Interior Douglas-fir Zone, in the dry valley bottoms of the Okanagan, Similka-meen, Columbia, Thompson and Fraser rivers, is the driest, hottest forest zone, the Ponderosa Pine Zone. Ponderosa pine predominates, and Douglas-fir is also found on cooler, moister sites. Some of the trees here were also logged by rail.

Like the coastal subalpine forests, those of the Interior, classed in the Engel-mann Spruce—Subalpine Fir and Montane Spruce zones, were inaccessible to railroad logging technology.

The central and northern forests of the Interior supported only one logging railroad, owned by Eagle Lake Spruce Mills at Giscome near Prince George. This was in the vegetation zone known as Sub-boreal Spruce, with Engelmann spruce and white spruce (*Picea glauca*) and their hybrids, subalpine fir, and lodgepole pine being the most common timber trees. Several other forest zones are recognized by ecologists, but because of the severe climate and short growing season, none is particularly productive. This factor, and the boggy, poorly draining ground, have made logging difficult and railroad logging totally impractical.[4]

Only a few of the tree species mentioned were economically important to the forest industry, especially in the logging railroad era. The prime commercial species were Douglas-fir, western red-cedar, western hemlock, Sitka spruce, and, particularly in the Interior, ponderosa, lodgepole and white pines.

Douglas-fir was the most highly regarded, as shown in the following quotation from a 1929 pamphlet on lumber grading rules for export:

Fir more than any other commercial timber, is the ideal wood for practically all buildings and structural purposes... [It] is practically impervious to water, holds nails firmly, takes stain well in any shade or color, and combines beauty, utility and durability. It is superior wood for bridge and wharf building, heavy joists where great strength is required, studding — in fact all ordinary framing material, ship plank, ship decking, spars, derricks, car sills, car siding, car roofing, car lining, flooring, ceiling, silo stock, sash and doors, interior finish...[5]

So important was Douglas-fir that at least in the early years of logging, the forest industry was highly concentrated in the Coastal Douglas-fir Zone, or in the dry subzone of the Coastal Western Hemlock Zone, where Douglas-fir predominated. Most mills were located on southern Vancouver Island or near Vancouver and New Westminster. In a study of the geography of the forest industry of coastal British Columbia, geographer Walter Hardwick noted, "The almost exclusive demand for Douglas fir by lumber manufacturers encouraged most loggers to operate their camps where Douglas fir predominated, on the land of low elevation around Georgia Strait.... Thus a whole forest industry became based upon the exploitation of a single major species, Douglas fir..."

However, by the early 1900s, other species were becoming increasingly important. Western red-cedar was considered "... unsurpassed by any other wood where durability, lightness of weight or ease of working are essential."[6] It

MacMillan
Bloedel's 1044,
one of the last
active steam
locomotives in
British Columbia,
eases onto
the log dump
at Chemainus
in 1969.
—ROBERT D.
TURNER

was, and still is, valued for exterior siding, decking and porch flooring, trellis work, laths, fences, hothouse frames, shingles and shakes. Additionally, in the early days, flumes, wooden drains, and boats were usually of cedar.

One alternate name for Sitka spruce was "aeroplane spruce," an indication of a particularly important use of this soft and light, yet tough and strong wood. In fact, it was contended that, "In aeroplane construction, Sitka Spruce has proven itself superior to any other wood in the world."[7] During both world wars, Sitka spruce took on great strategic importance for aircraft construction.

Western hemlock (sometimes called Pacific hemlock) was considered almost equal to Douglas-fir for ordinary building purposes. "It is suitable for inside joists, scantling, lath, siding, flooring and ceiling; in fact it is especially adapted to uses requiring ease of working, a handsome finish, or lightness combined with a large degree of strength..."[8]

The pine species, particularly white pine and ponderosa, or yellow pine, were used in construction, for sashes, frames, door mouldings, panelling, and cabinet work. Ponderosa has been considered "...second only to Douglas fir as a timber-producing tree in western North America..."[9] Lodgepole pine, which was logged by rail in the interior of the province, was used in general construction, for railway ties, poles and mine props.[10] Engelmann and white spruce are also valuable lumber species; white spruce has been described as "...one of the most important trees in Canada for pulpwood and lumber," and Engelmann spruce as "one of the most important species in the Interior of British Columbia..."[11] Quantities of these trees logged by rail, however, were apparently relatively small.

One practical consideration in railroad logging was the relative weight of the different woods. In the 1940s, for example, a typical carload of cedar being transported over the E&N from Lake Cowichan to Crofton weighed approximately 30 tons (27 tonnes), whereas a carload of Douglas-fir weighed about 35 tons (32 tonnes), and a carload of hemlock, about 40 tons (36 tonnes).[12]

Early logging in British Columbia, both along the Coast and in the Interior, was a primitive, laborious process. Little other than the brute strength of oxen or power of horses was available to move the logs. Where the timber was intended for milling into lumber, it was a major challenge simply to move the logs over the rugged landscape to processing areas. Sometimes, logs were felled directly into the water or in close enough proximity so that they could be jacked and pulled to the water's edge. Sometimes, as described by Dawson, primitive skid roads were built. Whatever the method used, cutting and moving the logs was tough, dangerous and exhausting labour.

There were several motivations for logging or for the removal of the forest cover. Some men wanted to settle and farm the land. Others, more entrepreneurial, looked for mineral wealth and saw the forests as an encumbrance to their search for treasure. Still others saw the potential for the development of a lumber industry. And a few took time to see the forests as natural wonders of great beauty.

Expanding settlement in North America and a growing potential for the export of prime lumber to many parts of the world led to the development of more and more sawmills in British Columbia and in western North America. Operating those mills required a reliable supply of logs. In the context of late nineteenth and early twentieth century technology, this need led almost inevitably to the use of steam machinery, steam railroads and the incredible variety of inventions and innovations that were developed using steam as a source of energy to haul logs.

Steam power brought a revolution in production methods and working conditions to the woods. It increased production tremendously and eased the work of the loggers. Moreover, it all but eliminated the cruel and dangerous use of bulls for hauling logs and left horses with but a minor role to play. The introduction of steam equipment was slow and faltering at first but by the beginning of the 1900s the use of steam technology had gathered considerable momentum. It would be a major part of the forest industry well into the 1950s and its application is central to the railroad logging story. The story begins, as do so many others, with the construction of the Canadian Pacific Railway through British Columbia in the early 1880s.

MacMillan Bloedel's 1066, just weeks before its last run.
—ROBERT D. TURNER

XVII

Loggers in a classic pose in front of a giant hemlock. Even though work was long and tough, the compensation often minimal, many spent a lifetime in the woods.—MACMILLAN BLOEDEL COLLECTION

CONTENTS

Logging by rail meant building the tracks through wild and often spectacular country. Timber bridges and trestles were essential. West of Chemainus on the Copper Canyon railroad of the Victoria Lumber & Manufacturing Company, the tracks spanned the Chemainus River on this rugged log bridge. The locomotive is No. 4, a machine that worked for 45 years in the Ladysmith and Chemainus regions of Vancouver Island before being preserved. —DAVE WILKIE COLLECTION

By the early 1900s, logging railroads had begun to penetrate the coastal forests of British Columbia. One of the first extensive networks of logging lines was developed by the Comox Logging & Railway Company, originally called the Comox & Campbell Lake Tramway Company. In 1909, this Baldwin 2-6-2 was ordered for a new railway through the fertile, heavily-forested lowlands of the Comox Valley on Vancouver Island.
—LEONARD FRANK, VPL

1 THE FIRST LOGGING LINES IN BRITISH COLUMBIA

Old "Curly" and the First Railroad Logging

Steam railroad logging began in British Columbia during the rapid spread of settlement and industry that characterized the last years of the 1800s. Beginnings were halting and tentative, often little more than a whisper of activity amid the vast wilderness expanses of the coastal forests. Yet it was a powerful, versatile technology and in the course of just a few decades, with its users driven by seemingly insatiable demands for lumber, it would change the face of the province forever.

Exactly when the first logging operation using a railway began in British Columbia may never be known for sure. Photographs indicate clearly that during construction of the Canadian Pacific Railway through British Columbia in the early 1880s workers on the Onderdonk contracts through the Fraser Canyon were using trains to haul logs to the temporary mills needed for the project. The railway needed thousands of ties and enormous quantities of timber for bridges and cribbing. Undoubtedly, similar activity occurred during the construction of the CPR through the Rockies and Selkirks to the east and also on the Esquimalt and Nanaimo Railway on Vancouver Island between 1884 and 1886. By 1887, the E&N was operating trains carrying logs to both Ladysmith and Chemainus, the start of many years of log hauling on the E&N.[1]

Railroad activity in British Columbia predates the construction of the CPR by nearly 20 years; the mining lines around Nanaimo and Wellington first began operating in the early 1860s. Logic suggests that the rail lines there were also used to move timber which was consumed in great quantities in the mines for pit-props and as construction material in the tipples, washeries and related buildings needed around the coal mines and shipping facilities.[2]

These sorts of operations, however, are not normally thought of as logging railroads like those that developed in later years. In any of the situations described, railroad logging was a by-product of other major activities — mining or construction — not a sustaining function as part of the forest industry. Early operations developed slowly as lumber production in British Columbia expanded and the companies reached farther afield for good timber.

The building of the Canadian Pacific Railway through British Columbia in the early 1880s was the largest project in the history of the young province. Andrew Onderdonk's crews used the railroad to supply logs for bridge timbers, ties and other needs.
—ONDERDONK ALBUM, BCARS, HP75145

"Old Curly" was used on the CPR construction in the Fraser Canyon. In 1888, it began its logging career that was to span nearly 40 years. A well-known photo taken by Vancouver photographer C. S. Brady in 1894 at Mud Bay near the Nicomekl River. —CVA

Before railways were used, a variety of transportation systems was developed for logging. In some areas, bull teams or horses could be used to drag logs for short distances. Because the trees along the coast and in the valleys were so massive, the logs had to be skidded along the ground but then only to the nearest body of water. Once in the water, the heavy logs could be rafted to the mills. Skid roads were constructed, and with the application of plenty of grease, the logs could be moved overland. However, this method was time-consuming and inefficient. Flumes and chutes were also used, applying gravity to the work at hand. Steam for log transport in British Columbia appears to have been first used by a logger named Jeremiah Rogers. He acquired two traction engines which had originally been brought to British Columbia for use on the Cariboo Road connecting the coast with the gold fields of the Interior. Unsuccessful as road engines, they proved better suited to hauling logs and were used to move out timber to Jericho Beach near the present site of the University of British Columbia in Vancouver. These machines were apparently in use until the early 1880s.[3]

Steam-powered winches, called donkey engines, could replace animal power for skidding logs along the ground or over the skid roads, but the winning combination was the railroad and the donkey engine used in a coordinated manner. The donkey engines provided the power to bring logs short distances to a railhead and then were used to lift the logs onto the cars for rail transport to the mills or the nearest suitable water body. Details of the earliest logging railroad operations remain sketchy.

Early use of railways in logging occurred in particular on the outskirts of Vancouver, in the Fraser Valley and along eastern Vancouver Island. The first applications of this rail logging technology sometimes were primitive, as the early photographs and the descriptions which follow show. The equipment was small, and not very powerful. Often locomotives were old, well-worn main line machines retired from service but resurrected for backwoods operation. The donkeys were small and light in weight, unsuited to moving the enormous logs of the mature, old-growth coastal forests. Sometimes, the logs were simply skidded between the rails by the locomotives.

In 1888, the Royal City Planing Mills acquired an 0-4-0 tank engine formerly used for the Onderdonk contracts during the CPR construction. This engine was known officially as "Emory" or No. 2 on the construction work, and unofficially as "Old Curly" — a reference to Satan — because on one occasion it moved unexpectedly and nearly killed its engineer. The ageing tank engine was used along with some other light equipment in the vicinity of Hazelmere, near Cloverdale in the lower Fraser Valley. Bob Harvie was the engineer and logs were dumped into the Nicomekl River and towed to New Westminster for processing. Bull teams were used to yard the logs into the railway landings. Logs from around the surrounding area from as far away as White Rock were hauled by the locomotives using the wooden-framed trucks to carry the logs. Bob Harvie's son, Claude, described the old locomotive during this period:

[It] . . . doubled as a lumber train and passenger train. He had no regular stops, no regular times, and if anyone wanted a ride, they would have to sit either right in the locomotive or else on top of the logs. It wasn't exactly the most comfortable ride for the adventurous passengers nor was it the fastest, but if a person wasn't in a hurry, and felt inclined to do a little sightseeing, it was truly an experience.[4]

"Curly" was one of the logging locomotives that, against the odds, survived long after it became obsolete. The Royal City Planing Mills became part of the British Columbia Mills, Timber & Trading Company which operated the Hastings Sawmill Company. Over the years, the little locomotive went through several reconstructions, the most noticeable being the addition of a trailing truck making it an 0-4-4T. " 'Curly' . . . is not the same 'Curly' as I knew," recalled Percy Des Brisay who worked on the logging train at Hazelmere, "as much of her is new; she was repaired so many times. She has a new boiler, most of the remainder is new but it is the same old bell and the same old frame . . . 'Curly' was taken north to Bear River in 1906, and kept in constant use till the year 1927."[5]

After the construction of the New Westminster Southern Railway (controlled by the Great Northern), which was to run from Vancouver and Seattle (although it was some time before the Fraser River was bridged), a connection was built between the new railway and the logging line permitting log trains to run through to a log dump on the Fraser River at Port Kells. For this heavier service, an old Great Northern 4-4-0 was acquired and this freed "Curly" for duty at Bear River.[6]

Hastings Mill retired the engine and presented the battered old hulk to the Vancouver Harbour Commission for display. After restoration by the CPR shops in Vancouver, it was placed on display at Hastings Park in Vancouver. There it remained until 1973 when it was moved to Burnaby's Heritage Village. Many changes were made to the old machine over the years but there are still many original parts in the veteran locie, and it survives as the oldest in western Canada.[7]

Another operation in the vicinity of Vancouver used railway equipment in the 1890s. A small railway was built for hauling logs near Kitsilano, in what is now Vancouver, for the Hastings sawmill. This operation employed a small, four-wheeled locomotive of uncertain origins to clear timber from what would become one of the most densely populated residential and commercial areas of Vancouver.

In the interior of the province, near Golden on the main line of the CPR, the Columbia River Lumber Company also began using a railway. The log supply for the company's mill had come from many points along the Columbia and logs were floated down to the mill. However, the accessible timber was largely depleted by the late 1890s and a railway was built near Nicholson to reach more distant areas. A well-worn locomotive was purchased from the CPR in April 1897 and put to work. Logs were moved by rail and the railroad was also used for hauling supplies from the steamer landing to the mill and the CPR main line at Golden.[8] The locomotive, built by Baldwin in January 1872 for the Northern

In the early 1890s, "Curly" was hard at work for the B.C. Mills, Timber & Trading Company, hauling logs from the lowlands of the Fraser Valley to a log dump near Port Kells on the Fraser River. Robert Harvie was the engineer.
— CVA

In the 1890s, a small logging railroad operated in what became the Kitsilano district of Vancouver supplying timber to the Hastings sawmill. The locomotive was an 0-4-0. In this photo, a single log is spanned between a single truck and a pair of connected trucks which have a platform between them for the hand brakes.
— CVA, LOGN11P15

5

Most early logging locomotives were small. This little 0-4-0T, built by the Canadian Locomotive Company in 1890, ran for the Royal City Saw & Planing Mills Co. This may have been the first new logging locomotive used in British Columbia. —CVA, LOGN25P40

A few old locomotives from the major railroads were used in logging service. This 4-4-0, acquired by B.C. Mills, Timber & Trading, from the Great Northern, replaced "Curly" in the Fraser Valley. The steam donkey engines yarded the logs to the landing; the horse returned the cable or "lines" to the woods. —RBCM

6

Pacific, gained fame on October 9, 1877 for being the first CPR construction locomotive to arrive at Winnipeg. Although actually owned by contractor Joseph Whitehead, the locomotive was lettered "Canadian Pacific" and was named *Countess of Dufferin*. Later it was acquired by the CPR. In 1910, a public subscription was raised in Winnipeg to purchase the machine and it was placed on display in the city.[9] This was one of the earliest locomotive preservation projects in Western Canada and it saved a machine of lasting importance for future generations.

Early Successes, "Paraphernalia," "Betsy" and "Walking Dudley"

On Vancouver Island, the Victoria Lumber & Manufacturing Company (VL&M) of Chemainus, which was to become one of the major operators of logging railroads, introduced steam to its logging with a small upright spool donkey in 1892. This was a simple machine with a small boiler and vertical engine, powering a single gear-driven drum which could be used to wind in a heavy rope or cable.[10] However, by the late 1890s, accessible timber was no longer available in many areas. Indeed, Victoria's *Daily Colonist* of January 2, 1899 commented in a story describing the lumber industry:

There has been a shortage of logs during the year owing to the more accessible timber being all cut and this shortage will continue until the mills can, by means of logging railways and such other methods, secure a normal supply of logs. Everyone knew that this state of things was coming, but the situation suddenly developed before people were ready for it and so it will take a few months to get everything straight again.[11]

Another important factor in the adoption of logging railroads in British Columbia was the availability of capital. The equipment was expensive and only the larger operations could afford the outlay for the locomotives and trackage. As more capital became available and foreign investment grew in the early 1900s, an expansion of railroad logging became more feasible.[12]

Later that year, VL&M began moving its timber by rail to keep the big Chemainus mill supplied with logs.[13] The Chemainus operations began with an older 4-4-0 locomotive and rapid expansion followed. In 1900, a Climax locomotive was added to the equipment roster. Another followed in 1901 and a third Climax in 1903. In 1902, a Shay locomotive was bought and two more came in 1906. Meanwhile, the old 4-4-0 had been sold to the Victoria and Sidney Railway (V&S) and a heavier 2-8-0 of 1879 vintage, originally built for the Pennsylvania Railroad, was acquired for use on the main line.[14] Climax and Shay locomotives were specially built for logging and were among the first of many geared engines to be imported from the major locomotive builders in the United States.

The Canada Lumberman, a trade journal, described the VL&M operations in 1902. This outline of the early application of steam equipment and railroads in logging on the Coast gives an unusually detailed insight into this pioneering railroad logging venture.

In the camps of the V.L. & M. Co. can be seen the latest methods of logging with steam power. Their method is as follows: A cruiser goes out through the woods, noting the lay of the land, the quality of the timber, and how it will have to come out. The cruiser is followed by an engineer, who runs the lines through the timber, taking elevations, etc.; when a suitable route is found the main line is surveyed, graded and track laid. This main line is built for a distance of two or three miles up into the timber, and from it spurs are built from either side, reaching from the main line to the boundary of the company's land on either side. Where the grades of these spurs permit, the logs are handled on cars down to the main line, in which case landings are built at intervals along the spurs. The tops of these landings are just level with the bunks on the logging trucks. As soon as the spurs are graded, and while the rails are being laid and the landings built, the fallers come in, falling the timber that is to come in over the spur. These are followed by the buckers, who cut the fallen trees into logs of suitable lengths, then the swampers clear out and get everything ready for hauling. When the landing is completed one of the large donkey engines is brought and placed on one end of the landing securely anchored to convenient trees or stumps; the end of the steel wire rope is taken by a line horse, hauled into the woods, one end of the rope is attached to the log, the signal is given and the log is hauled onto the landing, where it is taken in charge by the loaders, who, using the donkey engine, load it onto the cars. This operation is repeated over and over, until perhaps a radius of 500 or 600 feet [150 or 180 metres] is cleared of logs around the landing.

In some cases the lay of the land will not permit of the engines on the landing reaching out far enough to pick up all the timber laying adjacent to the landing, in which case skid roads are built out into the timber, reaching from the landing for perhaps 2,000 to 5,000 feet [600 to 1500 metres]. At the end of this skid road an engine is stationed, which hauls the logs onto the skid road; the end of the rope attached to the engine on the landing is hauled out to the end of the skid road by means of a haul back line, the rope is attached to the logs hauled in by the yarding donkey, which are made up into a turn of 10 or 15 logs, coupled together by dogs [a short metal stake with an eye on one end used to tie logs together], a signal is given, and the engine on the landing hauls the logs in onto the landing, where they are loaded onto the cars.

In event of the grade on the spur being too steep for the operation of cars, another system, called "trailing," is used. The ties in the middle of the track are covered with two inch plank, side pieces of 6 x 6 are placed just inside of each rail, donkey engines are placed at intervals along the road; they haul the logs out of the woods to alongside the road, a geared locomotive starting at the far end of the road takes charge of the logs, which are rolled into the centre of the track, dogged together, and hauled along on the plank between the rails; as the engine passes each donkey the logs they have ready are rolled into the track and attached to the turn; these are finally dragged down to a landing on the main road, where they are loaded onto cars.

The company are using a 25 ton [22.7-tonne] "Climax" geared locomotive, trailing over about two miles of road, which runs up and along the side of Mount Brenton.

For collecting the loaded cars from the different landings, spotting the empties, and making up trains, they use a 40 ton [36-tonne] "Shay" engine; when this engine has the train made up it is taken in charge by a 60 ton [54-tonne] consolidated, eight driver, locomotive, and hauled down to the unloading wharf at the head of Horse Shoe bay [Chemainus harbour], where by means of a crane and a donkey engine the logs are quickly unloaded into the salt water, and are later taken over to the mill. The company employ from 80 to 120 men in the woods, and run their camps all the year round.[15]

Victoria Lumber & Manufacturing Company of Chemainus used railways extensively by the early 1900s. Dragging the logs shown above at its Oyster Harbour log dumps soon gave way to using log cars, as seen below at Chemainus.
—GERRY WELLBURN COLLECTION

By planking over the ties, the loggers could haul the timber behind the locomotives without loading the logs onto cars. Grease helped, but the system was inefficient and dangerous. This scene is from the Mainland Cedar Company's Port Neville operation.
—W. J. VAN DUSEN, BCFS 263

"Dudley" was a home-made contraption built in 1900 or 1901 by the blacksmith and his crew at the Shawnigan Lake Lumber Company. Gerry Wellburn sketched the machine following interviews in the early 1940s with pioneer employees.
— *HARMAC NEWS*

Another early rail operation on southern Vancouver Island belonged to the Shawnigan Lake Lumber Company.[16] The rail haul was a primitive, low-budget affair that began in 1900 or 1901. At that time, a wooden-railed pole road was built from the west shore of Shawnigan Lake back into the timber. An eight-horse team pulled a log car, consisting of two, four-wheeled trucks, over peeled Douglas-fir poles. The cars had double-flanged wheels with, as Gerry Wellburn, who in later years was manager of the Shawnigan Lake Lumber Company and a life-long historian of the forest industry, recorded, "... several inches of play enabling them to follow irregularities in the track and go around the sharp angular turns."[17] The horses soon had trouble with their footing in swampy ground and the ever-resourceful blacksmiths at the mill built a locomotive to pull the car. This home-built, wooden-framed machine used a small boiler and engine connected with rods and gears to drive one of the "locie's" two axles. Some years later, Gerry Wellburn searched company files and interviewed employees to find out about its beginnings and short career.

When ready, the contraption was christened "Walking Dudley" by its proud makers. It was towed across the Lake on a raft and put on the pole road. Steam was raised and the dozen or so men of the logging crew clambered on board for the first ride. The engineer opened the throttle — a long piece of iron-bar: the engine hissed and sizzled but did not move. More wood was thrown on the fire. Still it would not move.

"Get off you men and give it a chance!" roared Frank Verdier, the logging boss and off jumped the logging crew and started to push. But still it would not go. So back onto the raft and over to the sawmill it went.

But the inventive geniuses in the blacksmith shop were by no means beaten. George Frayne changed the transmission and replaced the rods and cranks with a chain, which drove from a small sprocket to a very big one. The next time, when put on the log road, "Dudley" really rumbled along. It had no springs, and vibrated like a wet dog shaking itself. Its mournful groaning and clanking could be heard for miles around the Lake.

Frank Verdier did not take too kindly to the clumsy machine. In describing it, he used many interesting terms... but a very mild description was "It was just a damned old paraphernalia."

A mean problem was the drive-chain which kept stretching and breaking or coming off the sprocket. The sprocket wheel on the axle was really too big and kept plowing through the dirt and throwing off the chain. "Too many days I lay on my back in the mud, fixing that chain," recalled old-timer Herb Hawking.

"Dudley," driving one axle only, did not have enough traction on the rails until one bright lad said, "Loggers wear caulks in their boots — lets put caulks on the driving wheels!" That was tried but the spikes slivered and tore the rails so badly they had to be removed. But of all the problems "Dudley" introduced, the worst was fire. "Dudley" spat sparks from its smoke stack, and crunched up the wooden rails, until it set fire to them. A bad fire started on the pole road and spread through the logging operations and beyond to the Koksilah River. The loggers moved the yarding donkey into the swamp, and buried the logging lines and rigging.[18]

With a performance record as chequered as this one, it was small wonder that "Dudley's" career was short-lived. The change to steam machinery was not always popular. Joe Martino, one of the donkey engineers, is quoted as screaming

"Get rid of that dribbling pot and bring back the bulls!"[19] The company soon went shopping for something better. In 1902, William Munsie, Sr. came back from a trip to "the American side" having ordered a "knocked down" locomotive which was shipped to Shawnigan where the ". . . vital parts were assembled onto a wooden body, framed by George Frayne, Sr." The machine was a small, Class A Climax locomotive of 12 tons (10.9 tonnes) and like "Dudley" it was designed to run on the pole road. Unlike "Dudley" it was a success. Christened "Betsy," the little machine was to last nearly 20 years until destroyed along with the mill in a 1934 fire. Gerry Wellburn also recorded the story of "Betsy." He first became intrigued by the unusual machine after seeing it while it was being used by contractors during the construction of the B.C. Electric's interurban railway north of Victoria before World War I:[20]

Her engine was a two-cylinder vertical affair which drove through the centre of the floor to rather clumsy four-wheel trucks, the large double-flanged concave wheels which straddled the log "rails." Her boiler, which originally carried 150 lbs. [1035 kPa] of steam, was centered over the front truck, and on each side was piled the 2-ft. [0.6m.] wood used for firing. Her back was neatly rounded with an iron water tank about four feet [1.2 m] high, giving weight to her rear set of trucks. Special equipment included steam "jam" brakes, and a pail of skid grease. The grease was smeared on the log rails, as notwithstanding Betsy's short wheel base, she was apt to get stuck on the curves.

   She was a success from the start. . . . She handled two log cars, one at either end, each fastened to the locie with a 16-ft. [4.8 m] reach. She was always pulling a car and pushing a car. She averaged three miles [5 km] an hour, and extended the economic hauling distance to nearly four miles. But better yet, "Betsy" helped load the logs, which were ground yarded with a little steam-pot to skids alongside the track. The bunk load was rolled on with peavies and man-power, but to complete the load, "Betsy" was uncoupled and additional logs parbuckled with a line attached to her.

   The log cars, built at the sawmill, had wooden bunks faced with iron strips. Cheese blocks were secured with pins, and a tricky job was to pry out the pin at the dump, and release the block. Herb Hawking remembers more than one man flying heels upwards into the lake when the logs started rolling. The track was built with logs 12 to 14 inches [30 to 35 cm] in diameter, on a 6-foot [1.8-m] gauge.[21]

Before long, light-weight steel rails replaced the poles and "Betsy" was converted to standard gauge operation. Later, the railroad was extended and additional equipment was acquired including a two-truck Climax that, through the most unlikely chain of events, was eventually preserved at the British Columbia Forest Museum at Duncan. Even in the early 1900s, pressures to remain competitive were considerable and a make-shift operation could not provide the reliable supplies of timber needed for a major mill.

   Challenging the Shawnigan Lake Lumber Company for the most imaginative or unusual application of steam equipment in the woods was the McNair Timber Company in West Vancouver. There, in the early 1900s, another machine called the "Walking Dudley," but quite different in design from the Shawnigan Lake

The arrival of "Betsy" on the Shawnigan Lake Lumber Company's railway marked a dramatic improvement in the efficiency of the entire operation. "Betsy" began by running on poles for rails as shown above in this portrait of the proud crew with their new locomotive. Steel soon replaced poles and "Betsy's" performance was even more impressive. In 1910, Climax No. 2 (shown at right) joined the roster and worked for the company until the mid-1920s. Later abandoned, it was salvaged by Grainger Taylor and then acquired by the B.C. Provincial Museum. It is now on display at the B.C. Forest Museum.
—GERRY WELLBURN COLLECTION

The McNair Fraser operation on Hollyburn Ridge was unique in British Columbia because of its use of a Willamette cable locomotive built in 1908. Slow and awkward, the machine was nonetheless functional and could operate on steeper grades than the more common Shay and Climax geared locomotives. The logs were simply dragged behind the locomotive from the landings down to tidewater in West Vancouver near the foot of Seventeenth Street. In 1911, the machine ran off the end of the wharf and soon was scrapped. —VPL, 6728

"Walking Dudley" inched downgrade past camp on its way to the log dump about 1911. "The locomotive operates on rails laid on a cross skid road on which the logs are dragged," noted the Willamette company. "The engine is similar to an ordinary reversing donkey, mounted on a steel frame having two sets of trucks. The pinion on the crank shaft drives through a bull wheel, a large gypsy [winch] about 6 feet [1.8m] in diameter. Between the rails of the track, but at one side, is stretched a 1¼-inch [3.2-cm] cable which passes several times around the gypsy and is securely fastened at the summit and foot of the road." —CVA, LOGN34P50

The early operators of logging railroads were innovative and developed a number of home-built locomotives whose origins remain obscure. This machine, which ran in the Fraser Valley near Langley, is a case in point. —BILL KERR, ELMER WINTON COLLECTION

The Trail Lumber Company operated this ungainly locomotive with an elaborate spark arrester about 1908. Machines such as this one were usually constructed around a small donkey engine or a steam tractor. The capacity was limited to small loads. —BCARS, HP56350

Old main line power like this ungainly 4-4-0 could be the basis for home-spun modifications. This one received extra air tanks and what appears to be a home-made wooden tender. It ran for Cheakamus Timber near Squamish in the 1920s, hauling logs to the Pacific Great Eastern. It was scrapped a decade later. —TED ROBSON COLLECTION

15

Another primitive railroad operation was built by the A. G. Lambert & Co. sawmill west of Nelson in the Kootenays. Whimsically called the "Push, Pull & Jerk Railway," it was photographed about 1910. Normally, the small locomotive seems to have handled two of the small cars which were equipped with hand brakes. Later, a second similar machine, or perhaps this one rebuilt, was used. —WADDS BROS, DAVID THOMPSON LIBRARY

"We used to have a little flatcar for the men. It would hold eight or 10. It would run just plumb crazy and coast down to the sawmill. We used to take some awful chances going down Barkley's Hill [a 9 percent grade]—we liked giving a thrill to strangers." —JOE KERRONE REMEMBERING THE NARROW GAUGE WESTHOLME LUMBER CO.

The "Nanaimo," a British-made Manning Wardle 0-4-0T of 1874 vintage, was brought to British Columbia in 1877 to work at the coal mines at Nanaimo. In the early 1900s it was acquired by John Coburn for his Ladysmith Lumber Company which operated a mill near Cassidy. Joe Hickman was the engineer shown in the picture. Finally, the engine was used for construction work on the Pacific Great Eastern and eventually was scrapped. Charlie Snowden was another engineer who ran the "Nanaimo" and other early locomotives in the area including an unusual 2-4-4T that came from the New York Elevated Railways to haul logs for the New Ladysmith Lumber Company.
—BCARS, HP40327

16

locomotive, was used to skid logs down from the slopes of Hollyburn Mountain to tidewater. This "Dudley" appears to have been a Willamette machine or at least one of similar design. A few of these "cable locomotives" were built for operators in Oregon and Washington and were listed in a Canadian Willamette catalogue of about 1915.[22] E. S. (Ted) Pretious, a professional engineer, grew up near the right-of-way and described the ungainly machine:

The "Walking Dudley" consisted of a powerful, logging, steam donkey engine (or Dudley) bolted to a modified railway flat car, which ran on standard gauge railway track. The engine, through gearing, turned a special spirally-grooved steel drum around each end of which were wound two or three turns of steel cables, one lying along each side of the track and outside the rails. These cables were securely anchored at the logging site and tidewater and were constrained by "deadmen" to follow the curves by a series of chords. The logs of various diameters were attached directly to the "Dudley" by a steel cable attached to the leading log, the ones behind being linked or dogged together by steel grabs or hooks 1¼ inches thick [3.2 cm].

The engine could haul 16 to 20 logs averaging [in total] about 20,000 board feet [47m³] on each trip, down the mountain to tidewater. The engine was then literally able to wind itself back up the steep slope. The ties were recessed on their top surfaces to roughly accommodate the curved surfaces of the logs. Liberal applications of grease permitted the logs to slide easily down the centre of the track: the logs being held more or less in place by the recess in the ties. The leading edge of each log was cambered to prevent the logs from digging into the ties. Very seldom did a log jump the track. . . . It is readily understood that the "Dudley" required tangents with a minimum of curves and more-or-less uniform grade.[23]

Willamette described their cable locomotives as being used successfully ". . . on roads from two to three miles [3 to 5 km] in length and on grades as high as 25 percent. The locomotive runs either light or loaded at the same speed — about four miles [6 km] an hour."[24] The MacNair "Dudley" was used until 1911.

Machines like the "Dudley," pulling itself up and down Hollyburn Mountain by its own bootstraps, or the home-built "Paraphernalia" at Shawnigan Lake, were clearly not long-term solutions to the problems of supplying timber to the mills in British Columbia. Machines like this did not last long anywhere, although a few similar ones were used in the western states.[25] Much better, more flexible equipment was already available to the loggers. Change was rapid and, by the early 1900s, logging railroads were well established as part of the forest industry on the coast.

Development and Expansion of the Logging Lines

Increasingly, railways started fulfilling the important objective of assuring a reliable, steady supply of timber for the large mills being established to serve a growing domestic and export market for lumber from British Columbia. New, specialized equipment was brought in for the lines and a highly reliable and productive technology began to be developed, giving this equipment a distinctive and unusual character.

In the interior of British Columbia, development of the forest industry awaited the expansion of the major common carrier railroads. In 1898, the Canadian Pacific built a line through the Crowsnest Pass in the Rockies to the lower end of Kootenay Lake and by 1900, it had expanded westward all the way to Midway in the Boundary District.[26] Mining development was largely responsible for the expansion of the railways but lumbering in the area soon became a major industry. The mining towns of the 1890s — Nelson, Grand Forks, Rossland, Trail — were becoming established cities in the 1900s; settlers were farming the rich valley lands and with the rapid settlement of the Canadian prairies to the east, there was a ready market for lumber. As well, an increasingly important export trade in lumber was developing. The deep-sea shipping wharves at the big Chemainus mill, at Hastings Mill, and at other major coastal mills, bustled with activity. In the late 1800s and early 1900s, sailing vessels carried most of the lumber to Europe and ports around the Pacific.

In the East Kootenays, the timber was smaller and more easily moved by horses than were the huge logs of the coastal forests, but railroads were soon being laid into the forests of pine and interior Douglas-fir. In some areas, the mountain slopes were simply too steep to permit economical construction of logging railways, although in the flatter country around Cranbrook and in the valley lands near Fernie, several lines were built. The CPR itself operated a logging line at Yahk in the East Kootenays to supply its nearly unending need for railway ties. To the north, a few railroad logging operations developed along the main line of the CPR in the valley lands of the Columbia River between the major mountain barriers.

The expansion of the logging lines was very rapid. By about 1908, there were 28 logging railroads operating in British Columbia where, a decade earlier, there was probably only a handful. Twelve were on Vancouver Island, six in the Fraser Valley, one on the mainland coast, seven in the Kootenays and two more in other interior regions. This was really the beginning of the logging railroad era in the province. Most of the railways were small, with just a few miles of track, one or two locomotives and a few cars. However, for hauling logs they were so much more productive than any alternative means of transport that they became essential components of the lumber industry. Noteworthy is the number of donkey engines at work in the woods; there were 94, compared to only 36 locomotives. However, a single locomotive could keep more than one landing supplied with empty cars, particularly in this era of ground yarding where pulling the timber to the railroads was still a slow and laborious process.

In the next few years, several major logging areas would be opened up with railroads. In 1909, the Canadian Western Lumber Company of Fraser Mills began railroad logging in the Comox Valley on Vancouver Island using its subsidiary, the Comox & Campbell Lake Tramway Company (soon renamed the Comox Logging & Railway Company). On the mainland in 1910, the Howe

The International Timber Company developed an extensive railroad near Campbell River on eastern Vancouver Island. No. 3 or "Three-Spot" worked in company with several Shays. John "Spoolie" Kusha is the engineer in this 1917 photo. — GERRY WELLBURN COLLECTION

In the early 1900s, the large mills in British Columbia were major industrial operations that needed a reliable supply of logs. Logging railways were the answer. This is the Canadian Western Lumber Company's mill at Fraser Mills on the Fraser River. — FLETCHER CHALLENGE COLLECTION

Sound, Pemberton Valley & Northern Railway (which in 1912 became part of the Pacific Great Eastern Railway) began building trackage north from what later developed into the town of Squamish. This railway became an important carrier for logs cut from the region and eventually expanded to be a major system reaching Prince George and other parts of central and northern British Columbia.[27]

Over the next two decades the network of logging railroads expanded dramatically until nearly every coastal valley and hillside reverberated with the sounds of working steam locomotives and donkey engines. The use of logging railroads was much more limited in the Interior. Nevertheless, railroads were an important component of the forest industry, particularly in the East Kootenays, through the 1920s.

British Columbia Logging Railways, ca. 1908

NAME	CAMP LOCATION	MILES OF TRACK	LOCOMOTIVES GEARED	ROD	SETS OF TRUCKS FLATCARS	LOGGING ENGINES	DAILY OUTPUT# (bd. ft.)
Lower Mainland and Fraser Valley							
Abbotsford Lbr. Co. Ltd.	Abbotsford	3.00	1		-/3	2	50,000
B.C. Mills, Timber & Trading Co..	New Westminster	7.75		1		4	50,000
Heaps Tbr. Co. Ltd.	Narrows Arm	3.00	1			2	50,000
Ironside, Rennie & Campbell	Lake Buntzen	1.50				1	20,000
Landsborough & Burger	Silverdale	2.00	1		5/-	1	40,000
McNair-Fraser Tbr. Co.	North Vancouver	4.00	1		-/1	3	120,000
	subtotal:	21.25	4	1	5/4	13	330,000
Mainland Coast							
Sayward Milling Co.	Powell Lake	1.25	1		8/-	4	-----
	subtotal:	1.25	1		8/-	4	-----
Interior (CPR Main Line)							
Arrow Lakes Lbr. Co.	Galena Bay	5.00	1		40/-	1	-----
Columbia River Lbr. Co.	Carlin	3.00	1		*	2	50,000
Gibbons Lbr. Co.	Revelstoke†						
Hood Lbr. Co.	Taft	4.00	1		-/8	—	50,000
Mundy Lbr. Co.	Three Valley	6.00	2		18/2	2	80,000
	subtotal:	18.00	5		58/10	5	180,000
East Kootenays							
East Kootenay Lbr. Co.+	Jaffray	4.00	1		8/-	—	50,000
Eastern B.C. Lbr. Co.	Cedar Valley	2.50	1		10/-	—	60,000
Fernie Lbr. Co.	Fernie	2.00	1		8/-	—	60,000
King Lbr. Co.	Cranbrook†						
North Star Lbr. Co.	Cranbrook	3.00	1		6/-		50,000
Otis Staples Lbr. Co.	Cherry Creek	14.00	3		48/3	3	100,000
	subtotal:	25.50	7		80/3	3	320,000

NAME	CAMP LOCATION	MILES OF TRACK	LOCOMOTIVES GEARED	ROD	SETS OF TRUCKS FLATCARS	LOGGING ENGINES	DAILY OUTPUT# (bd. ft.)
Vancouver Island (and adjacent islands)							
Anderson Logging Co.	Union Bay	4.50	1		24/-	3	100,000
B.C. Mills, Tbr. & Trading Co.	Granite Bay++	5.00		1		5	55,000
	Thurlow Is.	3.00		1		3	45,000
	Rock Bay	13.00		3		11	150,000
	Salmon River	5.50		1		6	50,000
Brunette Saw Mill Co.	Comox	3.00	1		16/-	10	150,000
International Tbr. Co.	Campbell River	5.00	1		25/-	3	100,000
Jordan River Lbr. Co.	Jordan River	1.50	1		10/-	2	50,000
Nimpkish Lake Logging Co.	Broughton Str.	5.50	1		9/1	6	120,000
Shawnigan Lake Lbr. Co.	Shawnigan Lake	3.00	1		12/-	3	40,000
Victoria Lbr. & Mfg. Co.	Chemainus	21.00	3		54/2	16	250,000
Westholme Lbr. Co.**	Mount Sicker	15.00	2		4/-	1	20,000
	subtotal:	85.00	11	6	154/3	69	1,130,000
	Overall total:	151	28	7	305/29	94	1,960,000

# average daily output in board feet		++ Quadra Island
* used CPR cars		** narrow gauge (3-foot)
+ original directory uses "Kootenai"		† under construction

Source: complied from a directory of the Pacific Coast forest industry ca. 1908. (Photocopy RBCM). Note: these statistics are in some cases incomplete and may not be fully accurate. For example, from roster information, it is probable that VL&M had 6 locomotives by 1908. Also, company names often changed frequently.

From this early development and expansion of logging railways, a general pattern was emerging. Trackage had to be built farther and farther back into the timber and the railroad equipment required became increasingly sophisticated. Specially built, geared locomotives were becoming commonplace and although the old or small rod locomotives were still widely used, they were inadequate for log hauling. Many of the operations were still small with little rolling stock, but a few large, well equipped railroads had developed, particularly Victoria Lumber & Manufacturing at Chemainus, Otis Staples Lumber Co. at Wycliffe (Cherry Creek) and B.C. Mill's line out of Rock Bay. Vancouver Island was establishing its place as the centre of logging railroading in British Columbia with over 56 percent of the total mileage and nearly 60 percent of the average daily output.

The logging railways had a unique character, largely related to their function and the nature of the terrain through which they operated. These characteristics help explain the development of the lines in the busy years of World War I and the 1920s.

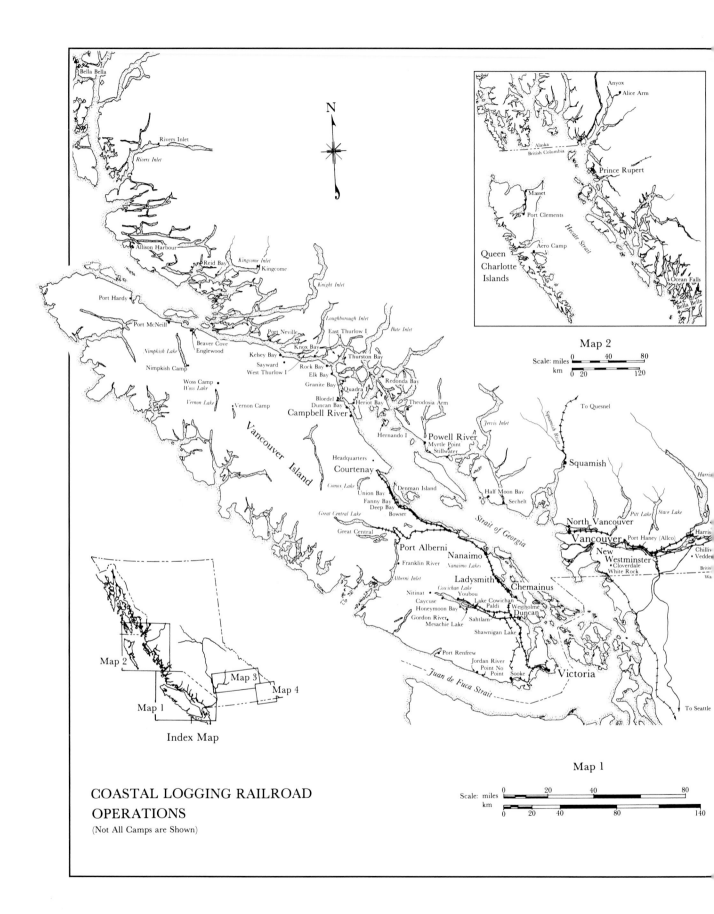

Map 2

Scale: miles 0   40   80
km   0   20   120

Map 1

Scale: miles 0   20   40   80
km   0   20   40   80   140

Index Map

Map 2
Map 3
Map 4
Map 1

COASTAL LOGGING RAILROAD
OPERATIONS
(Not All Camps are Shown)

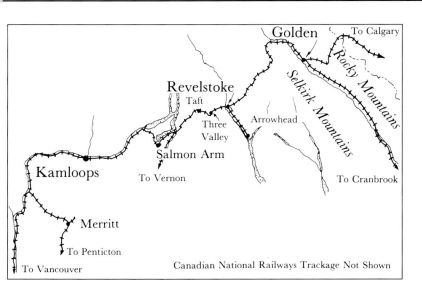

Golden

To Calgary

Rocky Mountains

Revelstoke
Taft
Three Valley
Arrowhead
Selkirk Mountains

Salmon Arm
To Vernon
To Cranbrook

Kamloops

Merritt
To Penticton
To Vancouver

Canadian National Railways Trackage Not Shown

Map 3

Scale: miles
0   40   80
km
0   40   120

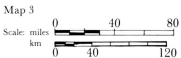

Map 4

SOUTHEASTERN
BRITISH COLUMBIA

Scale: miles
0   10   20
km
0   10   20

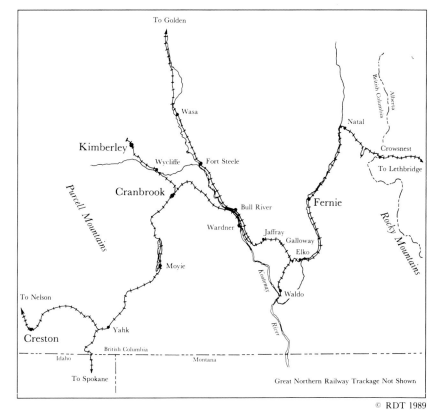

To Golden

Wasa

British Columbia   Alberta

Natal

Kimberley
Wycliffe
Fort Steele
Crowsnest
To Lethbridge

Purcell Mountains

Cranbrook
Bull River
Fernie
Rocky Mountains

Wardner
Jaffray
Galloway
Elko

Moyie

Kootenay

Waldo

To Nelson

Yahk
River

Creston
British Columbia
Idaho
Montana
To Spokane

Great Northern Railway Trackage Not Shown

© RDT 1989

Legend

Canadian Pacific Railway	┼┼┼┼┼┼┼
Canadian National Railways	┼─┼─┼─┼
Pacific Great Eastern Railway	┼┼┼┼┼┼
(British Columbia Railway)	
Great Northern Railway	┼──┼──┼
(Burlington Northern Railway)	

International Timber Company No. 4

RAILROAD LOGGING OPERATIONS
IN BRITISH COLUMBIA

ALSO SHOWING PRINCIPAL
POPULATION AND MILLING CENTRES

Logging railroads expanded rapidly along the coast in the early 1900s. Canadian Locomotive Company 0-6-0T No. 1 was operated by the B.C. Mills, Timber & Trading Company and was photographed in 1913 by H.R. MacMillan. The tank engine was built in June 1898. —BCFS, 3

On southern Vancouver Island, railroads were used along the shores of Juan de Fuca Strait. This Climax of 1907 vintage, with an enormous spark arrester, was operated by Cooke & Moore Logging near Sooke. —SOOKE REGION MUSEUM AND ARCHIVES

On the Mainland Coast, further expansion of railroad logging developed. This is the Brooks-Scanlon-O'Brien Company's Eagle River & Northern Railway at Stillwater, which operated from 1910 until 1955. —CVA

Rail logging began in the Alberni Valley on Vancouver Island following the extension of the E&N Railway in 1911. Weist Logging was the pioneer with, as the banner reads, the "First Trainload of logs hauled on West Coast Vancouver Island at Port Alberni, B.C. Aug. 7, 1912, Weist Logging Co. for Canadian Pacific Lumber Co." The Shay, later known as "Two-Spot," has been restored by the Alberni Valley Museum. —LEONARD FRANK, VPL

The Heaps Timber Company operated logging lines at Ruskin and at Narrows Arm near Gibsons Landing in the early 1900s. In the upper photo, well-maintained Heisler No. 3 pulls a long turn of logs over a pile trestle, likely at Narrows Arm operations about 1913. The second photo, apparently taken when equipment was being moved between the two logging shows, captures the Heisler and two donkey engines loaded onto a barge. A small tug is behind the locomotive.
—J. W. HEAPS COLLECTION

The Otis-Staples Lumber Company developed an extensive railroad near Cranbrook in the East Kootenays. The company operated three Shays and a Climax.
—FORT STEELE HERITAGE PARK COLLECTION

Logging railroads expanded along the east coast of Vancouver Island. This is the Shawnigan Lake Lumber Company and the locomotive is their small Climax, No. 2. The landing and small donkey engine are typical of yarding and loading arrangements in the period before World War I. —GERRY WELLBURN COLLECTION

From about 1916 to 1918, the Mundy Lumber Company logged near Three Valley in the Monashee Mountains along the main line of the CPR. John Boyd was the engineer of Climax No. 1. —BCARS, HP25907

27

Logging railroads are often associated with twisting mountain grades, but they were far more efficient on the flat lands. This photograph shows the timber lands penetrated by the International Timber Company near Campbell River on eastern Vancouver Island. In such country, the spur lines could be laid out in a systematic pattern as the timber was progressively cut. With magnificent stands of timber like this, it was small wonder that the forest industry flourished in the early decades of the 1900s. —LEONARD FRANK, VPL

Characteristics of the Logging Lines

The function of the logging lines was very simple and obvious. It was to provide a continuous, reliable supply of timber to the mills. Few logging railways had any other traffic or purpose except to carry the loggers, their equipment and supplies. Consequently, once the timber in an area was cut the tracks were usually pulled up and relocated a short time later. The result of this process and a practical application of economics was that there was little reason to invest heavily in high standards of construction and permanent roadbeds when the lines were so transient.

The grade profiles, permanent bridges, ballast and other features that tested the mettle of railroad engineers building main line routes through British Columbia were not the problems of the logging railroad engineers. They too had difficult engineering challenges but these were based on different operating and economic premises. On the CPR, for example, masonry and steel bridges were built to last decades and the grade was, wherever possible, limited to less than 2.2 percent (a rise of 2.2 feet in 100 feet, or 2.2 metres in 100 metres). Only the most unusual circumstances on a logging line would justify a steel bridge; timber trestles, often quite rustic, were the only feasible method of construction.

Any surveyor laying out a railroad strives for a minimum grade but on logging lines, once the flat lands were cleared, the engineers inevitably accepted steeper grades routinely because, almost always, the timber was being hauled from the mountains, so that the heavy loads were moving downgrade. Also, steeper grades meant shorter routes which saved time and money in construction. Building a high-class route to the timber might well have priced the logs out of the market. Practicality, not long-range growth in freight and passenger traffic, dictated the standards for the logging lines.

Topography was a critical variable in determining the layout of logging railroad trackage. On flat or lightly rolling land such as in the Comox Valley on eastern Vancouver Island or in the Fraser Valley on the Mainland, the tracks were laid out in a systematic, ladder-like pattern. A more permanent main line route led to the active logging areas and from this line, branches were built into the timber at regular intervals. The distance between the branches, unless rivers or other features intervened, was usually determined by how far the yarding equipment could pull the logs from where they were cut to the end of track.

Over the years, the technology of yarding improved but a general rule was that a small donkey engine could yard logs for perhaps 500 feet (150 metres) while a more sophisticated system of skyline yarding could move logs 1200 to 1600 feet (375 to 500 metres) to the landings. On occasion, this system could move logs up to about 3300 feet (1000 metres) but over long distances they became increasingly inefficient.[28] These types of yarding will be described in more detail in Chapter 3. The map showing the early lines of Comox Logging in the Comox Valley depicts clearly the regular, predictable pattern of trackage that developed after several years of operation.

Logging in more mountainous areas produced an entirely different set of problems and was much more expensive and complicated. Slope became an overriding consideration in planning routes. Even with the specially designed logging locomotives that were available to the loggers in the early 1900s, grades were still very important; two or three percent was considered typical for the main lines while five or six percent was common on the spur lines, with the normal maximum being seven or eight percent. Steep grades increased operating costs and reduced the hauling capacity of locomotives but these costs had to be balanced against the initial construction costs and the effect the railroad location would have on yarding and loading costs later on.

The track pattern that developed in rugged country varied with each operation. Usually, the engineers would try to follow a river course into the timber because this route provided the best gradient up the valley. From this line the spurs worked their way to the timber by the most economical route. This usually involved steep grades, sharp curves and, very often, switchbacks to gain elevation. However, it was not always possible to follow this procedure, and sometimes the main routes or spurs had to be laid along ridge tops. The problem in this situation was that then the logs had to be yarded uphill to the landings for transfer to the railcars. It was bad enough to have to haul empty equipment up into the timber but where the railroads had to haul the loaded cars uphill, their efficiency dropped dramatically.

In areas where switchback construction was impractical, or where the timber was to be logged either on a ridge top or in a valley without easy access, the tracks could be laid on an extremely steep grade in a generally straight line. This type of system was called an incline railway and it worked on the simple principle that the shortest distance between two points was a straight line. However, even the special logging locomotives could not operate on the grades of these railroads because they often exceeded 30 percent. One, built by Joe Kerrone on Mount Sicker, near Duncan on Vancouver Island, had a maximum grade of 62.5 percent.[29] Normally, a special donkey engine, (a "lowering engine," or "incline engine") was situated at the top of the grade and the cars were lowered downhill by cable.[30] Special precautions had to be taken in securing the loads, or cars with a bulkhead had to be used. The operation of an incline could be expensive and slow but in difficult situations it could provide an economical solution to problem areas, especially if a long circuitous rail route could be avoided.[31] Over the years many inclines were built for logging purposes in the western United States but few appear to have been used in British Columbia. Several were used on Vancouver Island and a few others were employed on the mainland.

Nearly all logging railroads in British Columbia were built to standard gauge — 4 feet, 8.5 inches (1.44 m) between the rails. A few companies which used

For over 40 years, Comox
Logging's trains crisscrossed the
flatlands of the Comox Valley
working north from Courtenay
nearly all the way to Campbell
River. The main camp was at
Headquarters and the big log
dump was at Royston. Each year
the tracks were extended into
new timber and the older spurs
were removed. In peak years, over
100 miles (160 km) of track were
in operation. The area was an
ideal setting for railroad logging.

The company also logged in
the Cruickshank Creek area near
Comox Lake. Bill Johnstone,
who retired as Superintendent of
the mining operations at
Cumberland, recalled how
Canadian Collieries (Dunsmuir)
Ltd.'s railway was used to haul out
the timber. "They towed the logs
down to the east end of the lake
where a big A-frame was used to
load up the cars. They would log
all summer and load in the
spring. They would switch the
crews during the winter months
to work some of the winter shows,
away from the snow. We would
haul the logs and use the
Collieries' locomotives. There was
a spur out of Bevan that went
right to the lake. We would haul
them down to Royston where they
had the booming grounds. The
14 used to do quite a bit of the
log hauling and the 20. We used
to pull some pretty big trains
down there, 25 or 30 cars. It used
to take about six weeks to two
months to clean them up."

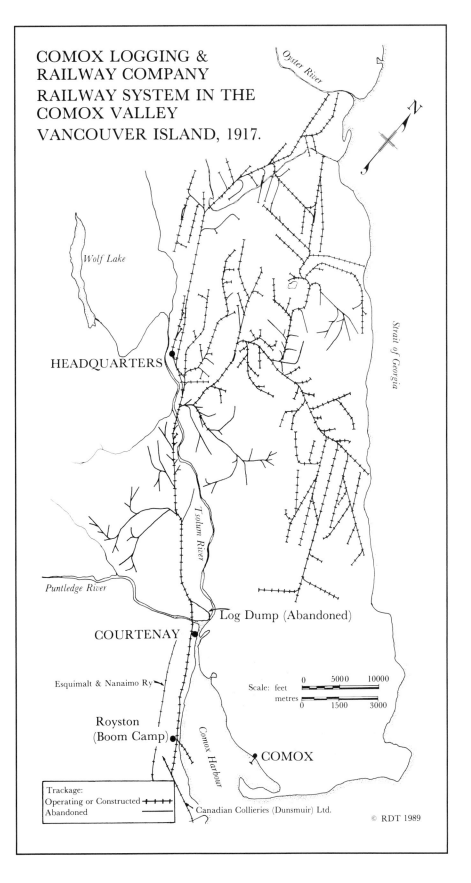

COMOX LOGGING &
RAILWAY COMPANY
RAILWAY SYSTEM IN THE
COMOX VALLEY
VANCOUVER ISLAND, 1917.

Oyster River

Strait of Georgia

Wolf Lake

HEADQUARTERS

Tsolum River

Puntledge River

Log Dump (Abandoned)

COURTENAY

Esquimalt & Nanaimo Ry

Scale: feet   0   5000   10000
metres   0   1500   3000

Royston
(Boom Camp)

Comox Harbour

COMOX

Trackage:
Operating or Constructed ┼┼┼┼
Abandoned ────

Canadian Collieries (Dunsmuir) Ltd.

© RDT 1989

Twisting track, temporary bridges and steep grades characterized many of the logging railroads. Three-truck Climax No. 2 of Vedder River Logging winds its way to the log dump in the early 1930s. —W. F. MONTGOMERY, BCARS, HP73768

Trestles such as this one over Copenhagen Canyon on the Eagle River & Northern Railway near Stillwater were typical of the structures built routinely by the logging railroad construction engineers. —CVA

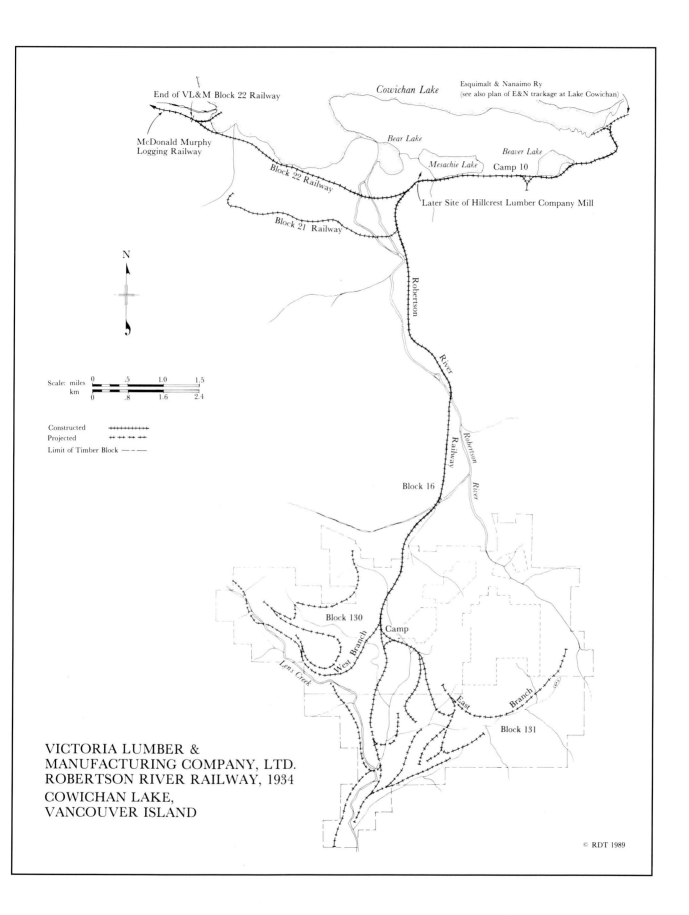

End of VL&M Block 22 Railway

McDonald Murphy
Logging Railway

Cowichan Lake

Esquimalt & Nanaimo Ry
(see also plan of E&N trackage at Lake Cowichan)

Bear Lake

Mesachie Lake

Beaver Lake

Camp 10

Block 22 Railway

Block 21 Railway

Later Site of Hillcrest Lumber Company Mill

N

Scale: miles
km

| 0 | .5 | 1.0 | 1.5 |
| 0 | .8 | 1.6 | 2.4 |

Constructed
Projected
Limit of Timber Block

Robertson

River

Robertson
Railway

Robertson River

Block 16

Block 130

Camp

Lens Creek

West Branch

East Branch

Block 131

VICTORIA LUMBER &
MANUFACTURING COMPANY, LTD.
ROBERTSON RIVER RAILWAY, 1934
COWICHAN LAKE,
VANCOUVER ISLAND

© RDT 1989

33

Inclines

"Amongst the more recent developments in railroad logging in British Columbia," noted the *British Columbia Lumberman* in April 1924, "is the Incline Road. . . . The fast disappearing number of easy stands have made it necessary to tap hitherto unapproachable timber, and in many cases the only practical solution is the Incline." This article referred to the use of steam equipment. Early, small-scale gravity inclines, often using horses to return an empty car uphill were used from the early days of coastal logging. For example, a gravity incline was built near Mill Bay north of Victoria.

One of the longest inclines was built by the Regina Timber Company at Sechelt. Capable of handling 200,000 feet (470 m³) of timber per day, the incline was over 1.25 miles (2.0 km) long and had a grade exceeding 45 percent. The company bought a special "snubbing" engine from the Smith & Watson Ironworks of Portland. It featured a large single, water-cooled drum and both air and mechanical brakes. The upper photo shows part of the 2500-foot (760-m) incline of Green Point Logging on the east side of Harrison Lake in the 1930s. The lower photo is of the top of the incline. In 1937, the operation, owned by P. B. Anderson and his son Dewey, was moved to the Salmon River area on Vancouver Island. —LEONARD FRANK, VPL; W. F. MONTGOMERY, BCARS, HP73685

poles for rails operated with wider gauge track but these were very limited in extent. Narrow gauge railroads, usually 3-foot (0.9-m) gauge, were not well suited to conditions in British Columbia. The track did not provide enough stability for hauling the large logs of the coastal forests and the light, narrow gauge locomotives seldom had the timber-moving capacity to justify their existence.

On Vancouver Island, narrow gauge had been used in coal mining at Wellington in the late 1880s and to a limited degree at Extension. It was also used on the copper-hauling Lenora, Mt. Sicker Railway near Duncan. These mining railways became a source of equipment for logging operators.[32]

After the Lenora, Mt. Sicker Railway closed in 1908, its three Shays found their way onto logging operations. Shay No. 1 was used at Lombard in the Fraser Valley, while No. 2 migrated, via the Westholme Lumber Company which operated near Mt. Sicker, to Hernando Island off Campbell River. There it was used until 1920 by the Campbell River Lumber Company. The last of the Mt. Sicker Shays was also used by the Westholme Lumber Company, and finally by the Eastern Lumber Company in the vicinity of Ladysmith. One other narrow gauge logging railroad in the Ladysmith area was run by Frank Beban. He acquired one of the small, very well-worn Baldwin saddle tank colliery locomotives and operated it in the early 1920s on a mile or two of track. However, engines of this type were not well suited for logging and Beban soon converted to standard gauge equipment.[33]

In the Powell River region, as early as 1905, a narrow gauge 0-4-0 saddle tank engine was used by Andrew Haslam to move timber near Vancouver Bay, but the operation quickly gave way to standard gauge. Another narrow gauge line near Powell River, which also used an 0-4-0 tank engine, was built to haul shingle bolts by Brooks, Bidlake and Whithall between 1921 and 1923.

Narrow gauge equipment, some of it from the Dolly Varden Mines Railway at Anyox, was also used on the north coast at Alice Arm. There were a few other lines along the coast using narrow gauge equipment but all were small and few lasted very long.

Overall, the largest narrow gauge operation in British Columbia was run by the Ross-Saskatoon Lumber Company, which used two Shays and about 25 connected trucks near Waldo in southeastern British Columbia. The system was built to the unusual gauge of 42 inches (107 cm), and 10 or 12 miles (16 or 19 km) of track were utilized. Like most of the other narrow gauge lines, it closed in 1923.[34]

Wrecks brought an end to the use of narrow gauge for logging. Lenora Mt. Sicker's No. 3 was involved in two bad wrecks in logging service. In both cases, the engineers were killed. Bob Swanson, who became Chief Inspector of Railways for British Columbia, started his long career with the logging railroads while still a teenager near Nanaimo. He recalled the end of the narrow gauge. "That engine ran away on them, and I saw it after. It piled up and it killed the engineer; his

Narrow Gauge Railways

Narrow gauge Shays from the Lenora, Mt. Sicker Railway found their way onto logging operations on the Coast. No. 2 is shown at left at Stag Bay, on Hernando Island, working for the Campbell River Lumber Company about 1914.
— MAY ELLINGSEN COLLECTION

At Alice Arm on the far north coast of B.C., narrow gauge equipment from the Dolly Varden Mines Railway was briefly used for log hauling for the Granby Consolidated Mining, Smelting & Power Company as late as 1927. The Abbotsford Lumber, Mining & Development Company also ran a small narrow gauge line in this area. — J. B. SCOTT, BCFS 1927

Campbell River Lumber's diminutive Shay No. 2 was really too small for West Coast logging.
— RBCM

The Ross-Saskatoon Lumber Company of Waldo in the East Kootenays used two Shays of 42-inch (1.07-metre) gauge on their logging railroad. No. 44 is pictured with the loading crew. The smaller logs of the interior forests were more easily accommodated on narrow gauge equipment.
— FORT STEELE HERITAGE PARK COLLECTION

Frank Beban acquired a Baldwin 0-6-0T that originally worked on the coal mining railroads in the Wellington area north of Nanaimo. Such machines were poorly suited to logging on the coast.
— LEONARD FRANK PHOTOS

The crew poses beside Shay No. 1 of the Canadian Robert Dollar Company at Union Bay in November 1918. At right is the Esquimalt & Nanaimo Railway's main line. The log dump is illustrated in the photograph above.

The Canadian Robert Dollar Company, a subsidiary of the Robert Dollar interests in the United States, operated a large mill at Dollarton near Vancouver. In 1917 and 1918, the company purchased logging railroads and timberlands on Vancouver Island at Deep Bay and near Union Bay.

—BOTH DOMINION PHOTO COMPANY, FRED SMITH COLLECTION

name was Batison. Then there was another one. Well Bill Rae, the Chief Inspector, came along and says, 'You can't run that way. That's too goddamn narrow. They roll over. You'll have to get a standard gauge.'" Soon after this pronouncement, the use of narrow gauge for logging was eliminated. In any case, Bob Swanson noted, "They were just trying to fill in. But narrow gauge never took on in the woods here. Only around the mining claims where the little engines had been used."[35]

The next chapter examines in detail the types of locomotives and other special equipment used on the logging railways and how they were employed. But steam-era logging railroad technology, like any other, clearly had its limitations, defined by topography and the capabilities of the locomotives. Even with improvements developed through the early 1900s until the Depression, there were only certain areas where logging lines could be operated effectively. When combined with the marketability of different timber species and distance from mills, the reasonable geographical extent of logging railroad operations became defined. Logging beyond these areas awaited market needs or the development of different technologies.

In general, these areas included the east coast of Vancouver Island, adjacent areas of the mainland coast and the Fraser Valley. There were few operations along the north coast because of the distance from the major milling centres on Vancouver Island and around Vancouver and New Westminster. The west coast of Vancouver Island was accessible for logging but, during the steam era, the areas to the north of Port Renfrew were generally too expensive to exploit because of the costs and hazards of towing the logs along the exposed, open Pacific coastline. Moreover, good supplies of timber — usually Douglas-fir, the most important species — were available closer to the mills. Nearly all of the coastal logging railroads brought the timber to booming grounds where the logs were assembled into rafts or flat booms before being towed to the mills. The sheltered inlets and protected waters of the Strait of Georgia provided a generally safe route for the fragile, but easily constructed, log booms of Douglas-fir. Logging operators who ventured beyond these waterways added greatly to their costs for log transport and increased the risks of losing their timber en route to the mills.

Rail Logging Ends in the East Kootenays: the Timber Wasn't Limitless After All

Even into the 1920s there still seemed to be endless stands of coastal timber that could be logged using the developing steam and logging railroad technology. The old-growth Douglas-fir forests of eastern Vancouver Island, adjacent mainland coastal areas, and the Fraser Valley still carpeted the flat coastal areas, valley bottoms and lower slopes of the mountain ranges.

In the Interior, particularly in the East Kootenays, a different picture was

Ties by the thousand were needed by the Canadian Pacific Railway for the maintenance of its huge transcontinental system. The company's Tie & Timber Branch was established to provide a steady supply. A major mill and tie operation was centred at Bull River on the Kootenay Central Railway but rail logging was not used. However, at Canal Flats and at Yahk, logging railways supplied at least part of the timber. Shay No. 1, shown near Canalflat (just north of the present Canal Flats), a three-truck Climax, and possibly other equipment provided the motive power through the 1920s. In 1930, two Heislers were apparently bought from the Crows Nest Pass Lumber Company. The Yahk operations began in 1911 and continued until 1942. — W. F. MONTGOMERY, BCARS, HP73546

The Columbia River Lumber Company at Golden used railroads to supply its large mill with timber. The company was a subsidiary of the Canadian Western Lumber Company of Fraser Mills which also owned Comox Logging & Railway on Vancouver Island. The Golden-based operations eventually acquired three Heislers like No. 1 pictured at left and one smaller machine. The three large Heislers were eventually transferred to Comox Logging.

The large mills had an enormous appetite for timber, as shown in this stockpile of logs awaiting shipment by rail to Golden. Heisler No. 1 is in the distance as is a Barnhart loader. In 1927, the year before the railroad was closed, 15 miles (24 km) of track were in operation. Three Heislers were on the roster as well as 111 log cars, four flatcars, three tank cars, and one speeder. Maximum grades on the line were 3.5 percent.
—W. F. MONTGOMERY, BCARS, HP73491

Canadian Pacific crews and equipment took over to move the logs over the main line of the CPR from the logging areas near Donald to Golden. CPR trains also handled Crows Nest Pass Lumber Company logs from its railway at Bull River to the mill at Wardner.
—W. F. MONTGOMERY, BCARS, HP73486

The smaller logs of the interior forests were much easier to handle than the coastal giants. This scene is probably on the Otis-Staples railway near Wycliffe.
—GERRY WELLBURN COLLECTION

Ed Denis (left), an unidentified crew member and Charles Rogers (right) pose beside Shay No. 1 of the Crows Nest Pass Lumber Company.—CHARLES A. ROGERS & SONS COLLECTION

The Crows Nest Pass Lumber Company, based at Wardner, operated several logging railways in the East Kootenays including a narrow gauge section near Bull River. They owned two Shays and two Heislers. Heisler No. 2, named "Bowen," shown in 1921, was a typical machine used by the interior lumber industry.
—BCFS, 18550

Huge spark arresters helped prevent forest fires during the dry summers. Arrow Lakes Lumber Company's No. 7 at Galena Bay on Upper Arrow Lake was certainly well equipped. The railway, shown in these two photos, lasted only until 1912. The Shay, apparently the only locomotive, was acquired new in April 1907 and operated on about five miles (8 km) of track bringing the timber down to the lake. —KELOWNA MUSEUM

Ross-Saskatoon narrow gauge Shay No. 44 winds its way to the mill at Waldo in the 1920s. — FORT STEELE HERITAGE PARK COLLECTION

By 1928, Elk Lumber Company's Climax No. 1 was lying derelict at Fernie. The next year, the river bank caved in and the wreck was carried away. — MAX MUTZ, DOUG RICHTER COLLECTION

Eagle Lake Spruce Mills at Giscome, near Prince George, had what was probably the furthest north logging railway in the British Columbia Interior. The company owned a Shay and a Heisler. The railway ran between 1924 and 1931 and was last recorded in 1933 by the government inspectors.
— W. F. MONTGOMERY, BCARS, HP73535

Nicola Pine Mills at Merritt operated a large mill and logging railroad. Climax No. 2, a 45-ton (40.8-tonne) machine built in 1913, eventually was used by at least six logging companies in B.C. The line had grades up to six percent and employed over 40 flatcars in log hauling. The locomotives burned coal from the local mines. Climax No. 3 (at left) was the largest engine the company had. Built in 1922, this 80-ton (72.5-tonne) machine later worked for Corbin Coke & Coal in the Crowsnest Pass and for Mayo Lumber, Salmon River Logging and Merrill Ring Wilson on Vancouver Island. By 1926, logs were supplied to the mill by contractors and the railroad was sold. —W. J. PRESLEY COLLECTION, VINTAGE VISUALS; NICOLA VALLEY MUSEUM-ARCHIVES

The major railways all carried large quantities of logs to the mills. Poles were another important commodity. This loading operation was at Falkland in the north Okanagan and the logs were destined for the Vernon Box & Pine Lumber Company on September 7, 1945.
—G. M. ABERNETHY, BCFS, 3329

emerging. The accessible timber was far from inexhaustible. By World War I, the mills around the mining and lumbering centre of Fernie were running out of accessible logs and the forest industry in the Crowsnest Pass area suffered a rapid decline. Terrible fires, including one in 1908 which engulfed the town of Fernie, destroyed large quantities of timber. The logging railroads operated by the Eastern British Columbia Lumber Company, the Fernie Lumber Company and the White Spruce Lumber Company, along with the large mills they supplied, were casualties of that decline, although in the early 1920s a small operation, the Elk Valley Lumber Company, operated a short logging railway with one Climax locomotive and 12 log cars.[36]

Southwest of Fernie, at Jaffray, the East Kootenay Lumber Company, which operated 10 miles (16 km) of railway, closed about 1920. Nearby, at Waldo, the Ross Saskatoon Lumber Company closed its mill in 1923 and its narrow gauge railroad operations ceased. Its competition, the Baker Lumber Company, closed in 1929. Each mill had been capable of a daily cut of 75,000 feet (175 m³) of lumber. Forest fires destroyed vast areas; in some places logging, followed by one heavy burn and then another, greatly retarded regrowth of the forests.

To the east, in the vicinity of Cranbrook, timber supplies lasted longer and the mills boomed in the early 1920s. However, by the end of the decade, the industry was also in a serious decline there. In 1927, the Otis Staples Lumber Company, which operated a substantial railroad (actually chartered as the St. Mary's & Cherry Creek Railway in 1906), closed down. Their mill had a capacity of 100,000 feet (235 m³) per day and when it closed, the town of Wycliffe, 10 miles (16 km) northwest of Cranbrook, all but disappeared. At Golden, to the north, the Columbia River Lumber Company closed in 1927 and its Heisler locomotives were sent to Vancouver Island to operate on Comox Logging's line out of Headquarters. Both logging operations belonged to the same parent company, the Canadian Western Lumber Company.

Expansion of the Logging Railroads on the Coast: 1920-1930

The years before World War I were times of tremendous population growth and development in western Canada. Immigration from Europe and settlement, tourism, and resource development were expanding. Two new Canadian trans-continental railways — the Grand Trunk and the Canadian Northern — were under construction and a new line penetrating the interior of British Columbia — the Pacific Great Eastern — was being built diagonally north-eastwards from the south coast. World War I shattered many dreams of limitless growth and business profits but materials needed for the war effort were in great and urgent demand.

World War I ended in 1918 and by the end of the year, the total length of logging railways in the province had more than doubled to 330 miles (530 km) from the mileage of just a decade earlier, and the number of locomotives on these lines had increased from 36 to 64. Not only was the increase in numbers significant, but the equipment in use was larger, more technologically advanced and considerably more efficient. Thirty-seven lines were in operation, with an average length of nearly 9 miles (14 km). With each passing year and the progressive cutting back of the old-growth forests, the lines had to be built farther and farther back into the timber stands.[37]

By the mid-1920s an even more dramatic expansion had occurred. Seventy-nine logging railroads, ranging in size from tiny, one-mile (1.6-km) lines of independent contractors to the extensive operations of Comox Logging & Railway with 55 miles (88 km) of track, were reported by the Department of Railways in 1924, although, for various reasons, not all of these were in operation. In just six years, the track mileage had doubled again to just under 700 miles (1125 km) and so had the number of steam locomotives. Logging railroads were operating 126 steam and 12 gas locomotives. Rolling stock rosters were vastly expanded to reflect the longer hauling distances and the increased scope of the operations.[38] In addition, the CPR's Tie & Timber branch at Yahk had three locomotives, 50 sets of trucks and 25 miles [40 km] of line.

In the 1920s, the development of steam technology for use in the woods reached its peak. New and efficient types of locomotives and donkey engines were available that were vastly improved over the machines in use before World War I. The logging suppliers had succeeded in producing equipment fully capable of carrying the giant logs of the old-growth coastal forests as fast as the loggers could cut and buck them. And, perhaps ironically, in that ability was sown the fate of the logging railroads and much of the old-growth timber.

Not only were the logging railways more numerous and equipment more extensive, but the use of logging railways had extended well up the coast of British Columbia, supplying timber to the developing industry from such remote locations as Kimsquit on Dean Channel, or Kingcome Inlet. These isolated logging camps were served by coastal steamers run by the major shipping lines, particularly the Canadian Pacific Railway, Union Steamship Company and Canadian National Railways.[39] Tugs brought the booms of logs from the remote camps to the mills. The steamers and tugs were the life-lines of these distant coastal communities. All mail, supplies and news of the world came in on the boats. So, too, did the loggers, following their periodic returns to civilization for a visit home or some "hell-raising," depending on an individual's inclinations, after life in the bush had become too much to bear. The steamer dock was to the coastal camps what the railway station was to rural North America.

Work in the woods was still hard, gruelling, hazardous labour characterized by isolation and long hours. The living conditions were often primitive. Jim Wolverton, who started railroading in 1913, worked in 1920 for Rat Portage Lumber on Harrison Lake, north of the Fraser Valley. He described the remote camp that was reached by sternwheeler or small boat via the Harrison River.

They had a tent camp there. There was the cookhouse and the bunkhouses and then there were two or three tents that families lived in. It was a small camp — a one side camp. There was about 50 men in it altogether, the fallers, buckers and rigging crew. Most of them single. There was a timekeeper who was married and we had a first aid man who was married. The camp foreman was married and another young fellow who was working in the rigging. I had a little tent up there in the woods, away from the mosquitoes; they would eat the pants right off you.

Winter came and the weather got rough and we shut her down and came out of there. After Christmas we came back but we were snowed out. After that, I went down to California![40]

Jack Payne, a contractor who built bridges for the logging lines on Vancouver Island, remembered work in the late 1920s:

If you were working for an outfit and they didn't have a mill, everything that went into that bridge was cut in the woods — the pilings, the bracing, the caps, the stringers — everything was hewed. There was no monkey business, and you worked. For a solid eight hours, you had no coffee breaks, you had no job security, you have none of this nonsense you have today. But fellows were agreeable, they all worked together, and we never heard anybody complain. The money was small, but everybody was happy to have a job.[41]

The late 1920s were the boom years of the coastal logging railroads; all along the coast and in a few interior locations, the hills echoed to the sound of the whistles of the locomotives and the donkey engines. As Gerry Wellburn recalled, "everything was motion, everything was moving and excitement...."[42]

In British Columbia, production from the forests reached a pre-war peak in 1928, and growth and expansion seemed boundless. Many companies were ordering new locomotives and equipment, and the manufacturers were producing an expanded range of improved machines to increase the efficiency of the logging railroads.

A mature technology had evolved that had reached the limits of its development but few people working in the woods realized this. Steam power was still largely unchallenged but the beginnings of the gasoline and diesel era, when trucks would be the main form of log transport, were evident. The Depression and technological change were ahead.

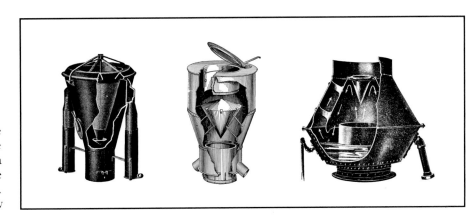

Spark arresters were the first line of defence against fires in the woods. The South Bend, Gorilla "Swem" and Davidson were popular designs in the 1920s.
— *B.C. LUMBERMAN*

Abernethy Lougheed Logging Company Ltd.

From about 1921 to 1931, George Abernethy and Nelson Lougheed ran one of the largest railroad logging shows in the Fraser Valley. They logged north of Maple Ridge up the lower reaches of the Lillooet River, a tributary of the Fraser.

This was a big enterprise, with the camps employing as many as 700 men in peak times. The railway extended onto the lower slopes of the mountains behind Haney in what became Golden Ears Provincial Park. A terrible fire destroyed most of the timber in the area in 1929 and the operation closed in 1931. The panorama shows Climax 99 backing down to the log dump with a seemingly-endless train of loaded skeleton cars near Port Haney. At left is Heisler No. 33, acquired new in 1923 and described in more detail on page 66. Climax 1662, shown in a builder's photo, became Abernethy-Lougheed's No. 66 and later became Lake Logging's No. 6 in the Cowichan District.

—W. MOORE PHOTO, VCA 650 PAN1; LEONARD FRANK, VPL; GERRY WELLBURN COLLECTION

The Powell River Company had a productive railway operation at Kingcome River from about 1912 to the mid-1920s. This train required both 2-4-2T No. 1 and 0-4-0T No.2 to move the timber. —V. C. RUSSELL

Pacific Mills, Ltd., based at Ocean Falls, operated logging railroads at several locations including Kimsquit, Kwatna Inlet, and Green Bay. Most railroad equipment was sold by 1928 or 1929. Shay No. 3 is shown on the long trestle approach to the log dump. —RBCM

By the 1920s, truck logging was becoming increasingly competitive with rail, particularly for moving small volumes of timber over short distances. Small operations began turning to trucks. This White truck was used by North Pacific Logging at Beaver Creek on Loughborough Inlet in 1920. The cook came out to have his picture taken.
—AUTHOR'S COLLECTION

International Timber Company at Campbell River had one of the largest logging railroads on Vancouver Island in the 1920s. In 1929, it had five steam locomotives (including three-truck Shay No. 4 shown at right), one gas locomotive and 224 pieces of rolling stock which it used over 47 miles (75 km) of track. In 1930, the assets were taken over by the Elk River Timber Company.
—A. A. PAULL, GERRY WELLBURN COLLECTION

International Timber's log dump near Campbell River. Note the shingle bolts in the water and the bulkhead flatcars for hauling them. —LEONARD FRANK, BCARS, HP39089

Hoard & Flaherty Logging ran a small railroad at Bainbridge in the Alberni Valley from about 1919 to 1923. The Shay then worked for Bainbridge Logging and after 1928 for Alberni Pacific as No. 3. —CLARENCE HOARD, VICTORIA CITY ARCHIVES, .8(98106-01)

Cedar poles were a major product of the forest industry during the logging railroad era. These loads, ready for shipment, were produced in 1923 by the Capilano Timber Company of North Vancouver.
—VPL 5943

The Imperial Press Conference visited the North Vancouver operations of the Capilano Timber Company in 1920.—LEONARD FRANK PHOTOS, 2034

Bernard Timber & Logging Company operated railroads at Orford Bay on Bute Inlet, Maurelle Island, and Port Neville during the 1920s. The equipment was sold in 1928 and 1929.—A. A. PAULL, ROOZEBOOM COLLECTION, BCARS, HP67989

Logging by rail required special equipment. Locomotives were built to
operate on rough, quickly-built trackage and over steep grades. The large
companies, such as Bloedel, Stewart & Welch, often acquired machines
from several manufacturers as this lineup of locomotives at Myrtle Point
suggests: Lima two-truck Shay No. 1; Baldwin 2-6-2 No. 2; and two-truck
Climax No. 3. All sported large spark arresters. — MACMILLAN BLOEDEL
COLLECTION

2 STEAM IN THE WOODS

Logging Locomotives

The rugged and transient nature of most logging railroads required special types of locomotives for efficient and safe operation. The standard designs of engines used by the major passenger and freight carrying railways in main line service were generally unsuited to logging operations. Usually they were too heavy and were equipped with large driving wheels to permit high speeds. Logging locomotives often had to operate on lightly constructed track and on bridges requiring lower axle loading than would be found on main line machines. Another feature of most of the main line or even branch line power on the major common carrier railways was that engines were designed to be turned at the end of their runs. Few logging lines had the luxury of turning facilities, which meant that logging locomotives had to operate in either direction with equal ease and safety. By the early 1900s, several specialized types of locomotives had been developed for use on logging railroads in North America.

In total, over 200 steam locomotives — we may never know exactly how many — operated on the logging railroads of British Columbia. Three-quarters of these were of the specialized geared types — Shays, Climaxes and Heislers — while the remainder were rod locomotives of more conventional appearance. Nearly all were built specially for the logging industry and were designed to meet the particular needs of log hauling. British Columbia's landscape challenged even the toughest and the most versatile machines. Equally, it challenged the men who worked with them and maintained them.

Shays, Climaxes and Heislers

The most famous type of logging locomotive was the Shay; it was also the most common type used in British Columbia. Its design was developed by Ephraim Shay, a Michigan logger, and it evolved into a highly successful and rugged logging locomotive. Built by the Lima Locomotive Works of Lima, Ohio, the Shay was unmistakable in appearance. The typical Shay had a three-cylinder engine mounted on the right hand side of its boiler over a crankshaft connected to a pair of trucks by a system of universal joints and couplings. Three-truck machines also were common. Each axle was geared directly to the driveshaft producing a very powerful, low speed, flexible machine.[1]

The powered trucks of a Shay, or other geared engine, typically might have had a wheel base of four feet, four inches (1.3 metres), while a rigid frame 2-8-2 logging locomotive of equivalent power would have had a wheel base of 14 feet (4.25 metres). The shorter wheel base meant that a Shay could run on much tighter curves than a conventional locomotive of equivalent pulling power. In this example, the Shay could operate on a curve as tight as 100 feet (30.5 metres) in radius while the 2-8-2 required twice that turning circle. Moreover, unlike typical main line steam locomotives or logging rod engines, no separate tender — unproductive weight needing to be pulled everywhere — was required to carry water and fuel. Instead, these vital commodities were carried on the locomotive itself over the powered trucks; in this way, all the weight of the locomotive was available for traction.

The biggest limitation of the Shay, and the other geared engines, was speed, but the Shay was designed to pull heavy loads on steep grades, not to be a greyhound. The geared drive system and small driving wheels gave the Shay great pulling power so that it could operate effectively on the steep grades that typified the logging railroads. Riding on trucks instead of a semi-rigid frame gave the Shay enormous flexibility in running over rough, undulating, sharply curving tracks.

Shays came in a large variety of sizes and types. Most were two-truck machines in the 40-50 ton range (36-45 tonnes) but some were as small as 10 tons (9 tonnes) while a few others topped 100 or more tons (90 tonnes). Machines such as Alberni Pacific's No. 2 or "Two-Spot," preserved at Port Alberni, and Bloedel Stewart & Welch's No. 1, preserved at the British Columbia Forest Museum, were typical woods engines in British Columbia and represented most of the Shays in use in the province before the 1920s. Later Shays, such as Mayo Lumber No. 3 (preserved at the British Columbia Forest Museum) and Comox Logging's No. 12 (displayed at the Ladysmith Railway Historical Society's museum) represent the heavier, improved Shays coming from Lima at the height of the mid-1920s logging boom.

The ultimate development of the Shay for west coast logging was the Pacific Coast Shay, first produced in 1927. This large three-truck locomotive, typically of about 90 tons (81.5 tonnes) although there were considerable variations in the weight, incorporated all of the advances, as company advertising noted, that Lima had developed for, or incorporated in, its locomotives over the years of Shay production: piston valves, superheaters, cast steel truck frames, heavy girder main frames, and improvements in the boiler, engine construction, and driving mechanism.[2]

Nearly 40 percent of all the logging locomotives in British Columbia were Shays — a testimonial to the popularity of the design with the loggers.[3] And of the Pacific Coast Shays, of the total production of 24 built by Lima, 17 operated in

Shays

*The Shay was about
the best locomotive in the woods.*
— BOB SWANSON

Mayo Lumber Company's little
two-cylinder No. 1, acquired in
1917 from North Star Lumber at
Jaffray in the Kootenays, arrived
on the Coast by flatcar. Lima built
the 18-ton (16.3-tonne) Shay in
1906. It is shown at right in
service at Paldi in 1922. The crew
was engineer Gus Schultz,
fireman Ernie Morris and
brakeman Ed McLean.
— GERRY WELLBURN COLLECTION

Comox Logging's Shay No. 6,
shown at Camp 3, in the early
1920s, was a mid-sized Class B Shay.
This 45-ton (40.1-tonne) machine
was built for Comox Logging in
1913. — RBCM

59

Merrill & Ring Lumber's No. 3, at Theodosia Arm, shows some of the improvements in Shay design developed by the 1920s. Its features included an enclosed steel cab, cast trucks and a heavy frame. The wood-burner operated with a large spark arrester. However, by the 1920s, most logging locomotives were oil-fired. —A. A. PAULL, ROOZEBOOM COLLECTION, BCARS, HP67877

The Lima Locomotive Works often photographed its new machines. The Island Logging Company ordered this 107-ton (97-tonne), three-trucker in 1927 for its Jordan River operations on the West Coast of Vancouver Island. It ran for 30 years until being scrapped in 1957. At that time it was B.C. Forest Products No. 6. Its specifications are shown at right. —GERRY WELLBURN COLLECTION

International Timber's No. 4 was representative of the Class C Shays. Built in 1920 and weighing in at 70 tons (63.5 tonnes), it worked in the woods behind Campbell River for over 30 years. —LEONARD FRANK

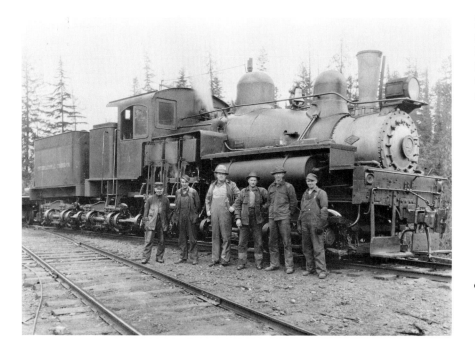

The ultimate expression of Shay development in logging service was the Pacific Coast Shay. No. 3 was built in 1929. —GERRY WELLBURN COLLECTION

LIMA LOCOMOTIVE WORKS, INCORPORATED
LIMA, OHIO

Class: 90—3 Truck Shay Geared

Road No. 3

Built for ISLAND LOGGING CO., LIMITED

GAUGE OF TRACK	DRIVING WHEEL DIAMETER	FUEL KIND	CYLINDERS			BOILER		FIREBOX	
			No.	DIAMETER	STROKE	DIAMETER	PRESSURE	LENGTH	WIDTH
4'-8½"	36"	OIL	3	14½"	15"	58⅛"	210 Lbs.	84"	58¼"

WHEEL BASE			MAXIMUM TRACTIVE POWER	FACTOR OF ADHESION	TUBES AND FLUES		
TRUCK	ENGINE	ENGINE AND TENDER			NUMBER	DIAMETER	LENGTH
4'-8"	30'-8"	43'-2¾"	42400	4.99	129 / 20	2" / 5⅜"	10'-11¼"

AVERAGE WEIGHT IN WORKING ORDER, POUNDS		GRATE AREA SQ. FT.	HEATING SURFACES, SQUARE FEET			
ON DRIVERS	TOTAL ENGINE		TUBES AND FLUES	FIREBOX	TOTAL	SUPER-HEATER
211400	211400	33.9	1037	138	1175	253

Capacity, Water 3500 Gallons

Fuel 1500 Gals.

Negative Order No. 473

Mayo Lumber's brand new Pacific Coast Shay No. 4 arrived in Vancouver on July 4, 1928. The Hofius Steel & Equipment Co., of Seattle, advertised on the locomotive, was the major Shay representative in the Northwest. This was the only Pacific Coast Shay built as a wood-burner. The heavy frame of the locomotive is shown clearly in this photograph by C. R. Littlebury.
—NORM GIDNEY COLLECTION

Pacific Coast Shays were put to work from California to British Columbia and were an immediate success. This is the Two-Spot of Cathels & Sorensen described by George Robertson on the opposite page. It was the only one of the type built as a coal-burner and was photographed amidst the desolation typical of clear-cutting.
—GEORGE ROBERTSON

Victoria Lumber & Manufacturing had three Pacific Coast Shays including No. 9 shown on the Robertson River Camp 10 operations south of Cowichan Lake. —WILMER GOLD

British Columbia, including both the first and last built. In the last years of steam operations where geared locomotives were used, the Pacific Coast Shays dominated company rosters. MacMillan Bloedel and its predecessors operated eight of the machines, B.C. Forest Products had four and Canadian Forest Products had three.[4] They were fine, well-built locomotives. "Pacific Coast Shay, you can't beat them!" remarked the late Pete McGovern, a veteran logging railroad engineer who ran many types of locomotives on Vancouver Island and in the East Kootenays over a 60-year career.[5]

The crews appreciated the improvements in the Pacific Coast Shays. Maintenance was reduced and the overall ease of operation was greatly improved. George Robertson, who worked at many of the camps on the west coast of Vancouver Island, remembered the advantages of these big machines.

The old 2-Spot, that went in there [to the Port Renfrew area on the west coast of Vancouver Island] brand new in 1929, one of the first Pacific Coast Shays to come to the coast here. On the older locomotives, the working of them engines [the three-cylinder Shay engine], used to give the fireman and the engineer awful trouble keeping the boiler up; it'd be leaky joints and it took an awful lot of overhaul work, maybe a couple times a year, especially when they got a bit old. But on the Pacific Coast type, there was a big frame and these engines were all on that big massive frame. So, your boiler and firebox was free from that, from the vibration and workings of them three engines working all the time, that's where the Pacific Coast type got its name from.

They were a pretty powerful locie.[6]

The next most popular type of logging locomotive used in B.C. was the Climax. Over 50 were used, representing about 25 percent of the total logging locomotives in operation. The Climax was also a geared locomotive, but of a distinctly different design. Typically, on the Class B (two-truck) and Class C (three-truck) types which were the most common designs, a single-cylinder engine was mounted on each side of the boiler, driving — through a gearbox — a central shaft that ran to each axle of the trucks.[7] The Climax design was tough and durable but remembered by veteran users as being rough riding. Older machines could develop a sway-back tendency that apparently had little effect on their ability to pull logs but added materially to their picturesque quality in vintage photography. Climax locomotives, like the Shays, were improved over the years. Later designs featured cast truck frames, piston valves, enclosed steel cabs and heavier frames. Hillcrest Lumber's No. 10, the last Climax operating in Canada, was typical of the best design Climax had to offer the logging market.

The use of Climax locomotives closely parallelled the application of Shays in logging. Most Climaxes which were operated in B.C. were smaller 40-50 ton (36-45 tonne), two-truck Class B engines while the remainder, with the exception of a few small machines, were heavier 70-ton (63.5 tonne) or larger Class C designs. Only one or two Class A types with wooden frames and centrally-mounted vertical engines were used. Shawnigan Lake Lumber Company's "Betsy,"

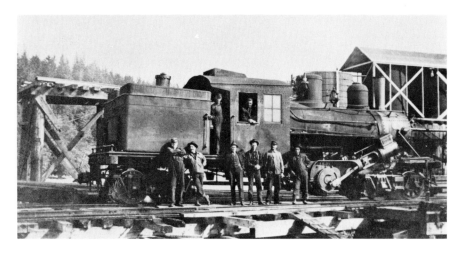

Climax Engines

Wilson & Brady's battered Climax shows its 1900 origins in its wooden cab and headlight. The history of this machine is confusing but it appears to have come to Vancouver Island in 1902 for Victoria Lumber & Manufacturing at Chemainus as No. 2. In 1912, it migrated to Heriot Bay on Quadra Island for Abbott Timber and in 1917 passed to Wilson & Brady (where it was No. 1, despite the number plate on the smokebox) who used it there and at Reid Bay. In 1922 Lake Lumber had it at Qualicum but in 1926 Frank Beban used it on his Beban Lumber & Shingle Co. at Extension. Timberland Development got it a year later, then in 1930 or '31 Henry Bay Logging used it on Denman Island. The vagabond's last record was in 1933 as a Rounds Burchett engine. —BCARS, HP44129

By 1910, Climax had modernized its locomotives with steel cabs and other improvements as shown in the Class B two-truck machine (centre) at Jordan River.
—SOOKE REGION MUSEUM & ARCHIVES

Bernard Timber & Logging's No. 4, photographed about 1926, was a standard Class B machine and was built in 1919. At 55 tons (50 tonnes), it featured a steel cab and Walschaerts valve gear.
—A. A. PAULL,
ROOZEBOOM COLLECTION,
BCARS, HP67983

About 16 Class C, three-truck
Climaxes operated in B.C
altogether. Capilano Timber's No.
2 of 70 tons (63.5 tonnes), built in
1917, was representative of these
large machines. Sold in 1931 to
Sisters Creek Logging and then
passed to Industrial Timber Mills,
it ended its days with B.C. Forest
Products. Empire Lumber's No. 1,
at right, was more modern. This
80-ton engine (72.5-tonne)
featured piston valves with
Walchaerts valve gear. Built in 1923
for Campbell River Mills of White
Rock, it also last worked for B.C.
Forest Products. W. F. Montgomery
set up his 8x10 glass plate camera
to record his classic portrait of No.
1 in the Cowichan District about
1925. — GERRY WELLBURN
COLLECTION; BCARS, HP73655

described and illustrated in Chapter 1, is typical of this design of lightweight Climax locomotive. "Betsy" also was one of the few steam locomotives used in British Columbia to operate on wooden rails. This rather primitive and inefficient mode of operation was soon replaced with conventional, albeit lightweight, steel rails and standard railroad wheels.

The third type of geared locomotive used in British Columbia was the Heisler. Apparently only 17 of these machines operated in the province and all but two were of two-truck configuration. The Heisler had a pair of cylinders mounted in a "V" pattern, one on each side of the boiler, driving a central shaft that was connected to one axle of each truck. The other wheels were driven by connecting rods from the powered wheels.[8] This arrangement produced a somewhat higher speed than the Shays and the Climaxes could attain. In 1924, the *West Coast Lumberman* noted that "Abernethy-Lougheed (of Port Haney in the Fraser Valley) decided to try a Heisler on the main line haul.... The new Heisler came fully up to expectations... it easily maintains a speed of 20 miles [32 km] an hour, and can go up to 25 [40 km] without tearing itself to pieces. They had been getting two trains a day, but because of its extra speed the Heisler started right in hauling three regular trains of 30 cars each, or more."[9] But they could be rough-riding, as Pete McGovern remembered from his days with Comox Logging, who operated more Heislers than any other company in B.C. "They were up and down and all ways. They were real devils. They'd go into the class of a Climax. They had the cylinder on each side, and they'd get going this way — in a rocking motion. They had to be overhauled more than the Shays, I think. Everybody used to run them and you could only run them for a few weeks maybe, and then they'd tie them up again."[10]

Heisler development, like that of the Shay, culminated in a locomotive designed specially for the Pacific Coast lumber industry. Heisler's answer to the Pacific Coast Shay was the "West Coast Special," offered in 70-, 80- or 90-ton (63.5-, 72.6- or 81.6-tonne) sizes. These were three-truck locomotives, with superheaters, feed water heaters, piston valves, deep girder-strengthened frames, enclosed steel cabs, and many improvements to trucks, running gear and boilers.[11] The new Heislers were impressive machines but so too were those of the competition. Just like Shay, Climax and Willamette production, Heislers would be a casualty of the Depression. Only one West Coast Special operated in British Columbia.[12] It ran for Malahat Logging as No. 4 and later for British Columbia Forest Products on the west coast of Vancouver Island. Malahat Logging ran it on their main line, just as its builder had intended.

The discussion of geared locomotive types in British Columbia ends with one, and possibly two, others. The Willamette Iron and Steel Works of Portland, long a supplier of logging equipment, developed and built its own design of geared logging locomotives in the 1920s. These engines were generally similar to Shays of the same vintage but with some differences in cylinder placement and other

Heislers

Capilano Timber Company's No. 3 shown near North Vancouver, on June 3, 1933 was a standard mid-sized Heisler. — KEN MERILEES

B.C. Forest Products' No. 8, formerly of Malahat Logging, was the most modern of the 17 Heislers to operate in British Columbia. — ELWOOD WHITE

features.[13] Willamette competed successfully with Lima in the American market but only one of their well-built locomotives came to Canada: Lake Logging's three-truck No. 3 which was built in 1928 and scrapped in 1956. Finally, there is an unconfirmed report that a geared locomotive built by the Washington Iron Works came to British Columbia. Details of this locomotive are limited and subject to conjecture.[14]

George Robertson summed up the loggers' view of the geared locomotives: "The Shay was the better locie of any really. The Climax was kind of a rough locomotive. There weren't too many Heislers used but they were good. It was mostly Shays, all over the coast...." Bob Swanson reflected that the Climax "wasn't the lady that the Shay was. The Shay was a well-built, well-balanced, beautifully-made engine. So was the Climax, but it was a bit crude. They used to run them to beat hell!"[15]

Rod Engines

Approximately 50 rod locomotives were used on British Columbia logging operations. Rod locomotives (sometimes called straight connected locomotives) were mechanically simpler than the geared locomotives. The power was transmitted directly from the cylinders by connecting rods to the driving wheels which were mounted in the locomotive frame under the boiler. The relative simplicity of the design usually meant that a rod locomotive was cheaper to maintain than a comparable geared locomotive. William Gibbons, in a 1918 extensive study of the forest industry in the western states, estimated that the cost of maintaining a geared locomotive averaged $400-700 a year while a rod locomotive averaged $300-400. These costs were offset to a degree by the costs of new rod engines which were usually somewhat higher than those of a geared engine. For example, in 1918, a typical 67-ton (60-tonne) rod engine might cost $13,900 while a 70-ton (63.5-tonne) geared engine cost $11,800. However, more important than the initial cost of the machines was their suitability for working in the conditions of a particular operation. Oil-burning equipment, used on nearly all logging locomotives in British Columbia, added another $400 to $500 to the purchase price.[16]

Most of the logging rod locomotives in British Columbia were modern machines from the major North American manufacturers, particularly Baldwin. In fact, there were more Baldwin logging locomotives in British Columbia than there were Heislers, giving Baldwin third place as the most important supplier of logging locomotives in British Columbia. Most rod engines were 2-6-2, 2-6-2T, 2-8-2 and 2-8-2T types. Overall, they ranged in size from small Porter, Baldwin or Davenport yard engines, such as 2-4-2s or 0-6-0Ts, through large 2-8-2s, and 2-6-6-2 and 2-6-6-2T articulated locomotives that topped the list in the 150-ton (135-tonne) range.

Many of the logging rod locomotives were fitted with side or saddle tanks to

Willamette

Only one Willamette geared locomotive operated in British Columbia and that was McDonald Murphy Logging Company's No. 3. This was the largest Willamette built and it was comparable to the Pacific Coast Shays built by Lima. Willamette had every right to be proud of its machines and if it had not been for the Depression it is likely that more would have been purchased by B.C. companies. The 80-ton (72.5-tonne) machine spent its entire life in the Gordon River area south of Cowichan Lake, following its delivery in 1928. Later, it was owned by Lake Logging and finally by Western Forest Industries before falling victim to truck hauling. It was scrapped in 1956. — W. F. MONTGOMERY, BCARS, HP73750

Tank Engines

Tank engines came in all shapes and sizes. B.C. Mills, Timber & Trading Company's 0-6-0T No. 6, shown at New Westminster on December 11, 1938, was typical of early smaller rod engines used in B.C. It was built by Montreal Locomotive Works in 1904.
—KEN MERILEES

Comox Logging's Baldwin No. 2, called the "Deuce" by its crews, worked at both Headquarters and Ladysmith. Built in 1910, it was not formally retired until 1960 when it was placed on display at Courtenay.
—H. L. BROADBELT COLLECTION

Timberland Development Company purchased a new coal-burning Porter 2-6-2T in 1924 for its railway north of Ladysmith. In the end, it was one of the last steam locomotives operating in B.C. It is shown in later years on the next page. —GERRY WELLBURN COLLECTION

This little, much-rebuilt 0-4-0T called the "Mabel Gwilt," ran for the Gwilt Lumber Company near Courtenay in the early 1920s. Gerry Wellburn worked on this engine as a young man in 1922 and memories of it encouraged Gerry to acquire the collection of small locomotives now at the B.C. Forest Museum. —GERRY WELLBURN

The service which a locomotive must deliver, and the conditions that are encountered,
widely vary in the logging industry, and accounts for the variance in the designs used

Specifications

Cylinders, 17 x 24″
Gauge of track, 56½″
Fuel, coal
Weight in running order:

Total	135,000 lbs.
On drivers,	106,000 lbs.
On leading truck,	14,000 lbs.
On trailing truck,	15,000 lbs.

Wheel base:

Rigid,	11′ 0″
Total,	25′ 2″

Diameter of drivers, over tires, 44″
Boiler pressure, 180 lbs.
Tractive force, 24,115 lbs.
Factor of adhesion 4.4
Height   14′ 0″
Width   10′ 6″
Length   31′ 4″
Diameter of boiler, 60″

Firebox:	Length	72″
	Width at top	50″
	Width at bottom	42½″

Flues: 221—2″ x 11′ 0″

Heating surface:	Tubes,	1263.2 sq. ft.
	Firebox,	97 sq. ft.
	Total,	1360.2 sq. ft.

Great area, 21.25 sq. ft.
Water capacity of two side tanks, 1800 gallons
Coal capacity, 7000 lbs.
Flexible staybolts
Boiler built to British Columbia requirements
Piston valves
Walschaert valve gear
Driving wheel—centers cast steel
Steel tired truck wheels
Leach air sanders
Pyle-National electric headlights
Collins flange oilers   Westinghouse No. 6 ET air brake
Fire extinguisher   with two 9½″ pumps

Victoria Lumber's 1044 shown at Chemainus on August 24, 1951 began its long career as Timberland Development's No. 4. In 1929 VL&M bought out the Timberland operations. The engine went through several rebuildings before making its last runs in 1969. Other photos are on pages 88, 213 and 252-257.
—ALBERT FARROW

All three locomotives shown on this page survived to be part of the last steam logging railroad operation in North America. Bloedel, Stewart & Welch's No. 4, shown at Menzies Bay in 1927, was a Baldwin product of 1925. It was an ideal main line engine for logging service.
—W. F. MONTGOMERY, BCARS, HP73735

Campbell River Timber's No. 2, a Baldwin saddle tank 2-8-2T, was one of the last two new rod engines built for B.C. logging railroads before the Depression. Locomotives like this one could operate equally well in either direction and carried nearly all their weight over the drivers. In later years it was sold to Alberni Pacific and worked for MacMillan Bloedel until the early 1970s.
—W. F. MONTGOMERY, BCARS, HP73691

carry water for the boiler, and a small fuel bunker was fitted behind the cab. This arrangement placed all of the weight of water over the driving wheels, increasing tractive effort and eliminating the need for pulling a heavy tender. However, operating range was reduced. Baldwin developed their tank engines to compete with the geared machines. Baldwin could produce convincing figures to argue that except under extreme conditions of grade or curvature, its 2-8-2T and 2-6-6-2T locomotives could handle trains as heavy as could the geared engines. In fact, Baldwin argued that the rod engines used less fuel.[17] But the geared engine proponents countered with figures to show less wear and tear on rolling stock and the ability of the Shays and other engines to operate on lighter rail due to their more even torque.[18] One logger added interesting comments in the same debate in *The Timberman* and probably summarized the feelings of most users:

Probably one reason that we got Shay engines for our work in the woods is that our country gets steeper in places, and we like the idea of having an engine that we can use to switch on grades up to 9 or 10 percent. Then we had the factor of the tower skidders. The weight of the tower skidder is 163 tons [148 tonnes]. We have moved a skidder with the one Shay on a 4 percent grade. We like the idea of having a geared engine for this particular work where the weight of the machine to be moved is great and as in the case of most all logging operations, our rails are probably lighter than they should be. We use 56 and 60-pound steel.* We feel that the geared engine can move this weight slower. The slower we can move the skidders the safer we feel about it if they go off the track. Then in the case of holding on the hills, we figure that a geared engine has more braking power than the rod engine. There are the same number of drivers in either case. The geared drivers are smaller and probably hold better in coming down grades with long logs. We are well satisfied with the performance of both machines for their respective work, and we rather feel that there is a place and there will continue to be a place for both types of machines.[19]

Some of the variations in design, special features and the details of minor locomotive builders are shown or described in the illustrations and captions. A general characteristic of the engines was that few looked exactly alike. Manufacturers did try to standardize production but they also provided a great variety of model types in their catalogues, as well as being very amenable to either customizing a locomotive or building one to special order. However, machines such as the Pacific Coast Shay were unlikely to be extensively changed from the basic catalogue design, although Mayo Lumber's No. 4 was built as a woodburner. But when a locomotive arrived on a logging line, it was the shop and operating crews' turns to add special appliances and equipment to suit local needs. A typical woods engine might feature a large spark arrester, both front and rear footboards, tool boxes, extra sanders, seats for brakemen, hose reels and a steam pump, a large siphon hose, fire-fighting equipment, and a snow plow for winter service. The list of extras was almost endless, and these variations contributed to the individuality of the locomotives. Some locomotives went

* Rail was measured in pounds per yard. The metric equivalents are 23.25 kg/m and 24.9 kg/m.

through extensive modifications having, for example, saddle tanks cut off or added, or tenders fitted for greater operating range, as requirements demanded.

The different types and sizes of logging locomotives were employed systematically by the companies to produce an efficient log transportation system. The choice between purchasing a locomotive from one manufacturer or another might depend on price, availability, personal preference or an attempt to standardize with one type of machine. However, a 45-ton (41-tonne) Climax could be used in the same ways as an equivalent Shay or Heisler. Where a company might own only one or two locomotives, the crews operated whatever they had available. However, on larger operations, with bigger equipment rosters, it was possible to employ the machines more efficiently, taking advantage of the special features of both rod and geared locomotives.

Geared engines were most efficient on steep trackage in rough country; there lay the advantage of their power and flexibility. However, on flat land, which in British Columbia meant the valley bottoms or coastal plains, they were too slow for efficient long-distance hauling. In these areas, rod locomotives were preferable because of their greater speed.

Employing the qualities of each type of locomotive to best advantage produced a typical pattern. Crews worked geared engines from the landings, where the timber was loaded onto the railcars, to transfer points along the main lines of the logging railroads. Main line crews, working with rod engines, gathered the loaded cars and returned empties for the other crews to take back to the landings for more logs. The destination for the main line crews was usually the log dump, but it could be a transfer point with one of the major rail lines. In this way, a company might employ several geared locomotives while requiring only one or two rod locomotives. However, if a main line were particularly hilly or rough, a heavier geared engine — perhaps a 70- or 90-ton (64- or 82-tonne) machine — might be used for the long haul down to the log dump. In theory, if grades on the main line exceeded two percent for loaded trains or five percent for empty trains, geared engines became a practical choice.

Rod engines generally worked best where grades for loaded trains were less than one and a half percent and for empty trains did not exceed three percent. However, logging operators simply used the equipment they had to best advantage and could not always abide by manufacturers' guidelines or what was theoretically the most economical approach in a particular logging situation. "A rod engine," reflected George Robertson after many years in logging, "won't work on a grade over about three percent; four percent's about their limit. Whereas a geared engine will work on eight, nine, they've been know to work on 13 percent but that's a little bit on the tricky side; six or seven was nothing. A 90-ton (82-tonne) Shay would handle 10, 12 empty cars up a nine percent grade going back into the woods. Or they could haul six or seven loaded cars out of an adverse grade of about eight or nine percent. Very seldom they had to haul out much of an adverse, [except for] getting empties back in the woods."[20]

74

Bloedel, Stewart & Welch's No. 2 or "Two-Spot" 2-6-2 was a typical mid-sized rod engine used in the woods. It was built by Baldwin in 1913 and worked at Myrtle Point, Menzies Bay, Great Central, and Copper Canyon. It received the new steel cab, shown at right, at the Menzies Bay shops. As MacMillan & Bloedel's 1022, it was photographed on the Copper Canyon railroad from Chemainus on May 26, 1953.
—MACMILLAN BLOEDEL COLLECTION; ALBERT FARROW

Unusual, because of its 2-6-0 wheel arrangement, Baldwin No. 1 worked for the Eagle River & Northern, a Brooks-Scanlon-O'Brien operation, at Stillwater. The engine ran from 1909 until its retirement in 1952. —CVA

Elk River Timber Company's No.5, was a big Porter 2-8-2 built in 1928. It was used on the main line. —W. F. MONTGOMERY, BCARS, HP73677

Elk River Timber, near Campbell River, had several Shays and a large Porter 2-8-2 which functioned in an effective combination on their extensive logging railroad. Pete McGovern worked as an engineer on the line before World War II and recalled the pattern of operations.

The Shays were run up in the woods, feeding onto the main line. Of the two smaller ones, one was on the steel gang laying and picking up track all the time, and the other one was switching and hauling the crew up, in and out of camp. The two bigger engines [the Porter and the Pacific Coast Shay], they would haul the logs out, they'd be in different areas. The Pacific Coast Shay would handle the biggest bulk of the trains coming in. From Camp 9, they used to have the main line engines go out at one o'clock for the first trip in the afternoon. The Pacific Coast Shay would pick up loads and bring them into Camp 8. The Porter would go to the beach [the log dump] and then back to Camp 8. Then the Pacific Coast Shay would meet him at Camp 8 with his train and then they'd switch engines and carry on that way.

The Porter would handle it to the the dump and back to Camp 8. The first trip they went all the way down and then back to Camp 8. And the next trip, they went from Camp 8 down and then back to Camp 9 which was about 40 miles [66 km] from the beach.[21]

On the west coast of the Island, Malahat Logging also used different locomotives on the branch lines and main line. George Robertson described how different geared engines were used to advantage, the heavy new geared engines on the main line and the lighter machines working the branches.

That Heisler [three-truck West Coast Special] never done much switching in the woods, it was just strictly running on the main line, which was about 16 miles [26 km] to camp and then out to the woods. They had the one machine on the main line, and it runs double shift. There was a day shift, run a nine or 10 hour shift, and there was a night crew on another nine or 10 hour shift. Then there was a switch engine out in the woods. Very seldom that had to work night shifts, only maybe in the summer months a bit.

It was the same on the Hemmingsen side [of the San Juan Valley near Port Renfrew]. They ran one locie on the main line, and then a switch engine out in the woods.[22]

The strengths of the different locomotives — hauling power on grades, or capacity for speed on the flat land — account, in large part, for the much greater number of geared locomotives than rod locomotives in British Columbia. In 1928, for example, when the forest industry was doing well in the years just before the Depression, there were only 24 rod engines in operation, mostly in main line hauling, while there were 113 geared locomotives in use in the province.[23] Later, however, as trucks became increasingly important for moving timber, it was the rod engines that were to become the dominant type of locomotive on the surviving logging railroads. The geared engines were replaced by trucks hauling the timber from the mountain slopes down to the logging main lines.

The life span of logging locomotives varied considerably. Some seemed to go on forever; others lasted only a few years. A great deal depended on the stability of the lumber market and the demand for used equipment. Some of the longer-surviving machines were in the rosters of the large companies. Comox Logging's No. 2, a Baldwin 2-6-2T built in July 1910, survived on the property until it was preserved at Courtenay in 1960. A 40-year life span was not uncommon, although 20 years was probably more typical. Some engines, like Comox Logging's No. 2, stayed with one company throughout their careers in the woods and may have been moved very little, while others passed through six or eight owners in widely separated parts of the province, moved from place to place by barge along the coast or occasionally by common carrier railroad. Sometimes they were even moved overland on a sled, skidded along by a donkey engine until they reached the end of track. Each machine had a unique history; the stories of several individual logging locomotives are presented in the accompanying illustrations.

Train Handling, Safety and Locomotive Maintenance

Operating trains on the steep grades and twisting, turning trackage of the logging lines required special skills learned from years on the job and constant attention. "I always used to tell the guys," remembered Pete McGovern, "'you don't try to see how fast you can go coming down the hill, you try to see how slow you can go.'" He recalled two incidents in handling heavy trains on the steep grades of the Copper Canyon operations west of Chemainus:

We usually used retainers [for retaining air brake pressure] on the heavy grades. The main thing on the steep grade is keeping your train down to a slow speed instead of letting it go. . . . I used to come down no trouble at all, just about eight, 10 miles [15 km] an hour all the way. Some of them would come down 20 miles [25 km] an hour, and they just risk running away all of a sudden, because they didn't keep it under control. I went down the switchbacks over at Copper Canyon and every time I'd make an application going down the hill, I'd stall. I said to the brakeman, "How many retainers you got on there?" He said, "We got 'em all up on high pressure." I said, "No wonder it's stalling."

   You just touch them and they snug right up and I said, "Just put up one high, and maybe two or three on low and then alternate it through the train." The next time we come down there, it was smooth all the way down, same speed all the way. Apparently the other fellow on day shift, with the same engine, No. 9, they said every time he came down the hill, they had them all up on high pressure and he pretty near had a run-away every time he was coming down [because he had used up all his air pressure by keeping the retainers on high all the way down]. They weren't under control.

Handling the big donkeys and skidders brought another set of problems:

I brought the big No. 2 skidder that weighed about 250 tons [227 tonnes] down from the Three-mile, down over a mile or so of grade . . . about four percent . . . with the 1044. Well, we put in extra cars, rigging cars and oil cars to help brake the skidder, to hold it back. Just kept it down to a slow speed. If it once got rollin' on you, well. . . . The main thing is to keep it down to where it only took a little shot of air to keep it that way. Don't let her get moving on you.[24]

78

Main line power was supplied mostly by Baldwin. An exception was M&B's first 1055 which was built by Alco in 1920. The 135-ton (122.5-tonne) 2-8-2 was brought to B.C. by Alberni Pacific in 1939 and was for many years the largest logging locomotive in the province. Its early career was in Oregon on the Portland, Astoria & Pacific and with the Oregon American Lumber Company. From APL the engine went to Chemainus as shown on the Copper Canyon line on May 26, 1953. The engine survives as Canfor's 113. — ALBERT FARROW

Baldwin built Comox Logging's No. 11 in 1923. It is shown at Ladysmith on May 26, 1953. The 2-8-2 was a standard Baldwin logging Mikado type or "Mike" featuring piston valves, and 44-inch (112-cm) drivers. It worked for both Simpson Timber and the Donovan Corkery Logging Company in Washington before being purchased by Comox Logging in 1937. — ALBERT FARROW

The largest steam locomotive in logging service in B.C. was Canfor's 111. This machine was a 2-6-6-2 type rebuilt from a 2-6-6-2T at Tyee Machinery in Vancouver. Built for Weyerhaeuser in 1929, it was purchased in 1946 by Canfor to provide heavy power on the main line in the Nimpkish Valley. — ELWOOD WHITE

Hazards of the Trade

Despite every precaution by the crews and regular equipment maintenance, accidents did happen all too often on the logging trains.

Scottish Palmer Logging's No. 1 was caught in the engine shed when a fire started in 1926. The intense heat from the burning building and fuel oil destroyed the cab and damaged the cylinder assembly. The Shay was rebuilt and became Royston Lumber No. 2.

Less seriously damaged was Alberni Pacific's No. 6 when it lost its footing at Alberni in 1938 and needed the steam crane to get it back on the tracks. APL trains passed through the outskirts of the city and a wreck such as this one became a subject of great interest.
—VPL; GERRY WELLBURN COLLECTION

Bloedel, Stewart & Welch's Shay No. 15 went right through the middle of the trestle in this wreck near Franklin River in December 1939. It, too, was rebuilt.
—ARNOLD EDWARDS

On steep grades it was frequently necessary to "double the hill." This meant taking half of the cars up at a time so that a short section of excessive grade did not limit the hauling capacity of a locomotive for the entire trip. There were several ways of handling this operation. The locomotive could be placed in the middle of the train and when it reached the bottom of the hill, the cars behind would be cut off. The locomotive would then push the cars in front over the summit and then return for the rest of the train. With a siding nearby, it was possible to keep the engine on the front of the train and run around the extra cars. Pete McGovern recalled an incident on Elk River Timber's Campbell River line when things became somewhat more complicated. The main line crew was "doubling the hill" with the big Porter 2-8-2:

You'd start out with 26 or more on the head end and you'd have a caboose at the front. The brakeman rode the caboose. Then, you'd push the 26 or so on the head end, kick them up over the hump, two, three miles up the track. You run them down hill and up hill [rolling up the next hill until they came to a stop]. . . . One night we had a brakeman on there, I guess he fell asleep instead of being awake to pull the air when they [got to the point where they] started to roll back again. They met the train coming up with the second bunch. Oh wow, what a pileup! There was trucks piled up to above the smokestack on the No. 5.

The engineer and fireman, they didn't know what happened. The fire, when it hit, blew right back. They thought the boiler had blown up or something. Anyway, the brakeman didn't feel much at the caboose because by the time the slack had pushed into the caboose, more or less, the caboose stopped. So he comes down, going on about making a rough coupling![25]

Where the grade was just beyond the capacity of a locomotive, it was sometimes possible to work your way over the summit. Richard James described how the Cathels & Sorenson's crew worked their 2-6-2 No. 1 (later MacMillan Bloedel No. 1077) over an adverse grade near Port Renfrew on Vancouver Island in the mid-1920s:

The 1-Spot pulled 19 skeleton cars from the upper camp to the booming grounds. She came down forward and backed back up to the camp. There was one place where she stalled on the grade. The brakeman would go back and set the brake on the last car. Then they would let the engine brake off and roll back to bunch up the slack. The engineer would blow the whistle and would bump ahead maybe 20 feet [6 m]. As soon as she stalled again, the brakeman would set the brake again. After about two or three times, the engine would make it over the top. That was on a two or three percent grade with heavy fir.[26]

This type of situation used equipment to the limits of its capability, but pulling an extra carload or two on each trip made a significant difference in productivity when a crew might be able to complete only two or three runs a shift from the woods to the log dump. Trial and error showed what was possible but there were many variables including weather and rail conditions. The train crews had to know their equipment well and safety was a priority. Accidents in remote locations, away from medical help, were even more of a threat than in settled areas.

Maintenance on the locomotives in the woods presented many problems to the crews. Some large operations had fully-equipped shops and machinists and boiler makers on staff, but many smaller operations had only basic facilities. In any case, once they were out in the woods, the responsibility fell to the train crews to bring their equipment into camp. The men took pride in their locomotives and in their ability to maintain them.

Safety and inspection were major concerns of the British Columbia Government's Railways Department over the years. The inspectors routinely examined locomotives, tested boilers, spark arresters and safety appliances. They worked with the companies to examine used equipment being imported to make sure it would pass provincial standards. They also examined engineers, firemen and other train crewmen before giving them their "tickets." In the small, out-of-the-way operations an inspector might have his hands full dealing with financially marginal operators. Larger railroad operations could not afford to be shut down or have problems and were generally more cooperative. The inspectors had to know the equipment and have a good practical knowledge of operations in the woods. "The early ones [inspectors] were tough," recalled Tom Coates, who at an early age developed a keen interest in safety in the woods. One inspector was "... a miserable bastard. But when Bob Swanson [for many years Chief Inspector for the Department of Railways] got the chief's job everything changed in that Bob was reasonable to deal with. It didn't mean that he was soft, but he was reasonable." Tom recounted an incident with an earlier inspector from his years with Salmon River Logging at Kelsey Bay.

This 90-ton Shay was stopped at the siding when they should have been heading for camp and I came along with the speeder. I wondered what was wrong because when I had checked with the dispatcher, I was cleared to camp, following the locomotive. Johnny said, "There's a leak in the boiler, of some kind. There must be a rivet gone or something. I don't know whether I should keep going or not."

I said, "Well, cut the steam and roll downhill into camp anyways and we'll find out what's wrong."

So they cut the steam down, that's the blowoff valve, cut it down to 20 or 30 pounds [140 to 200 kPa] and headed on into camp. We got to camp and took the lagging off the boiler and there was a crack about eight inches [20 cm] long. Not a lateral crack, but it went from the seam out. This was an unusual thing. I got on the phone and called the chief Inspector. He said, "What's the matter?"

"Well," I said, "she's developed a crack, we have an eight-inch crack across the bottom of the plate in the boiler."

He said, "Bullshit!"

And I said, "Not bullshit! We've got a crack there!"

"Oh, impossible!" he said, "You must be looking at a rivet leak."

"No," I said, "it's a crack. We can see it."

"If you had a crack like that," he said, "the boiler would have gone sky-high!"

"They brought some Shays up from Pysht down on the Peninsula, and I had to get those going. But the boilers didn't match the B.C. code. So I said I could fix that. I figured if it didn't blow up in the States, it wouldn't blow up here. The air was the same. So I converted those joints by putting a new outside butt strap on them. Russell Mills sent a slide rule down to me and I did the calculation and laid it all out and did the job and they ran 'til they scrapped them."
—BOB SWANSON

Safety was an ever-present concern for the men working on the logging trains. Onni Parta had a near-fatal accident on December 2, 1947 as the following quote from the Department of Railways accident file reveals: "...at 10.55 p.m. Loco 17 with fourteen skeleton cars being pushed from log dump to Siding 1 for overnight storage. Head brakeman [conductor] Onni Parta fell beneath first car and two rear wheels ran over his right leg. He then grabbed air hose coupling between first and second cars and was dragged 450 feet. His left foot badly mangled with compound fractures..."

Twenty-two years after that accident, Onni checked the air pump on MacMillan Bloedel's 1066 before working turns of cars down to the dump at Chemainus in 1969. —ROBERT D. TURNER

83

George Stevenson of Alberni Pacific connects up the air brakes between two skeleton cars. Air brakes were essential for controlling trains on the steep grades. — MACMILLAN BLOEDEL COLLECTION

The backhead plate from MacMillan Bloedel's second 1055 read: "Going down 6% to 9% grade have water line at gauge cock No. 1. Going up 6% to 8% grade do not have water line below gauge cock No. 3."
— ROBERT D. TURNER

The loggers used the tools at hand to work on their locomotives and rolling stock. Canfor's 112 had its boiler lowered onto the running gear with the big steam log unloader at Englewood (right).
—STAN UNSWORTH

"We were putting a new barrel on the Two-Spot out in the snow, and I says, 'Why don't we put it on in the shed?'

Matt [Hemmingsen] says, 'If the goddamn shed burned down where the hell, we would have nothing, would we?' So we had to work out in the bloody snow, and I says, 'you've got three stumps— two would have done.'

'Well,' he says, 'I'll show you something else mister you don't know. You get everything under snow now, you just get the hot water hose—all the bolts and nuts are on the top of the stump and nobody's going to steal them.'

You can maintain a Shay between two stumps but you can't do a rod engine. You've got to have a drop pit to do a rod engine."
—BOB SWANSON

Spare parts, boiler tubes and anything that might be useful for fixing equipment were kept close to the shops because sources of parts could be a long way away. This cluttered scene (centre right) is from B.C. Forest Products with Heisler No. 8 in for repairs.
—GERRY WELLBURN COLLECTION

Ross-Saskatoon Lumber's narrow gauge Shays were repaired out in the open, or as Bob Swanson described above, "between two stumps." —AUTHOR'S COLLECTION

The camp and shops of Merrill Ring Wilson near Rock Bay on Vancouver Island were very well equipped. This pre-World War II scene shows the variety of the equipment used on the railroad. —TOM COATES

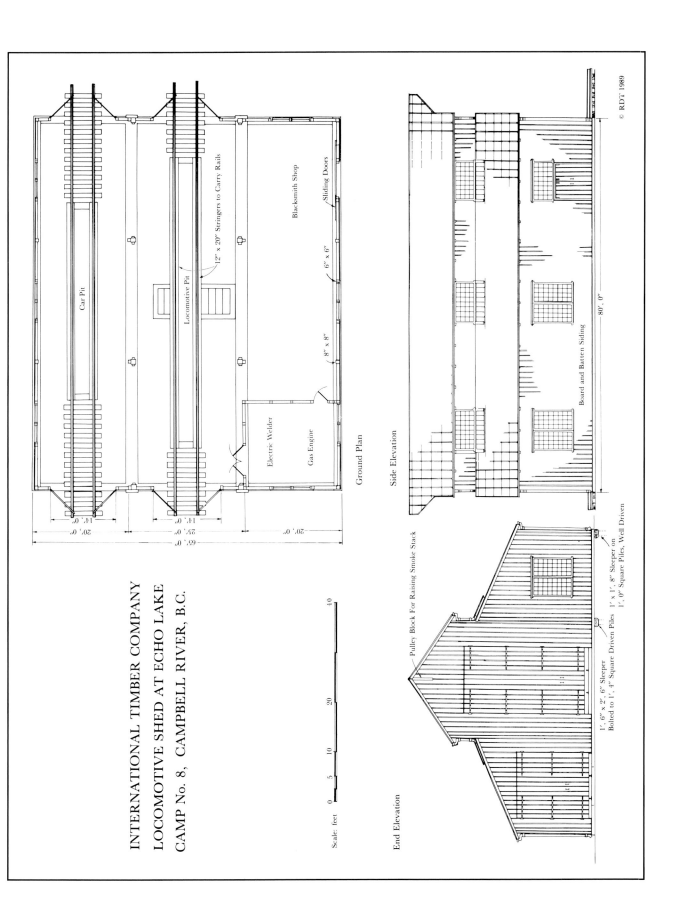

INTERNATIONAL TIMBER COMPANY
LOCOMOTIVE SHED AT ECHO LAKE
CAMP No. 8, CAMPBELL RIVER, B.C.

Scale: feet

0   5   10   20   40

Ground Plan

Car Pit

Locomotive Pit

12" x 20" Stringers to Carry Rails

8" x 8"

6" x 6"

Electric Welder

Gas Engine

Blacksmith Shop

Sliding Doors

14', 0"

14', 0"

20', 0"

25', 0"

20', 0"

65', 0"

Side Elevation

Board and Batten Siding

80', 0"

End Elevation

Pulley Block For Raising Smoke Stack

1', 6" x 2', 6" Sleeper
Bolted to 1', 4" Square Driven Piles

1' x 1', 8" Sleeper on
1', 0" Square Piles, Well Driven

© RDT 1989

Some of the large operations, such as VL&M at Chemainus, had fine, fully-equipped shops and the crews were able to carry out extensive repairs, build equipment such as speeders, or completely rebuild heavy equipment. In this photo by Jack Cash, No. 4 (later 1044) is receiving an overhaul at Chemainus. This locomotive went through many changes in appearance over the years. It operated on the main line, with and without sidetanks and was fitted with an old CPR switcher tender. Later the tanks went back on and it lost the tender. Its original appearance, as built for Timberland Development, is shown on page 71. Other views appear in Chapters 4 and 5.—MACMILLAN BLOEDEL COLLECTION

"Well," I said, "the boiler's still there but we got the crack!"

Well he came up and we did have the crack. But I couldn't convince him it was a crack until he came up to see it. We had to put a whole new course in the boiler. That's half the boiler renewed. She was tied up for a couple of months. They did that up in camp. Vancouver Machinery did the boiler work, but we did it up there.[27]

Whether or not the provincial inspectors were always appreciated at the time a particular piece of machinery came under scrutiny may be debatable, but few men in the woods doubted the necessity or value of the inspectors' contribution. Work in the woods was dangerous enough without having unsafe equipment, and the regular inspections enforced a standard that greatly improved conditions on the railways. Even so, on the logging railways alone, in 1925, which was a particularly bad year, there were seven fatal accidents. None, however, was attributed to equipment failure. The causes of the fatalities were a sad litany to tough working conditions or, all too often, moments of carelessness. On Abernethy-Lougheed's operation, one man was struck by a stack and killed (the details were not recorded) while another fell under a locomotive. At the Frank Beban Lumber Company, a man died after jumping off a moving train. The Lamb Lumber Company lost a crewman who fell off a car and died, while an employee at Deep Bay Logging was crushed by a log when his speeder jumped the tracks. At Merrill & Ring Lumber a man stumbled and fell between the cars of a moving train and was killed as was a logger at Wood & English who stepped in front of a moving car. Each year during the peak years of logging railroad activity several fatal accidents could be anticipated. It was a depressing prospect.

Inspection and approval by the Railway Department also helped determine the rates charged by the Workmen's Compensation Board. The two organizations cooperated to encourage safe operations. At times, the quest for better conditions was a challenge and the threat of higher WCB charges helped encourage better and safer equipment. One Department engineer wrote to H. B. Gilmore, Commissioner of the WCB, "...with regard to the Gwilt Lumber Company, I am awaiting the return of the Hon. Dr. MacLean to take up the question of shutting this railway down immediately as I consider writing them just a waste of time." To Island Logging, the Department wrote in 1925, "It is hardly necessary to remind you that it is to the interests of the logging company to build a good railway and furnish up to date equipment not only for the protection of the employees, but to secure a low rate from the Workmen's Compensation Board; this will depend upon what we find when making a final inspection of your completed road."[28]

For the men working on the logging railroads, the best assurance of safety was being careful and maintaining the equipment. The men took pride in their locomotives and often spent long hours keeping them in repair. In hard times, labour was often the cheapest commodity and much of the heavy work was done in the camps by the train and shop crews. In the isolated camps, large repair facilities, machine shops, foundries or sources of parts could be many miles away. "In the steam days," recalled Tom Coates, "you did all your own work. You could make everything. You had a blacksmith, machinists. . . . You'd make your own bearings and shafts which you can't do with the gas and diesel equipment."[29]

The steam locomotives were the most dramatic and interesting equipment on the logging railroads. Certainly they were enduring. In the next chapter, the story of their retirement and the conversion to truck and diesel locomotives brings their use in the woods to a close. But there was more to the logging lines than just the locomotives. There was an extensive array of specialized equipment that made logging railroads unique in other ways.

Speeders and Gas Locomotives

Gas-engined speeders were common on many of the lines. These useful pieces of equipment came in a variety of types and sizes. The smallest were open, four-wheel cars typical of those on railroads anywhere in North America for track patrol and moving maintenance-of-way crews. However, the logging lines required other types of cheap and convenient vehicles and the speeders were developed to meet many additional needs — moving logging crews, switching a few cars around the yards, constructing new trackage into the woods or removing spurs from cut-over lands, carrying supplies, acting as ambulances, delivering mail, moving families and visitors to and from the camps, carrying children to school and even bringing in shipments of milk and mail order packages. In some ways, the speeders (often called "crummies"), perhaps more than the logging trains themselves, were central to the life of the logging camps. There were many jobs that a crew could carry out with a speeder instead of having to use a much more expensive locomotive. They were general utility vehicles — the logging railroad equivalent of a pickup truck and a bus rolled into one.[30]

The British Columbia Railways Department worked closely with the logging companies and the equipment manufacturers to improve safety and equipment standards. Safety in these vehicles was a particularly important consideration when 50 or more men could be riding a speeder over the steep logging grades. By the late 1930s, what became the typical British Columbia speeder design had developed. There were variations in style and construction, but usually the speeders were fully enclosed — an important feature in the west coast rain-forests — with a central, elevated seat for the operator who could face in either direction. Most rode on four wheels and were powered by a gas engine mounted in one end, driving the wheels via a chain drive. The speeders were equipped with air brakes as well as hand brakes. Air sanders, flange oilers, boxes for saws and tools and other features could be added as needed.

Some of these speeders were substantial cars and could carry a large crew and their equipment while others were comparatively small vehicles. Speeder designs

For the woods crews, travelling to and from camp was just part of the daily routine. Often speeders were used for this purpose. The scene above is from Thomsen & Clark's camp near Harrison Mills in the 1930s. At right, Vedder River Logging crews used this speeder and trailer for track maintenance.
—W. F. MONTGOMERY, BCARS,
HP73654 AND HP73767

Safety was a major responsibility of the government inspectors. As Chief Inspector William Rae advised Island Logging in 1924, "...it is a very dangerous practice to allow men to be carried on open cars as considerable accidents have occurred. It will be necessary for your company to have a suitable car for conveying the workmen, provided with racks for carrying saws and axes."

Speeders, like this one at McDonald Murphy's camp near Cowichan Lake, gave some protection from the weather.
—CEDRIC MYERS

Bob Swanson's Speeders

"When I went to Chemainus in 1937, they had just built the 105, with two Godfredson truck wheelrims and steel tires; [and] a Zephyr V-8 engine...which burned a lot of gas. Then they had a little pimple on the roof for the guy to sit in and look out. Streamlined diesel trains were coming out in the States and I was intensely interested...So, I said, 'Well, the next time we build one we'll do it a little differently.'

We bought a speeder from an outfit in Vancouver but it ran along like a hopping toad and it jumped off the track all the time. But, the Chief Inspector said, 'No, you can't have any more than an 8-foot wheel base,' but, the thing was 20 some feet long...So I took it all to pieces and started from scratch. I put the wheels up to 12 feet, so it was not on a node in the middle; to get away from the sine-wave curve. He didn't say a word. They took it out. We couldn't get it off the track! I made the cab full width... and put a headlight up on top of the cab...I got a Westinghouse twin horn...you could hear it coming for miles. Oh! we were just having a great time."

No. 107 at Fanny Bay in 1940 and with the shop crew at Chemainus. Bob Swanson is seventh from left by the speeder he described above. A speeder takes shape at Chemainus.—AUTHOR'S COLLECTION; JACK M. HOWE; MACMILLAN BLOEDEL COLLECTION

were enlarged and improved in the 1930s making them, in effect, enclosed utility locomotives and crew cars. The speeders came in many styles and a larger speeder might be matched with an unpowered trailer for increased capacity. The Gibson Manufacturing Company of Seattle was an early builder of this style of speeder, supplying one to Alberni Pacific in 1938 that, with its trailer, could transport 100 men.[31] The next year, the Vancouver firm of Hamilton Bridge, Western, Ltd., developed an enclosed speeder powered by a six-cylinder Hercules engine that could carry 60 passengers with improved stability and power.[32] The logging companies also built their own speeders and worked to established safety and construction standards. Bob Swanson, who was then master mechanic for the Victoria Lumber & Manufacturing Company at Chemainus, took a particular interest in the recent development. In the accompanying sidebar, he recalled the developments. Under Bob Swanson, the VL&M crews developed and built several speeders which established standards for the industry. Bob Swanson went on to work as an Inspector with the Railways Department and in this position he continued to contribute to the development of the modern speeders.

The labour shortages of World War II complicated the regulation and inspection of speeders as the Railways Department *Annual Report* described in 1945:

Considerable time was spent in supervising the construction of gas rail-cars to comply with the Department's regulations as to safety appliances. Operators for this equipment are very scarce. Men made application for operator's permits who did not have the necessary experience on railroads nor knowledge of air-brakes, and in order to keep this equipment in service instructions were given them and they were allowed to operate without a permit until they had more experience, when they were given an examination and permits issued. This worked out satisfactorily and we did not have serious accidents.[33]

By the post-World War II years, these streamlined rail cars, usually painted bright yellow for high visibility, were a common sight on the surviving logging railroads. Through the late 1940s, there was a surge in the construction of these cars as the companies modernized their operations. The Railway Department *Annual Reports* noted a large car of 80-passenger capacity built in 1946 (for the Victoria Lumber Company at Chemainus), eight new "power rail cars" in 1947 and 12 more in 1948, some of which were diesel-powered.[34] Railway Department regulations, specifications and inspections helped assure a high standard of safety on these vehicles.[35] They were detailed and specific, defining construction requirements and the location of appliances and equipment such as saw-racks, seats, headlights and other fittings. These efficient cars were a great improvement over the assortment of old and often near-derelict equipment that had been used for transporting logging crews in the early years of the logging railroads. The speeders were safe, fast, economical and comfortable.

The speeder design was very adaptable. Alberni Pacific, for example, built a fire-fighting speeder powered by a Mercury V8 engine at its Camp One. All the work was done at the camp's machine shop under the supervision of Walter Murray and Jimmie Magnone. The speeder carried enough equipment for 85 men and could seat 60. A tank of 560 gallons (2545 litres) provided an immediately available water supply. In addition, the speeder carried a large pump with a capacity of 90 gallons (410 litres) per minute, as well as smaller pumps and hoses. In good fire-fighting tradition, it was painted bright red.[36]

In later years, as shown in Chapter 6 on diesel operations, some of these versatile machines were rebuilt to carry cranes or with open decks for track maintenance work. They were interesting and highly variable vehicles that added much to the character of the logging lines. Speeders continued to be important to the surviving logging railways well into the diesel era. Even in the late 1980s, Walter Infanti, who was then Railway Superintendent of Canadian Forest Products, commented that nothing really had come along that could replace them.

The speeders were not the only type of equipment used to move the crews from the logging camps to the woods. Before the speeder designs evolved into small enclosed rail buses, the companies used a variety of old passenger cars, boxcars or cabooses which were fitted with seats or benches. Racks might be attached to the outside of the cars to carry saws and axes. Sometimes leaky, dilapidated and rickety, these cars generally were strictly utilitarian, although there were a few exceptions. A. P. Allison's operation, which became Aero Timber during World War II, on the Queen Charlotte Islands even acquired a former Morrissey, Fernie & Michel Railway rail motorcar for moving its logging crews from the camp on Cumshewa Inlet to the woods. Generally, there were few comforts for the loggers except a dry, perhaps heated, place to sit; after a long day in the woods in the rain even that was most welcome. The eventual replacement of these old cars by enclosed speeders was an important improvement for the loggers and the companies.

In describing new improvements to speeder designs in 1937, *The Timberman* noted that "An important element in these days of labor unrest is the comfort of the woods crews. Less labour turnover and better morale among the men are vital factors in logging costs. Speeder transportation of the crew has solved these problems to a great extent. In several cases, the adoption of speeders for this purpose has removed the necessity for building new camps, saving their cost before they went into service."[37] The improvement in conditions for the loggers was not just limited to their time on the speeders. Not having to move camp meant that more permanent homes could be established in the company camps; families could settle with a greater feeling of stability and comfort. The speeders were a step along the road that would eventually lead to the virtual disappearance of the isolated woods camps.

Bloedel, Stewart & Welch's speeder
No. 4 on the Franklin River
railroad in the 1940s. — VPL 6146

Merrill Ring Wilson used this large,
two-truck speeder on Vancouver
Island. The loggers would probably
have preferred a design with more
windows. — TOM COATES

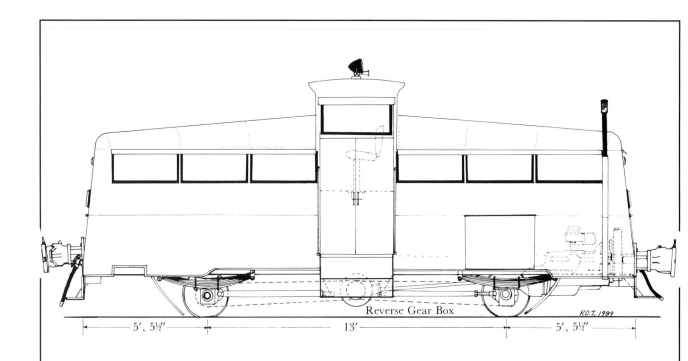

Reverse Gear Box

R.D.T. 1989

5', 5½'' ——— 13' ——— 5', 5½''

VICTORIA LUMBER COMPANY, LTD.
CHEMAINUS, B.C.

SPEEDER NO. 102
AUGUST, 1946

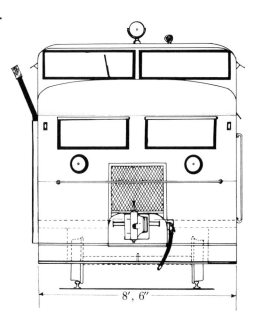

8', 6''

Brake Rigging not shown
Based on Original Company Drawing
Scale: ¼'' = 1', 0'' (1:48)

NOTES: VL&M speeders were painted yellow with black lettering. Unpowered trailers were built to the same design but without the raised operator's cupola. Uses for these speeders included fire fighting, track maintenance, ambulance service, inspections, camp supply, transport of woods crews, mail delivery and shopping trips for families living in remote camps.

Speeders could be as long-lived as the logging locomotives. The versatile VL&M design, shown in these drawings, proved highly successful. The 102 was in ambulance duty in the photograph above. Years later, former VL&M speeders were still hard at work on Canfor's logging railroad. In the middle photo, taken at Nimpkish Camp in 1973, the 130 shows the scars of hard work. Two rebuildings followed. The first removed one end to produce the equivalent to a pickup on rails. Then the other end was removed to produce a double-ended flatdeck as shown in the lower photograph from 1984.
—JACK CASH, MACMILLAN BLOEDEL COLLECTION; ROBERT D. TURNER

97

A Speeder for All Seasons

Speeders became an essential part of the post-World War II logging railroads; witness the speeder lineup at Bloedel, Stewart & Welch's Camp 5 inland from Menzies Bay. They moved the crews, (as shown in the Canfor speeder below left), delivered the mail and milk (in this case to Brewster Lake Camp) or were used for track work (as shown on VL&M). They ranged in size from two-truck monsters such as Canfor's 121 at right to small machines like 402 below run by Gordon Roberts on the Salmon River Branch in 1949. Unless noted, all are from BS&W's Menzies Bay operation about 1950.

—STEVE STARK COLLECTION

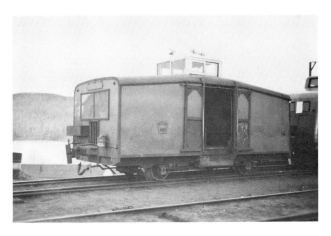

—JACK CASH, MACMILLAN BLOEDEL COLLECTION

Similar in function to the speeders, on many operations, were the small gas, or later, diesel locomotives. These machines were not seen — by the larger operators at least — as replacements for steam locomotives in the major tasks of log hauling, but rather as lightweight utility locomotives. However, in the 1920s, before trucking began to make serious inroads into the use of logging railroads, small operators might use one as their sole source of motive power. Typical examples on this scale in the early 1920s were the Sing Chong Logging Co., operating at Mud Bay on Vancouver Island over about two miles (3 km) of trackage with one gas engine and one skeleton car, and Superior Logging at Nanoose Bay, with 2.25 miles (3.5 km) of track, a single gas locomotive and two cars.[38] Small operations such as these were early casualties to truck logging because one or two trucks could easily handle the same tonnage of logs over simple forest roads, eliminating the cost of track construction and maintenance.

Some of the small locomotives were little more than a Fordson engine, on a frame, driving railroad wheels. Some were made to operate on poles rather than on steel rails. For this use, double-flanged wheels were fitted. One example of the use of this type of machine was on the Queen Charlotte Islands in the late 1920s and early 1930s. Supplied by the Westminster Iron Works, and called "Tugaway Tractors," they were used to haul cedar poles in the Port Clements area and on Kumdis Island. Fortunately, one of the machines, long abandoned in the woods, has been salvaged by the Port Clements Historical Society.[39]

Several manufacturers supplied speeders or small gas locomotives to the B.C. logging railroads. In 1917, the Maritime Motor Car Co. of Vancouver built a five-ton (4.5 tonne) gasoline locomotive with a six-cylinder engine for Brooks–Scanlon–O'Brien.[40] An even smaller machine of just two and one half tons (2.25 tonnes) built by Maritime Motor Car was used by Merrill, Ring & Moore Logging at Duncan Bay on Vancouver Island. In 1920, *The Timberman* reported George Moore's opinion of the machine.

The locomotive is the handiest rig he ever used for logging road construction. He has two hopper cars carrying three yards [2.3 m³] each which he uses for ballasting. The gasoline engine is also used for taking up track. It requires but one man to operate the locomotive and the elimination of the fire hazard is quite a consideration. In building new track the gasoline locomotive is kept on the job. There is no switching of locomotives with the attendant delay and expense.[41]

Six years later, George Moore was again cited in *The Timberman*. The report noted that the Duncan Bay camp had very successfully operated Plymouth gas locomotives of seven and 10 tons (6.3 and 9 tonnes) and that, "... in road building and switching cars these gasoline locomotives have served efficiently in the place of a steam locomotive for the past nine years."[42] Presumably, the tiny Maritime Motor machine had been replaced by one of the larger Plymouths.

Another supplier of gasoline locomotives was the Reliance Motor & Machine

Cheap to buy and economical to run, gas locomotives were the answer to some of the financial problems of small operations. The Westminster Iron Works produced Fordson-powered locomotives for several companies. Usually, they were used to move one or two cars over short distances. However, they were very vulnerable to truck competition because of the high cost of railroad construction. The upper view is probably of Superior Lumber at Nanoose Bay which ran in the 1920s and was owned by Japanese-Canadian interests. The other photo, unidentified, is from 1930. — GERRY WELLBURN COLLECTION; BARR PHOTO, BCFS, 3012

Hillcrest Lumber, known in later years for its Climax locomotives, was one of the first companies to use gasoline-powered machines. About 1918, company founder Carlton Stone, and his crew built, for $1500, a small locomotive using a 20-hp Russell engine on a wooden frame to pull a simple trailer. Standard gauge track was laid with light rail. A second nearly identical machine was built. Eventually, the little home-built engines were replaced with Hillcrest's first Shay.
— GERRY WELLBURN COLLECTION

The Maritime Motor Car Company of Vancouver was responsible for this five-ton (4.5 tonne) gas engine built in 1917 for Brooks-Scanlon-O'Brien. — *The Timberman*

Westminster Iron Works "Tugaway" locomotives were built during the mid-1920s to run on either steel rails or wooden poles.
— *B.C. Lumberman*

102

Tupper and Steele of Vancouver built this impressive gas locomotive for the Mainland Timber Company in 1924. A chain drive powered all wheels and it could travel up to 15 miles (24 km) per hour. It was powered by a 40-hp engine and was 20 feet (6.1 m) long.— *B.C. Lumberman*

An "economical hauling outfit" was the description of this railroad tractor—it hardly seems appropriate to call it a locomotive. It had three speeds forward and reverse. The Fordson-powered machine was built by the Reliance Motor & Machine Works of Vancouver for Dawson & Taylor of Courtenay in 1924 and operated on about two miles (3.2 km) of track.—A. A. PAULL, *B.C. Lumberman*

Merrill & Ring was another purchaser of gasoline locomotives. The well-maintained machine (above) was typical of the four-wheeled Plymouth line of locomotives. The company also bought this 20-ton (18-tonne) Davenport for its Theodosia Arm operations in 1925.
—ROOZEBOOM COLLECTION, BCARS, HP67857; *B.C. Lumberman*

104

Works of Vancouver which offered locomotives powered with Fordson gas engines or Twin City heavy-duty oil-engines. Some were equipped with one log bunk and pulled a trailer fitted with a second. Their products found their way onto the lines of the Port Alberni Canal Shingle Co., the Dawson Taylor Logging Co. and the Fanny Bay Logging Co.[43] Tupper & Steele of Vancouver also offered Fordson-powered gas engines for the logging market in the mid-1920s.[44] Perhaps the most successful local manufacturer was the Westminster Iron Works, established by John Reid in 1874, which offered a wide range of light, gas-engined locomotives and speeders in their catalogue and supplied machines to a number of operators including the R. B. McLean Lumber Company operating at Bainbridge, north of Port Alberni.[45] Fortunately, the McLean machine survived to be preserved by the Alberni Valley Museum.[46] Major North American manufacturers were usually represented by local equipment dealers. The Vancouver Machinery Depot Ltd. acted as agents for Davenport, the large American manufacturer of industrial locomotives, while Brown, Fraser & Co. handled the well-known Plymouth line of gasoline locomotives.

Comox Logging's 107, a Whitcomb, shown at Ladysmith in the mid-1940s, moved south from Headquarters. In fire season, each of its four stacks sported a spark arrester. The hood featured a large steam locomotive bell. This engine survived the end of railroad logging at Ladysmith to be preserved by the Ladysmith Railway Historical Society.
—TED ROBSON

Another of Comox Logging's gas engines was photographed at Headquarters on September 20, 1940. Note the chain drive visible under the cab, and the spark arrester. The origin of this machine is uncertain but it may have been rebuilt from a Westminster Iron Works engine.
—AUTHOR'S COLLECTION

Logging railroads required special equipment for moving the huge logs
cut from the forests of the Pacific Coast. Controlling the trains on the
steep grades was hazardous and took considerable skill. These seasoned
brakemen stand beside a typical three-log load ready to roll over Comox
Logging's railroad at Headquarters on Vancouver Island in 1919.
—LEONARD FRANK, VPL

3 ROLLING STOCK, CAMPS, TRESTLES AND SKIDDERS

Disconnects, Flatcars and Skeleton Cars

The logging railroads used a variety of types of rolling stock in their operations, but the most important were the log cars. These were of three basic types: disconnected trucks, or "disconnects," flatcars and connected trucks, or "skeleton cars."

The simplest of these cars were the disconnected trucks. These were operated in pairs. Heavy-duty, four-wheeled trucks were equipped with a coupler (very often a link and pin pocket) at each end and a log bunk was placed across the bolster of each truck. Hand brakes were fitted and usually footboards were attached for the brakemen to stand on. These trucks were versatile because a pair could accommodate almost any length of log spanned between them. Some loads of poles could be so long that, because of the natural sagging of the logs between the trucks, they nearly touched the ground. However, they could not be equipped with air brakes and as a result they could be dangerous and difficult to control. After air brakes became mandatory, the disconnects were no longer used on a regular basis.

It was dangerous being a brakeman on the early trains equipped with the disconnected trucks. The brakes had to be set manually by the crews, who had to ride either the loads or the footboards of the cars as they clattered down the steep logging grades from the landings. On steep grades, it was necessary to have at least one brakeman for every two or three pairs of trucks. Accidents were frequent and many a brakeman was injured trying to control the trains of disconnected trucks. An engineer could also find he had pulled the train apart with a sudden increase in speed, causing delays and a real chance of injury. Jim Wolverton worked disconnected trucks during his teenage years.

We used those disconnect trucks and hauled whole trees out. The trees would drag on the ground between the trucks; they were that long. They had two brakemen on there and they would handle nine or ten loads. They got by with them fine but . . . you have to know the road, so that you know when to speed up your train when it's on the hills or to get it over the flat or decreased grade. And then catch it again before you get too far down on the steep grade again. To slow it down and accelerate; to keep it under control at all times.

They would switch out the short logs and the light loads and put them on the tail end of the train and the heavier loads next to the engine. Well, we were switching out and the brakeman gave me a kick sign and I kicked them with the Shay and he gave me a stop sign and I clamped down on the brake and I peeled a load of logs off on a bridge; they fell out like a boom right on the bridge.[1]

Some of the men who worked these early types of equipment would become legendary in the woods. George Robertson described the abilities of Charlie and Willie Jones from the west coast of Vancouver Island.

The brakeman had to set up the brakes and knock 'em off at the bottom of the hill and then set them up again going down the hills. That was a pretty tricky business. One of the best men they ever had for that kind of work in the olden days was an Indian from Renfrew, he worked at Jordan River. His name was Willie Jones. His brother Charlie Jones [hereditary Chief of the Pacheenaht Band[2]] and Willie were both brakemen. They were both supposed to be very good at the old hand brake system. They could run up along the loads, it didn't matter what speed they were going or where they were travelling. They'd get off, set up brakes and then be at the other end to let them off again and back and forth...very capable of doing anything.[3]

Flatcars, fitted with log bunks, were used on some lines for log hauling. In many cases where flatcars were used, they were owned by either the CPR (most often the E&N on Vancouver Island) or the CNR and were moved at least part of the way over the major railways. Campbell River Mills, operating at Vedder Crossing in the Fraser Valley, used cars from the Milwaukee Road (Chicago, Milwaukee, St. Paul & Pacific). Comox Logging and its successors remained committed to the use of flatcars throughout its long history of railroad logging on the coast. These were the company's own wooden-framed cars and they were used through the steam era. Later, these were replaced with steel cars which were in use until the end of log hauling by rail in 1984. While they were structurally stronger than skeleton cars, typical flatcars of comparable capacity were about 6 tons (5.4 tonnes) heavier; a decided disadvantage. The large deck of the flatcar could also accumulate a large quantity of bark from the logs which, particularly when wet, added even more weight to be hauled back to the woods.

Despite their added weight, flatcars could be used to advantage under some circumstances, as Comox Logging's Robert Filberg pointed out in 1932 to a logging congress in Seattle:

One of our operations is on a steep sidehill where there are 14 switchbacks on the main line of the railroad. The grades are steep and we could not get sufficient cars up the hill to keep the skidders working in the small timber they are working in, about 400 feet board measure [0.9 m³], to the log. We use all flatcars anyway, so we tried to stake the loads [in the same way] as cedar poles are loaded. It costs about 60 cents per carload for stakes and wire but we get an average load of about 8000 feet [19 m³], on the cars and that has reduced the number of empty cars we have to put up the hill. We now load all small logs in that manner because our haul is more than 30 miles [48 km] and we get so much more out of our cars. We don't think this slows the loading up much if any.[4]

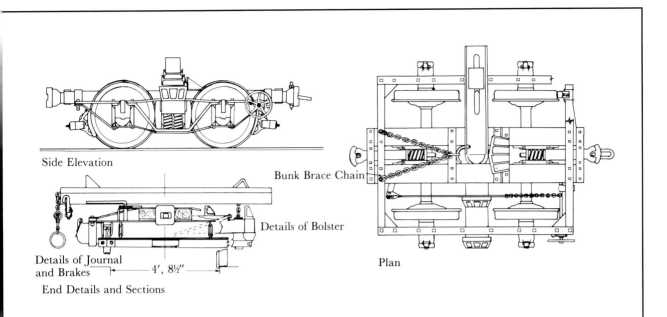

Side Elevation

Bunk Brace Chain

Details of Bolster

Details of Journal
and Brakes

4′, 8½″

Plan

End Details and Sections

HERCULES LOGGING DISCONNECT TRUCK
(As Manufactured by Seattle Car & Foundry Co.)

Scale   ¼″ = 1′, 0″ (1:48)
© RDT 1989

The disconnect trucks so prevalent in the early days of railroad logging were capable of carrying huge loads of variable lengths. However, they lacked air brakes. The photograph at right shows loads of Sitka spruce on the Pacific Great Eastern in 1917. Spruce, light in weight and strong, was in great demand at that time for use in aircraft construction.
—LEONARD FRANK, VPL

Several logging railroads operated in the Squamish area and some shipped timber over the PGE. The lines included Squamish Timber, Newport Timber and Cheakamus Timber. The largest operator was Merrill & Ring. Their railroad opened in 1927 and it ran with some closures until 1940. Normally, they used about 15 to 20 miles (24 to 32 km) of track, several locomotives and about 80 cars.

Flatcars were used on some of the logging railroads in British Columbia. Often the cars were supplied to the logging companies by the major common carrier railways. In the Cowichan Lake area both the CPR and the CNR connected directly with the logging railroads and handled the loads over part of the distance from where the logs were felled to where they were milled. — W. F. MONTGOMERY, BCARS, HP73646

In the Interior, where the logs were usually smaller than on the coast, flatcars were also used on many of the log hauls. Logs and poles were an important commodity on many CPR branch lines in the forested areas of the province. CPR equipment was used on several logging lines in the East Kootenays. On the CNR and PGE, both virtually devoid of branch lines during the steam era, logs and poles were also important sources of traffic but these operations are another story.

The Interior logging railways generally used short flatcars for log hauling. These cars were usually fitted with wooden stakes to increase their load capacity and in this way up to three dozen logs could be piled up six to eight feet high (1.8-2.5 metres) on the cars. The Columbia River Lumber Company, which was owned by the Canadian Western Lumber Company, used these cars extensively until the late 1920s when the operation was closed. The CPR moved trains of these cars over its main line from Mile 52.8 on the Mountain Subdivision to the lumber company's mill at Golden. Their equipment roster for 1926 showed 120 cars and three Heisler locomotives on the line.[5] These short, wooden-framed flatcars were fitted with rails so that a small steam-powered loader — probably a Barnhart which was really a small crane — could run down the length of the train lifting the logs onto the cars.

The skeleton car, which consisted of a pair of railroad trucks with a log bunk mounted over each and joined by heavy timbers, was the last major type of log car to be used by the logging railroads in British Columbia. Overall, it was also by far the most common type. These cars were light in weight — important when the limiting factor in log hauling often was the ability of the locomotives to pull the empty cars back uphill to the landings — and were cheap to build. Air brakes were fitted easily. A typical skeleton car was 41 feet (12.5 metres) long and could accommodate logs 42 feet (12.8 metres) long. Empty, the cars weighed 12 tons (10.8 tonnes) each and could carry about 40 tons (36 tonnes) of logs. Longer cars, sometimes reinforced with trussrods, were built to move poles, pilings and "boom sticks" — long logs used in assembling the log booms. These cars could be as long as 70 feet (21.3 metres) and would sometimes have extra log bunks mounted on the centre sill between the trucks to help carry the loads.

A 1925 quotation from the Vancouver Equipment Company (acting as agents for Pacific Car & Foundry in Seattle) to Bloedel, Stewart & Welch gave prices of $1822 for ten 70-foot (21.3-m), two-bunk cars using second-hand trucks, and $1596 for ten 42-foot (12.8-m) cars of 80,000 board foot (188 m³) capacity.[6] Relatively safe to operate, versatile, light in weight, easy to repair and economical to build, skeleton cars became standard equipment for most companies on the Pacific coast.

Skeleton cars were made by most of the larger firms supplying equipment to the logging industry. Major suppliers in the northwest United States, acting through agents in British Columbia, competed to supply the logging operators, and local firms also set up production. In 1929 for example, the Vancouver Engineering

Skeleton cars were the most important log cars in the woods. They were light in weight and had air brakes. These cars on Lake Logging Company's Cowichan Lake trackage were owned by the Canadian Pacific. The locomotive is Lake Logging's Willamette.
—NICHOLAS MORANT, CPCA M287

Cathels & Sorensen on the West Coast of Vancouver Island used a skeleton car developed by the North Western Equipment Company. The "All Steel" truck was designed not to "come to pieces even under circumstances where one might reasonably expect to find disaster."
—LEONARD FRANK, VPL

Works expanded its production facilities to increase its output of skeleton cars and other logging equipment.[7] In some cases, a logging operator might buy just the castings and have his own shop crews assemble the cars. The E&N Railway, the CPR's Vancouver Island subsidiary, was also a major builder of skeleton cars. In 1930, the company began production of 200 cars for service on Vancouver Island at its shops in Victoria West.[8] CPR wooden skeleton cars were still in use on the E&N and on MacMillan Bloedel's Nanaimo River operations until the closure of the Nanaimo Lakes line late in 1969.

The capacity and flexibility of the skeleton cars increased over the years with the addition of drop stakes on the log bunks and the use of heavier trucks. Earlier cars had simple "cheese blocks" or "chocks" at each end of the bunk to hold the logs. The drop stakes, which could be released from the opposite side of the car for dumping the logs, meant that higher loads, and loads composed of many small logs, could be carried safely. This became increasingly important in the post-war years when smaller timber — often second-growth — was being hauled on the surviving railroads. In their most modern form, the skeleton cars were of all-steel construction with permanent, fixed stakes which permitted large loads to be carried and unloaded easily. The load could be lifted as a single unit by a large front-end loader or transfer facility. Roller bearing trucks improved operating efficiency. This design was used only in the diesel era by Canadian Forest Products and is shown in detail in Chapter 6.

Equipment use changed significantly in the period between 1900 and the mid-1920s. By about 1910, when railroad logging was becoming established in British Columbia, there were nearly 30 lines in operation. At that time, 305 sets of trucks were available for log hauling but only 20 flatcars, including those used for track construction and other purposes, were owned by the companies.[9] However, additional flatcars, owned by the CPR, were used by some logging operations. Skeleton cars, with their improved safety features, were as yet not utilized in the region. In contrast, by 1924 nearly 70 companies, some having several camps, operated a total of 305 flatcars (200 of which were operated by Comox Logging at its Headquarters Camp in the Comox Valley), 1237 skeleton cars (connected trucks) and 504 disconnected trucks. Not only do the figures reflect the growth in railroad logging but they show clearly the emergence of the skeleton car as the dominant type of logging rail car in British Columbia. Regulations in effect by this time required that "at least 85 percent of the number of cars in every train shall be equipped with air brakes." Because skeleton cars and flatcars carried air brakes and disconnects did not, the demise of the dangerous disconnect trucks was inevitable.[10]

Bull Cars, Snowplows and other Special Equipment

Other types of rolling stock seen frequently on the logging lines included tank cars for carrying fuel and water, and a few old box cars for tools and equipment.

Heavy-duty flatcars, often called "bull cars," were employed for moving donkey engines and other logging machinery. They were versatile pieces of equipment and could be used for any type of heavy transport on the lines. The large donkey engines, or skidders, had to be relocated frequently and special, heavy-duty rail trucks were employed for this purpose. Snowplows were a luxury that only the larger operations could afford even using home-made equipment. Comox Logging built one from the tender of a retired locomotive for a frame.[11] Sometimes, with a little ingenuity, a "bull car" could substitute for a more conventional snowplow. George Robertson remembered with amusement, the technique used in the San Juan Valley on Vancouver Island.

They would take the bull car, it was a heavy car, weighed 40-ton [36-tonne], and they had systems of mats made up. They would drop timbers down over the front and hang 'em down so that they just touched the ties. They would brake the two wheels on the front so they couldn't turn. And they would kind of ride up onto these timbers so that they wouldn't wear much on the railroad track and they just shoved them down the track . . . and it just pushed the snow off that way. Finally, it would have to go over the side somewhere. In them days there were so many bridges and trestles that it would only be a quarter of a mile or a few hundred yards you were bound to come to a bridge anyway.[12]

Fire-fighting equipment for logging rail operations was not as well developed as some other types of equipment, at least to begin with. "Fire was always a big problem," recalled Tom Coates who spent a lifetime working in the forest industry in British Columbia. "They made a real effort to stop them, just as they do today. They didn't have any good equipment. We had bad fires during those years because we didn't have the equipment they have now. I remember in the upper Allouette Lake area on Abernethy Lougheed, they had a spitter [thunder storm] there and it started a fire on the back lot and the crew on the machine couldn't get out. They were all picked up in Stave Lake the following day. They just had to gallop, and the fire went into Stave Lake. Oh, God, we had some terrible fires!"[13]

Many types of cars were eventually developed for fire-fighting. The most common were tank cars equipped with pumps, hose reels, and tool boxes. Sometimes, flatcars were fitted with large wooden storage tanks for water. Larger operations placed tank cars with fire-fighting equipment at strategic points on their railways so that in the event of fire, cars could be moved in quickly. In the 1940s on Alberni Pacific's extensive railway, six tank cars were used, each with a capacity of 8,000 gallons (36,370 l) of water and fitted with a centrifugal gas or steam pump and 2,000 feet (610 m) of hose.[14] In later years, tank cars were fitted with track sprinklers to dampen down the tracks and bridges, helping to prevent fires started by a passing train. In some situations, sprinkler systems were built on the large bridges to reduce the danger of fires.

In the hot summer months, sparks from a locomotive or from dragging

The highest bridge on Bloedel, Stewart & Welch's newly-built railroad
from Menzies Bay into the vast forests of eastern Vancouver Island was
recorded in 1927 soon after its completion. The train, led by BS&W's
Two-Spot 2-6-2, consists of a heavy flatcar or "bull car" for carrying
special equipment like the early gas-driven shovel.
—W. F. MONTGOMERY, BCARS, HP73737

Special Equipment

Forest fires were a constant threat during the dry summer months. All logging operations were required to maintain firefighting equipment. Some examples used in the woods: VL&M fitted a flatcar with wooden tanks and also mounted a small tank on a trailer pulled by a speeder; Comox Logging placed a tank car body on a log car for track sprinkling; Capilano Timber had everything but the kitchen sink on this car; and Canfor used many of these

well-equipped cars. This one carried 6000 gallons (27275 L) of water, a 500 gallons (2275 L) per minute centrifugal pump, 2000 feet (610 m) of 1.5-inch (3.8-cm) hose and equipment for 20 men.
—TWO PHOTOS, JACK CASH, MACMILLAN BLOEDEL COLLECTION; ROBERT D. TURNER; A. A. PAULL, BCARS, HP67747; J. REVEL, BCFS, 15381

Comox Logging's Ladysmith operation rated this handsome snowplow built on the frame of a steam locomotive tender.
—ROBERT D. TURNER

Pile drivers were essential equipment on the logging railroads for building the many trestles and bridges they required. This one belonged to Allison Logging on the Queen Charlotte Islands in the late 1930s. Trestle work also could be used to support the tracks over wet, marshy country.—H. W. WEATHERBY, BCFS, 2447

117

Canadian Forest Products used a refrigerator car to move provisions between Englewood and Camp L on Nimpkish Lake. Climax No. 7, shown above, eventually was rebuilt with a diesel engine.
—ELWOOD WHITE

Cabooses were rare although the larger operations often had one or two on the property. This is Comox Logging's No. 1 at Ladysmith in the early 1950s. —NORMAN GIDNEY

Steam, gasoline or diesel shovels were useful, particularly in roadbed construction. This machine worked for Pacific Mills at one of its coastal operations which fed timber to the company's mill at Ocean Falls. Note the ballast cars, both in this photo and the one above. —RBCM

brakeshoes could easily start a fire but, noted Tom Coates, "... more of them I think were caused by lines and faulty blocks and lines burning over logs and rubbing on snags. A certain number were caused by sparks and steam machines, but they had pretty good spark arresters."[15] It was part of the routine in the logging camps to check out and fit spark arresters, which came in a variety of styles, to all the steam equipment as the dry months of summer approached. The use of oil as a fuel in the locomotives and donkey engines also reduced the fire hazard and by the 1920s, nearly all locomotives and donkey engines operating in the coastal forests burned oil.

The constant cycle of laying new spur lines and removing the tracks from logged out areas required rolling stock and, on larger lines, special equipment. Flatcars, for moving rail and other materials, ballast cars, and even track-laying machines were important. Steam shovels, and later gas or diesel shovels, were used on larger operations for roadbed construction. Similarly, many companies had a pile driver for working on the complex wharfs, log dumps and pile trestles used on the lines. The pile drivers were usually mounted on a sled and were transported from place to place on moving trucks or heavy flatcars. Many operations also had one or more steam cranes. Often self-propelled, they were used for anything from loading carloads of lumber and placing spark arresters on locomotives to building bridges or rerailing wrecked equipment. Adapted with loading tongs, they could be used efficiently in the woods for assembling a few carloads of timber or picking up lost logs from a derailment or other accident along the right-of-way. Some of the more important manufacturers of cranes were American Hoist & Derrick, Brownhoist, Erie, and Ohio Locomotive Crane. Larger operators often would have a full crew, locomotive and work train assigned permanently to railroad construction and dismantling.

Bridges and Trestles

The rugged topography of British Columbia presented the loggers with many challenges not the least of which was bridging the many turbulent rivers and deep canyons that cut through the major stands of timber. Bridging was expensive but unavoidable. Engineers laying out the routes for the logging lines had to be careful in choosing a right-of-way that would minimize construction costs yet produce an efficient log cutting and hauling pattern. Another important consideration facing the construction engineers was the volume of timber to be moved. It made little sense to build an elaborate, permanent structure that would see short-term use, in some cases only a couple of years.

Early bridges were usually built with the materials at hand — logs. These were simply stacked up in criss-cross patterns to fill a ravine. Timber was cheap and available. Larger crossings required more traditional railway trestle work. In some places piles (long poles, often of Douglas-fir) were used, while in others, sawn

Bridges and Trestles

Logging railroads constantly faced streams and rivers to cross. One solution was simply to fill up the stream bed with stacked up logs. Victoria Lumber & Manufacturing tried this about 1908 at a time when logs were cheap.
—L. CUMING, BCFS, 15495/2

The Capilano Timber Company logged the dense forests behind North Vancouver. Laying tracks around the rugged sidehills and mountain slopes often dictated trestle work. A pile driver crew is hard at work on this impressive structure. — GERRY WELLBURN COLLECTION

Comox Logging needed a major pile trestle and truss bridge across the Puntledge River north of Courtenay. The bridge builders have finished their work but the tracks have yet to be laid.
—VPL, 6058

It was essential to protect bridges and trestles from fires. Sprinklers were sometimes laid across the bridges to keep them well soaked. This scene is from Green Point Logging near Harrison Lake.
— CVA

timbers might be employed. For long spans, substantial logs might be used for the centre sections of the bridges. Trestles were the expedient way of crossing swampy areas. A good crew with a pile driver could make steady progress across wetlands that would have been extremely expensive to cross by any other means. Douglas-fir was the preferred construction material because of its durability, structural strength, and availability in long, clear lengths.

The trestles were an enduring feature that seemed as much characteristic of the logging lines as were the Shays and Climaxes. The bridges ranged in size from modest structures involving little more than a few logs laid across a small stream to enormous engineering projects involving trestle work and bridge spans across major rivers and canyons. Individual bridges could consume millions of feet of timber. They were also a vulnerable link in the log hauling system. Larger, more permanent structures required regular, expensive maintenance and fire protection. If a bridge were burned or damaged for any reason, the whole log hauling operation might be closed down or seriously disrupted until repairs or an alternate route could be developed.

There were many impressive bridges on the logging railroads but the most spectacular in British Columbia was unquestionably the magnificent structure over Bear Creek on Malahat Logging's line in the San Juan Valley on the west coast of Vancouver Island. Built in 1939 to carry the railroad into new stands of timber, the bridge was a necessary component of a $5,000,000 expansion inland by Malahat Logging that included 15 other trestles on the line. Reportedly the highest-towered wooden structure (at 243 feet or 74 metres from stream bed to bridge deck) in Canada, the bridge was reminiscent of the massive timber bridges built by the Canadian Pacific on its original main line over the Selkirk Mountains in British Columbia in the 1880s. The Bear Creek bridge measured 548 feet (167 m) in length with the deepest part of the canyon being crossed on three 90-foot (27.5-m) Pratt deck truss spans (built with treated timbers) supported by two massive towers and trestle approaches.

The bridge required an enormous amount of materials:

Pilings in approaches	5,000	lin. ft.
Sawn lumber in approaches	24,600	ft. b.m.
Hewn stringers in deck	2,300	lin. ft.
Hewn caps in deck	700	lin. ft.
Round timber in central towers	125,300	ft. b.m.
Sawn timber in central towers	6,000	ft. b.m.
Hardware in central towers	11,000	lbs.
Treated timber in trusses	77,076	ft. b.m.
Untreated timber in lateral systems	16,560	ft. b.m.
6-inch Teco split-ring connectors	3,860	
Hardware	10,314	lbs.

(*Source*: A. K. G. Blakeney, in *B.C. Lumberman*, August 1940)

(*Metric conversion*: 1 ft. b.m. or 1 board foot is equivalent to a piece of wood 1″ x 1″ x 12″. For conversion, 1000 board feet = 2.35 cubic metres of wood.)

Bear Creek Construction

The great bridge over Bear Creek on Malahat Logging's railroad in the San Juan Valley of Vancouver Island was the largest logging structure in British Columbia—an engineering landmark. This series of photographs shows the complexity of its construction. This bridge was 243 feet (74 m) above the stream bed and was an amazing piece of design work.—ERIC BERNARD COLLECTION

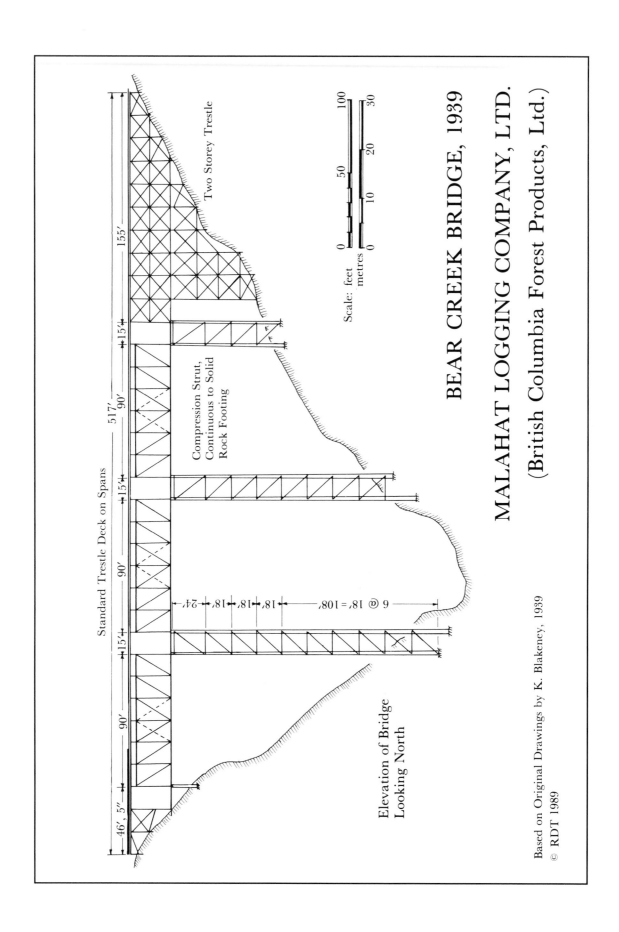

BEAR CREEK BRIDGE, 1939

MALAHAT LOGGING COMPANY, LTD.

(British Columbia Forest Products, Ltd.)

Based on Original Drawings by K. Blakeney, 1939

© RDT 1989

Two Storey Trestle

Compression Strut,
Continuous to Solid
Rock Footing

Standard Trestle Deck on Spans

Elevation of Bridge
Looking North

Scale: feet
metres

Bear Creek Bridge dwarfed the logging trains. On a bridge of this size, variables that would have been unimportant in a small span, including wind resistance, had to be accounted for in the planning. —CAM CHOUINARD

124

Fire protection for the bridge was very important. If fire threatened the bridge, the response had to be immediate, in this case Shay No. 6 with a firecar. — ELWOOD WHITE

Bridge building with timbers became an engineering art on the logging railroads. The Davie Creek trestle of Canadian Forest Products, photographed in September 1956 with Shay 103, was a fine example. A. Kelso Blakeney, who designed the Bear Creek Bridge, also built many for CFP.
—ELWOOD WHITE

The trestle over Rough Creek on Victoria Lumber & Manufacturing's Copper Canyon line was a classic of conventional trestle construction.
—JACK M. HOWE

The Salmon River on northeastern Vancouver Island was bridged by Merrill Ring Wilson for its logging railroad from Rock Bay. Heavy timbers were used to construct the centre span. At right, Pacific Coast Shay No. 4 backs over the bridge high above the river.
—TOM COATES

Bloedel, Stewart & Welch also had to cross the Salmon River at their Camp 5—Menzies Bay operation. The photograph is from 1950.
—TED ROBSON

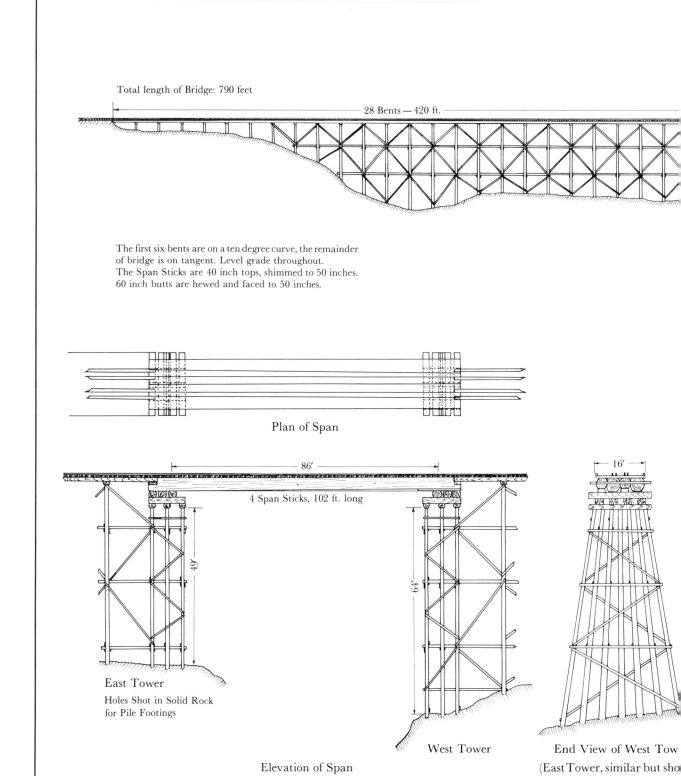

Total length of Bridge: 790 feet

28 Bents — 420 ft.

The first six bents are on a ten degree curve, the remainder
of bridge is on tangent. Level grade throughout.
The Span Sticks are 40 inch tops, shimmed to 50 inches.
60 inch butts are hewed and faced to 50 inches.

Plan of Span

86'

4 Span Sticks, 102 ft. long

49'

East Tower

Holes Shot in Solid Rock
for Pile Footings

64'

West Tower

16'

End View of West Tow

(East Tower, similar but sho

Elevation of Span

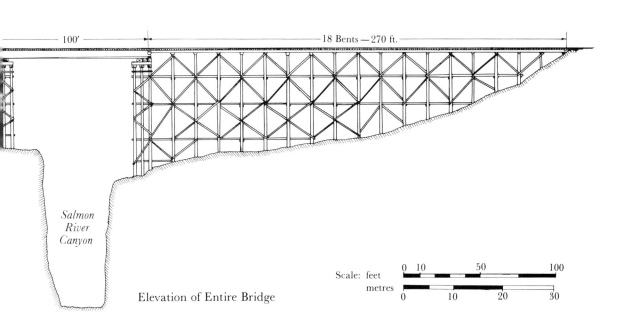

100′ ——— |————— 18 Bents — 270 ft. —————|

Salmon
River
Canyon

Elevation of Entire Bridge

Scale: feet
metres

0 10   50   100

0   10   20   30

Merrill Ring Wilson No. 4

MERRILL RING WILSON LIMITED
SALMON RIVER BRIDGE
SAYWARD DISTRICT,
VANCOUVER ISLAND
APRIL 20, 1938

Based on Original Company Drawings

© RDT 1989

Structures such as the Bear Creek bridge required skill and innovative engineering to design and construct. For this project, A. Kelso Blakeney was the engineer in charge of construction while Russell Mills was resident manager for Malahat Logging. Al Kallberg was construction foreman.[16]

The expensive timber bridges and trestles were one of the logging railroads' greatest weaknesses as trucks became increasingly competitive. Railroads were severely limited by the curvature of the tracks that locomotives and rolling stock could negotiate. Trucks were not. A logging railroad might have to bridge a canyon to maintain reasonable grades and curvatures but a truck road could simply run up to the head of a canyon, make a sharp curve, and then come back down the other side. The savings could be enormous.

Some bridges survived after the abandonment of the railways, to be used by the truck roads. However, most were simply abandoned as the tracks were removed, and left to disappear into the regrowing forests. In remote areas, the remains of a few still stand decades after the sound of the locomotives has passed from memory, and virtually all traces of the rights-of-way have vanished under the second-growth forests. Of the mighty bridge at Bear Creek, only the end trestle sections survived into the 1960s. The centre spans were destroyed when they became unsafe for road traffic a short time after the railway was abandoned.

Log Dumps

Log dumps, whether in a mill pond of a small sawmill or on the shore of an isolated coastal inlet, were the terminus of most logging railroads that did not act as feeders to the common carrier railways. These important facilities could be simple arrangements permitting one or two carloads of logs to be dumped, or elaborate, efficient unloading facilities built to handle trains of 30 or 40 cars.[17]

Small operations could use a dump as simple as an incline built of a few logs sloping from track level down to the water. Usually, the tracks were tilted towards the water, by elevating the outside rail 12 to 16 inches (30 to 40 cm) above the inside one, to aid in rolling the logs off the cars. A crewman could release the dogs or cheese blocks on the log bunks and, in most cases, gravity would finish the work. Sometimes it would be necessary to — very carefully — get the logs moving with a pike pole, or peavey. Logging jacks might also be used to roll the logs off the cars. Three men, working together, could handle seven or eight cars in about half an hour using this method.[18] Some larger lines, handling substantial volumes of timber, needed faster, more reliable methods of dumping the logs; an inefficient log dump could slow down the entire railroad operation.

A number of mechanical devices were developed for unloading log cars. Because the log dumps were often in use for many years, greater investment was justified. Where the logs had to be towed to the mills, adjacent facilities were needed for sorting and rafting the logs or making them up into booms. Usually pile trestles

Log dumps were built in many different forms. This one at B.C. Mills, Timber & Trading Company's Rock Bay operation used a series of A-frames.
—LEONARD FRANK, VPL

The dump at Reid Bay in 1923 was very simple. The Climax pulled a cable through blocks to unload the logs.—ALEXANDER PHOTO, BCFS, 2071

133

Each log dump, it seemed, was different: gin poles were used by both Alberni Pacific (above) on Alberni Inlet and Wood & English (above right) at Englewood; an overhead beam worked for Merrill & Ring at Theodosia Arm in the 1920s; and at Green Point Logging's boom camp (right) at Harrison, a Jill poke was used.
—LEONARD FRANK PHOTOS;
A. A. PAULL, BCARS, HP67874; BCFS, 2857-2; VCA

135

The Jill poke was an efficient log unloading machine used by many operators including Green Point Logging at Harrison Lake (left) and Campbell River Timber at Menzies Bay shown below. The Jill poke was put under considerable stress requiring the base to be heavily supported. —VCA; W. F. MONTGOMERY, BCARS, 73678

had to be constructed out into the water away from the shore line to reach water deep enough to dump the logs. Tidal areas could require long approach trestles to reach beyond the low tide line. In some situations, such as Comox Logging's large dumping facility at Royston or Elk River Timber's dump at Campbell River, the trestle work was extensive and represented a major investment. The life of untreated pilings in salt water was often as short as three or four years although in fresh water they might last twice that long. Maintenance was a constant requirement.[19]

One of the common arrangements was to use a simple device called a "gin pole." Often several of these were used together to make a more flexible dumping system. William Gibbons described the "gin pole" system:

The gin pole, which is about 35 feet [10.7 metres] in height, is erected along the track on the land side, with the 7/8-inch [2.2 cm] parbuckle line leading through a sheave block at the top of the pole. In unloading, the open end of the line is passed under the load to the opposite side of the car and fastened to the brow skid. When the line is tightened by power applied at the other end, the load is raised from the car bunks and pushed from the car...

The power as a rule is furnished by the locomotive, the hand work being done by the train crew. When a number of gin poles are used, the locomotive is the only practical source of power. In some cases, where it is desirable to unload as quickly as possible, the power is supplied by an ordinary logging engine, generally an old one, necessitating the employment of an unloading engineer in addition to the regular train crew.[20]

There were many developments and innovations on this basic idea of using a line run under the logs to lift them off the cars. In fairly permanent situations, large A-frames, or systems using two poles with cables might be built instead of the simple "gin pole." There was great variation and more elaborate arrangements could be used to lift the load off the cars.

Another ingeniously simple device was the "Jill poke." Gibbons described this practical unloader:

The track for the entire length of the dump is slightly superelevated. Parallel to the track on the land side, and about 5 feet [1.5 m] above the level of the track, there is a timber with notches cut at proper distances. The arm of the poke is a stick of wood 4 by 3½ inches by 6 or 8 feet [10 x 9 cm by 1.8 or 2.4 m], which is shod with a sharp steel prong at the pointed end and has a collar at the blunt end. In operation the pointed end of the poke is placed against the logs and the heel is inserted in one of the notches in the timber, the positions of the poke being such that it will push the logs from the car when the car is put in motion. Thirty-two cars, containing 150,000 feet [354 m³], have been unloaded with this method in 20 minutes.[21]

More sophisticated "Jill pokes" might have two horizontally-mounted, centrally-pivoting arms, or sweeps, in an X shape to push the logs off the cars. This system required more substantial construction but, "... with the chock blocks tripped, the train crew can unload several cars of logs per minute." With the larger unloaders, "... the train moves toward the unloader slowly, seldom finding it necessary to stop."[22] As the train moved by the unloader, one of the arms would push a load off, turning on a central bearing, bringing the next arm into contact with the following load and so on until the train was emptied. These devices could be extremely efficient and an entire train could be dumped in a matter of minutes.

In situations where more flexibility in dumping was required or simply to improve efficiency, a mobile unloader was operated on a track parallel to the dump. These machines, usually steam-powered and self-propelled, incorporated a winch and an arm which extended above the load. A cable was passed under the load and secured to heavy timbers along the edge of the trestle work at the dump called the "brow skid." The cable was then tightened and the logs were lifted and rolled off the car. Another variation had a swinging arm which, when raised, would lift the logs off the car. This system was developed to a high degree by Comox Logging with its "Humdurgin" unloader used at Ladysmith and described in detail in the next chapter.

Camp Cars and Mobile Camps

The isolated logging camps of the steam era featured a type of building that has all but disappeared in its original form. This was the portable camp car. Entire camps, including cookhouses, bunkhouses, washhouses, and buildings for saw filing, equipment repair, blacksmithing, and accounting and management, were moved regularly as the timber was cut back into the mountains. "The buildings of a portable camp on skids are moved from one location to another on logging cars or by means of donkey engines. They must be of a size that can be loaded readily on the cars," noted William Gibbons in 1918. "This type of camp has proved more satisfactory than the ordinary permanent camp. With the exception of the initial cost, [the permanent camp] has no advantage over the camp on wheels, and it has some fundamental disadvantages."[23]

Pending the next move, some operators preferred to leave the camp cars permanently mounted on trucks. These cars could be moved with very little lost time and it was possible to relocate an entire camp between breakfast and supper without disrupting the work schedule of the men in the woods. Speed of relocation could be particularly important if fire threatened the camp. Normally, the camps would be moved every few years but the distances were not usually very great. Seven or eight miles (10-12 km) would place the camp close to the timber so that the men and equipment did not spend long in transit between camp and their work at the beginning and end of each shift or when they returned to camp for meals. This was important to the loggers as Tom Coates recalled:

In those days, it was an hour and a half for lunch and everybody went to camp, even at IT [International Timber Company near Campbell River], even at Bloedel's at Myrtle Point. You'd be out in the woods, and when the whistle would blow at noon, you'd all run, get into the

Logs at Sea

The overall system of log transport along the coast often entailed the towing of the logs to the mills. Few logging railroads ended at the mills; most ran to a sheltered bay where the logs could be dumped into the ocean. From there rafts or booms were assembled and tugs towed these slow, awkward cargoes to the mills for processing. In the protected waters of Georgia Strait, the booms were usually safe but in the exposed waters of the West Coast, and in northern British Columbia, much more complicated rafts such as the Davis raft had to be constructed from the logs.

Cathels & Sorensen's railroad ended at Port Renfrew on the West Coast of Vancouver Island. The top photograph from the early 1920s shows 2-6-2 No. 1 at the log dump and in the distance the assembly area for the Davis rafts. A late 1930s photograph, also from Port Renfrew shows rafts being constructed. The locomotive was eventually traded to the Victoria Lumber Company for Climax No. 7 whose number it adopted. Later it became MacMillan & Bloedel's 1077. —LEONARD FRANK, VPL; BCFS, 5108

A tug off Brotchie Ledge near Victoria with a large boom of Douglas-fir and cedar. Long logs called "boom sticks" formed an outside frame for the logs. Tug boat skippers had to know their business well to control the huge booms. —DAVID SCHOLES

139

crummies [crew cars], and into camp and into the dining room, eat; you're on the run all the time to get back to work in that hour and a half.[24]

New camp cars for the Capilano Timber Company, logging in part in the watershed of Vancouver, were featured in *The Timberman* in 1918. The article, "Camp Cars De Luxe for B.C. Operation," noted that ". . . in the competition for labour, logging camps with special conveniences for the men are becoming a matter of importance. . . . In the case of the Capilano Timber Co . . . the camps had to be perfectly constructed from a sanitary point of view," in order to protect Vancouver's water supply. The cars were all 40 feet (12.2 m) long and 14 feet (4.25 m) wide. They were well-ventilated with monitor roofs and large windows. Each car was electrically lit and steam heated, and hot and cold water connections were provided. The steam heating plant, the article noted, ". . . will be constructed on skids so that it can be set to one side away from the main buildings. This feature will lessen the fire risk considerably as this is the only building in camp from which there will be any danger of fire spreading." The article went on to describe the cars:

Each bunk car contains a toilet, a shower bath and sink, supplied with hot and cold water. It will be unnecessary for the men to leave the bunk house as is usual in camps where they have a central bath house. This should be appreciated by the men, especially in the rainy season. The bunk cars are also equipped with a clothes hanger and a locker for each man.

The kitchen will compare favorably with up-to-date hotel kitchens. Large drawers for the supplies are placed on rollers with special cabinets for pastries and other foods. There is also a cabinet for setting bread to rise and a cooler for storing meat and butter. The serving table is metal topped. Sinks are installed for both vegetables and dishes with hot and cold water drainage connections to each . . .

In the dining car there are six tables set crosswise, each sufficient to seat from eight to ten men and instead of the benches usual in camps heretofore, each man is provided with a stool. In this building, there is a window at each end of every table.

The car containing the laundry equipment will also contain accommodation for the cookhouse crew and, in one end, a filing room in which special attention has been given to the overhead lighting, there being a continuous glass window on one side and a full-length skylight overhead.

One end of the office car provides sleeping accommodation for the timekeeper and foreman; the other end has a room for the superintendent.

The exterior of the cars is painted in dark green with canary trimmings. The interior is painted in a pearl gray.[25]

Not all camps were as well thought out for the comfort of the men. Tom Coates remembered some of them well and others all too well, ". . . some of the little ones, you'd have to go out and do your laundry in a tin tub on Sunday. Get your hot water out of the boiler, as long as the engineer, whoever was running it, was cooperative. Most of those old camps, the big ones, God, you could be a quarter of a mile away from the cookhouse, or the washhouse or anything else. Toilets, quite

Bloedel, Stewart & Welch's camp at Myrtle Point about 1919. Life in the early camps could be rugged with few comforts for the loggers. The double rows of windows in the cars suggest that they had double or triple bunks. The cupolas on the roofs were for ventilation.
— MACMILLAN BLOEDEL COLLECTION

The Capilano Timber Company's camp cars, built in 1918 were considered deluxe accommodation in their day.
— *The Timberman*, MAY 1918

Moving camp was a routine matter for the loggers. An entire camp could be relocated in a day or two with only a minor disruption in the logging activities. This is an International Timber camp on the move near Campbell River.
—VPL, 6040

Camp cars in a long train pass through Lake Cowichan. They probably were part of Victoria Lumber & Manufacturing's Camp 10 equipment. —KAATZA HISTORICAL SOCIETY

Bloedel, Stewart & Welch's camp near Menzies Bay in 1927 had just been established following the closure of the company's logging activities at Myrtle Point. As a safeguard, a fire break was usually maintained around the camps.
—W. F. MONTGOMERY, BCARS, 73728

a walk." In contrast, there was a camp at Kingcome Inlet, ". . . in the very early '20s which was all on wheels and never came off. They had sidewalks outside the buildings that used to let down when they weren't moving. There were only four men to a room, which was really something in those days, and the bath house and the wash house and whatnot were in the middle so it was always strung out in one long line. But you were under cover the whole time, because, as well as the sidewalk which let down, they also had a canopy which would let down. . . . That was the most modern camp I ever saw. Powell River built that . . ."[26]

These transient camps were the working homes for the loggers. Where more permanent camps were located, families might live and the camps would become small communities with a school, a social hall and other features. Some loggers or their families even planted gardens. "Married quarters at Rock Bay were very good," Tom remembered. "Phil Wilson, [of Merrill Ring Wilson] he was remarkable in some ways, he was tough in some ways, but he was very good to the men. He was the first man that I know that used just single beds instead of double and triple bunks. He was the first man who brought in spring mattresses. . . . He built good married quarters. But in most places, they were not so good. You'd have to build your own. Company didn't provide them at all. So a man would just get a little lumber and put up a little shack and that was it."

Tom Coates also worked at Theodosia Arm which

. . . wasn't a large operation. The thing I remember so well about it was they had a hundred pigs roaming around the camp. That was half the pork supply to keep the crew going. Another place I remember well for pigs was . . . Lamb Lumber Company. No pig pens, just roamed loose and they'd feed them at the back of the cookhouse, and they'd drop all the slops into the trough. I went there one summer and stayed five or six weeks and then I left. Lamb had quite a steady crew for some reason, I don't know why. But there were a lot of men who'd work for Lamb for years and years. The same at the old Hastings company. I would say 70 percent of them stayed there year in and year out, that is they never worked for anyone else but Hastings.[27]

Wartime labour shortages brought women into the camps as kitchen staff and domestic help during World War I. Conditions improved, at least partly to attract and keep labour which was in high demand. In his early working days Tom Coates had to supply his own blankets at the camps,

. . . But by the end of the war, almost everyone was providing blankets, sheets, and putting in laundries, hiring girls for flunkies. A lot of girls by the war's end were working in the cook houses, there at the camps. I never remember any problems. I know at IT [International Timber Company] first time I worked there, they had all-girl flunkies. I know one very happy couple, he was a locomotive engineer who married one of the flunkies at IT shortly after I was there. They had eight or 10 girls as flunkies plus two girls in the laundry. When they first started providing bedding, they put in a couple of these big steam washing machines and did all the laundry in camp.

I don't remember any problems. The loggers were not as wild as the stories you hear.

All scrubbed and heading for town. Loggers from one of Cathels & Sorensen's camps are ready to take the speeder down to Port Renfrew.
—GEORGE ROBERTSON COLLECTION

The big camps were impressive, if austere communities. This one belonged to Brooks-Scanlon-O'Brien at Spring Lake on their Eagle River & Northern Railway running inland from Stillwater near Powell River. The camp was destroyed by a forest fire in 1926.
—BCARS, HP67905

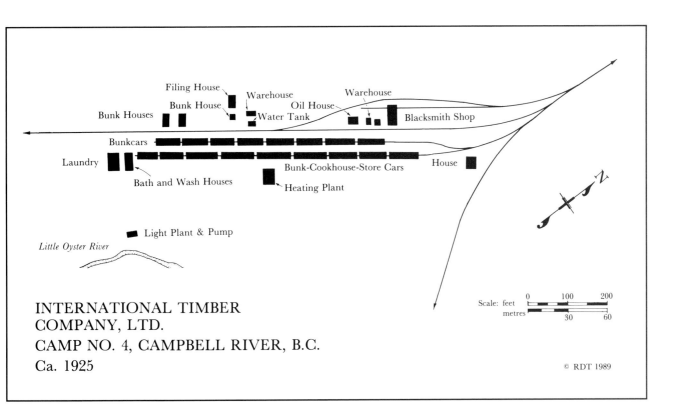

Filing House
Bunk House
Warehouse
Oil House
Warehouse

Bunk Houses
Water Tank
Blacksmith Shop

Bunkcars

Laundry
Bath and Wash Houses
Bunk-Cookhouse-Store Cars
House

Heating Plant

Light Plant & Pump

Little Oyster River

INTERNATIONAL TIMBER COMPANY, LTD.
CAMP NO. 4, CAMPBELL RIVER, B.C.
Ca. 1925

Scale: feet
metres

0	100	200
	30	60

© RDT 1989

International Timber's Camp 4 in the Campbell River area was representative of the medium-sized woods camps. Nearly all of the camp is laid out on two parallel tracks. The bath and wash houses are a long hike from some of the bunkcars. This photograph is taken from north end of the camp looking south. Note the small speeder powered by the gas engine.—GERRY WELLBURN COLLECTION

"We used to travel up and down on the Union boats—mostly on the *Chelohsin* which called in twice a week at Menzies Bay. Quite often if there were a lot of people coming in they would put on the old caboose behind the locie to carry everybody."—DICK HERRLING REMEMBERING LIFE IN THE 1930S AT CAMPBELL RIVER TIMBER'S CAMP NEAR BREWSTER LAKE.

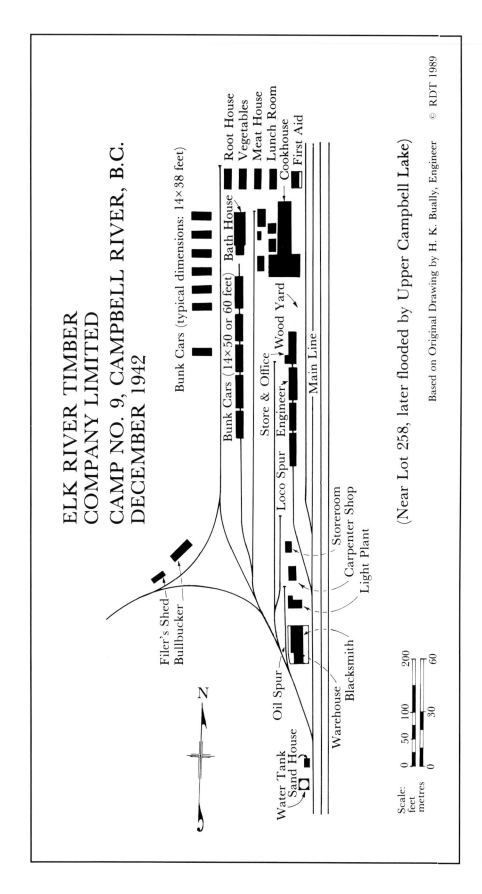

ELK RIVER TIMBER
COMPANY LIMITED
CAMP NO. 9, CAMPBELL RIVER, B.C.
DECEMBER 1942

Bunk Cars (typical dimensions: 14×38 feet)

Root House
Vegetables
Meat House
Lunch Room
Cookhouse
First Aid

Bunk Cars (14×50 or 60 feet)   Bath House

Store & Office   Wood Yard

Loco Spur   Engineer

Main Line

Storeroom
Carpenter Shop
Light Plant

Filer's Shed
Bullbucker

Oil Spur

Warehouse
Blacksmith

N

Water Tank
Sand House

(Near Lot 258, later flooded by Upper Campbell Lake)

Based on Original Drawing by H. K. Bually, Engineer   © RDT 1989

Scale: feet   0 50 100   200
          metres   0   30   60

The layout of Camp 9 was similar to many other woods camps. Bunkcars were backed onto the sidings and others were placed nearby. The cookhouse—a central feature of any camp—was well located. A turning wye, and oil, sand and water facilities were built for the locomotives.

146

Elk River Timber's Camp 9 was located on the shore of Upper Campbell Lake in a large clearing in an unusually picturesque setting. The camp site was flooded following the construction of the hydro-electric dam at Elk Falls. —RAY COMPTON, MIKE CROSS COLLECTION

Camp 9 was clean and well maintained. Most of the camp cars were mounted on trucks but some were moved off the tracks. —RAY COMPTON, MIKE CROSS COLLECTION

"It was great to grow up there [at Campbell River Timber's camp]. Most people couldn't get out of a place like that fast enough but it was really nice as a kid. Quite often they's take a string of cars down around supper time in the summer months. They would be back by 9:30 or 10:00. Sometimes we'd be allowed to go down for a ride and sometimes we'd just climb on. That was good for a licking if you were caught!" —DICK HEERLING

The Gordon River Valley near Cowichan Lake was the site of a large camp established by McDonald Murphy and taken over by Lake Logging in 1934. Lake Logging named the camp "Rounds" after one of its founders. These scenes show some of the activity at the busy camp: loggers boarding old E&N coaches used to take them to the woods; Climax No. 2 about to leave camp; the rush to the cookhouse; an overview of the camp; and finally, Willamette No. 3 with a log train.
—NICHOLAS MORANT, CPCA, M284; FOUR PHOTOS, CEDRIC MYERS

Living conditions in the camps improved over the years and the camps tended to become more permanent with fewer moves. As equipment was upgraded it became easier to move the men to the woods from permanent facilities and the nomadic camps slowly disappeared. Some of the camps such as Rock Bay, Nimpkish Camp, and Camp 5 at Brewster Lake evolved into stable communities that lasted for 10 or 20 years or more, while others were abandoned and simply disappeared with the timber that was logged. But even the more permanent settlements were abandoned once the timber was cut and there was no longer any reason for their existence. Woss Camp on northern Vancouver Island is the last company-owned railroad logging camp in British Columbia.

Of the rail-mounted camp cars, very few survive. Occasionally, in logging areas, a tool shed or storage building will show in its construction that it was once used as a camp car. Fortunately, Gerry Wellburn made sure this important feature of forest history was preserved at the B.C. Forest Museum at Duncan. Four camp cars from Victoria Lumber & Manufacturing's Copper Canyon operation and one from the Nanaimo Lakes camp form a major exhibit. The four Copper Canyon camp buildings, a bunkhouse, a timekeeper's and first aid building, a surveyor and engineer's office, and a cookhouse, were all built in 1942. They were purchased in 1956 and were moved to Gerry's property at Deerholme and in 1977 they were relocated to the Forest Museum at Duncan. A fifth building, the rail camp dining room, was moved to the Museum in 1979.[28]

Donkey Engines, Loaders and Skidders

"There is no exaggeration in the statement that no class of machinery is called upon for such extremely severe service as logging engines. The demands upon them are frequently far beyond their normal capacity and from the nature of their work it is difficult to give them the attention which such machinery should have" (Willamette Iron and Steel Works Catalogue, ca. 1915).[29]

Steam was the most important source of energy. It powered the locomotives on the railways and ran the saws and equipment in the mills. It also powered the donkey engines that yarded and loaded the logs in the woods. There were so many types of donkeys and variations on the designs that it is impossible here to review them all in detail. Instead, we can examine some of the major types and how they were used in conjunction with the railroads.

The donkeys ranged from small, very simple portable winches to enormous and complex, multi-engined machines that could perform several functions at once. There was also great variety and flexibility in the way this equipment was used in the woods. Some companies preferred one type of equipment and method of yarding timber while another operator had different ideas of what worked best.

Comox Logging's Robert Filberg summarized the situation at a logger's conference later published in *The Timberman*. "Surely though, no logger has ever failed to justify and defend his purchase of equipment or his system of yarding and loading, it's just not done. That is, of course, unless someone else bought the equipment or installed the system of yarding and loading. We are all, therefore, quite within our rights to pick the 'bugs' out of the other fellow's systems while defending our own."[30]

In its simplest form, the donkey engine comprised a small vertical boiler which supplied steam to a single-cylinder steam engine which drove a winch. The early machines often had the spool of the winch mounted vertically (a vertical windlass or capstan). The donkey was mounted on a large wooden sled built of heavy timbers. The sled made it possible for the donkey to pull itself along over extremely rough terrain to where it was needed. When simple, single-drum machines were used, a horse was often used to take the line back out to the timber. These early donkeys were first used in the Douglas-fir forests of the Pacific Coast in the late 1880s. They had been used in California a few years earlier following the patenting by John Dolbeer of a steam logging machine in 1882. Soon a larger, powered drum, mounted horizontally across the sled, became standard and this type evolved into multi-drum machines. By the turn of the century, steam-powered ground yarding had all but replaced the use of horses or oxen along the coast although horse logging remained important in the Interior pine forests until much later.[31]

In the interior of the province, particularly in the East Kootenays, the steam equipment used was generally much smaller than the machines of the coastal logging camps. Horses were used for much of the ground yarding, and machines such as Barnhart loaders lifted the small pine and fir logs onto the railcars. The Barnhart was a small, steam-powered crane on wheels that ran along rails attached to the tops of the logging flatcars. Another type of loader was the McGiffert, which had retractable wheels to move along the logging railway tracks. Log cars could be pushed directly under the loader. These types of machines greatly increased the efficiency of loading the logs and complemented the hauling capacity of the railways.

On the coast, the size of the logs presented a problem of a much greater magnitude. Steam-powered ground yarding systems were a vast improvement over animal power, but it did not take long before the loggers developed more efficient systems. The biggest problem with ground yarding was that the logs had to be pulled over rough country and that required a lot of power to overcome the drag of the heavy logs. Not only that, but the valuable timber could be damaged. The answer was to lift the logs at least partially off the ground using heavy wire ropes. This reduced or eliminated the drag and meant that the logs could be moved with much greater speed. Overhead and high-lead yarding became the standard in Pacific Coast logging operations in the early 1900s — the famous Lidgerwood design was introduced in 1904 and high-lead methods came into use about 1905. Slack-line systems were operating in 1908. However, it took some

The steam donkey engine was essential to the yarding and loading process. Moving the massive logs of the coastal forests required powerful, tough machinery. This one belonged to the Canadian Robert Dollar Company at Union Bay in 1918. It illustrates well the features of a woods donkey: vertical boiler with spark arrester on the stack; heavy wooden sled; fairleads for guiding the lines (wire ropes); a crude shelter over the machinery to protect the crews from the weather; and the massive drums of the donkey. — DOMINION PHOTO COMPANY, FRED SMITH COLLECTION

The spar tree and skidder were the focus of yarding and loading activity at the landings. This skidder is probably one of Fairservice Gierin Logging's at Cowichan Lake in the 1920s. The big unit includes both yarding and loading engines. —W. F. MONTGOMERY, BCARS, HP73657

The landings were a site of almost constant activity. Yarding and loading were often done simultaneously. The crews handled the loading tongs and other heavy equipment with skill but the work was dangerous and a moment's carelessness could have serious consequences. A typical yarding crew might consist of one hooktender (the foreman), two choker men, one unhooker, one signalman, one engineer, one fireman and, if necessary, a wood buck. The loading crew could require a fireman, engineer, head loader, second loader and third loader. This photograph is of Lake Logging at Cowichan Lake. —NICHOLAS MORANT, CPCA, M266

The big skidders or "units" were highly complex and included steam winches, powered from the main boiler, for yarding, loading, and spotting cars. — FRED BELL

Elk River Timber, Side No. 2 in the early 1930s. Among the crew are Leslie Taylor; Bill Smith, engineer; Ray Morrison, head loader; Black Jack Kerpin, leverman; Sam, Head Loader and "One-eared" Pete. — JOHN BUCHANAN COLLECTION

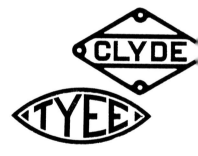

Sometimes landings had to be located on switchbacks on steep hillsides. At this site on McDonald Murphy's operations at Cowichan Lake in the early 1930s, a spotting line was used to move the cars under the loading boom. — CEDRIC MYERS

years for these systems to see widespread use and there were innumerable variations and developments of the equipment.[32]

Normally, the high-lead and skyline arrangements required the use of a spar tree to hold the blocks; some are illustrated in the accompanying photographs. "The principle of hanging the main-line lead block high on a spar tree to give a lift on the log to overcome obstructions obtained double the output of the ground lead [type of yarding]," noted J. Kenneth Pearce, an authority on logging methods. "The high lead is the most commonly used and therefore, the most important of the cable-hauling systems." In fact, ". . . more logs are yarded on the Pacific coast, from the redwoods through the Douglas-fir region to Alaska, with the high lead than with any other systems."[33] By making use of the enormous power of the steam donkey engines, the lines could be operated at speeds of up to 20 miles (32 km) per hour.

The spar tree itself was a large, straight tree trimmed of its lower branches and cut off as much as 150-200 feet (45-60 m) above the ground, usually at a point where the tree was 24-30 inches (60-75 cm) in diameter. The tricky operation of topping was done by the "high-rigger," usually of a breed of young men who took pride in their skill at climbing and working on the high spars. They also rigged the spars with supporting cables and attached the blocks and other rigging for the yarding and loading operations. Sometimes, it was not possible to use a standing tree for the spar and one would be cut and brought in to the landing site and raised in the desired place.

The high-lead and skyline systems had important differences in the way the rigging was set. High-leads usually operated with a single spar so that the farther away from the spar the logs were hauled, the more difficult it was to get them clear of obstruction. With the skyline methods, a second spar was used at a distance from the landing. A skyline was rigged between the two. As Brown noted, "All skyline systems have the following elements in common: a heavy wire rope skyline is suspended by 'shoes' or 'jacks' or blocks hung on straps on the spars between the head spar or tower at the landing and a tail-spar tree at the back end of the yarding or swing road. The lift on the turn of logs is provided by a carriage riding on the skyline."[34]

Often, to extend the reach of the yarding systems, a second donkey engine would be situated at the end of the skyline or high-lead. This machine would be used to yard in logs from the surrounding area to a "cold deck." From there, the logs were transferred to the main yarding system and hauled in to the landing. Cold decking had the advantage of providing a steady supply of logs to the landing but it did increase the complexity and cost of the yarding process.

Once the timber was yarded to the end of the rail line, it still had to be loaded onto the rail cars. In the early days, logs could be parbuckled onto the cars using cables, running through blocks, to either the locomotive or a donkey engine to roll the logs up an incline onto the cars. However, this method, like ground yarding, was inefficient and soon gave way to more sophisticated and efficient techniques in which the logs were lifted onto the cars using cables rigged to the spar tree.

"The gradual evolution of logging engines has given the industry the compound-geared, ground-yarding engine and the long-range, high-speed roading engine, both of which seem to have reached perfection, also fairly satisfactory overhead and high-lead logging engines, which without doubt are susceptible to further improvements," wrote William Gibbons in 1918.[35] By that time, the logging engines had become sophisticated pieces of industrial machinery being supplied by major firms such as Willamette of Portland (represented in B.C. by Canadian Willamette of Vancouver) and the Washington Iron Works of Seattle.

The typical donkey engine of the early steam era in the western woods normally had a minimum of two drums, a main line drum for the line used in log hauling and a haulback drum for the line which was used to pull the heavy main line back to where the logs were cut. Many donkeys also had a smaller third drum for a light "straw line" which could be used for rigging and other purposes. When additional power sources were required, either a second donkey was used or a larger machine with additional steam-powered drums was acquired. Machines that included both loading and yarding engines were called "units." The larger machines were often permanently mounted on heavy-duty railroad trucks. Loggers often called the big machines "skidders" and as logging methods developed, the machines evolved into enormous, complicated multi-drum and multi-engine behemoths. The ultimate expression of their growth was the tower skidder, a huge machine that carried a collapsible steel spar, which eliminated the need for rigging a spar tree at each location. Consider the complexity of this skidder described in 1918 by William Gibbons:

The one designed to handle timber of average size in this region is equipped with 12 by 12 inch [30.5 x 30.5 cm], double-cylinder, high-speed engines, with five drums. Then there is the utility engine with 10 by 10 inch [25.4 x 25.4 cm] cylinders and four drums. On the front of the machine there is a 12 by 12 inch swinging-boom loading engine, mounted on a turntable. This engine drives three friction drums. Up in the tower, underneath the steel spar, there is a four-drum, guy-tightening engine. The skidding engine has a hauling-line speed of from 500 to 800 feet [150 to 245 m] per minute, and a return-line speed of from 1,800 to 3,000 [550 to 915 m] per minute. The machine is mounted on a steel frame. This frame with its supporting legs is raised or lowered by hydraulic jacks, to allow empty cars to pass beneath it.[36]

Some companies had a small donkey that was used by the rigging crews to prepare the spars before the arrival of the yarding and loading machines. Tom Coates, who rigged hundreds of trees during his long career in the woods, described a typical one. "The goat was a small donkey, 9 by 10, 10 by 11 inches [23 x 25.4, 25.4 x 28 cm], small sized machine, on a sled, mounted on a skeleton car, and you carried on it straps of all different sizes that would suit whatever size tree you had. You carried extra shackles, extra rigging of every type and claw bars and hammers, railroad spikes, everything you need."[37]

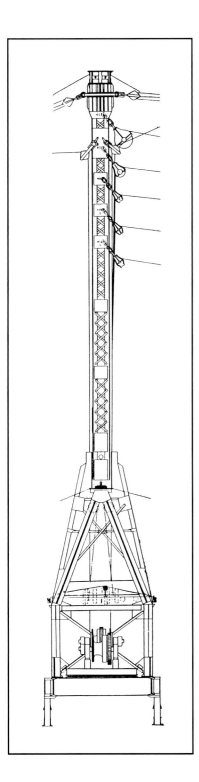

The tower skidder took the development of large scale steam yarding and loading equipment to its zenith. The drawing shows the tower of a Lidgerwood, while the photograph shows Bloedel, Stewart & Welch's machine at Franklin River in the 1950s. — *The Timberman*; MACMILLAN BLOEDEL COLLECTION

157

Comox Logging was one of the earliest operators of high lead logging equipment in British Columbia. Lidgerwood machines were purchased in 1910 and used with great efficiency. A typical Comox Logging setting is shown above. —W. F. MONTGOMERY, BCARS, 73713

Lake Logging at Cowichan Lake had to build up this landing site with cribbing to support the tracks and two donkey engines at this landing. The destruction of the forest cover was complete and much of the timber would be left behind. —NICHOLAS MORANT, CPCA, M279

Donkey engines and the railways were the two major components of log transportation during the steam era. Efficient planning of the yarding and railway operation was very important to financial success in logging. The engineers and managers had to know their equipment and how to employ it to take advantage of the topography, the nature of the timber stand and the particular characteristics of the machines at hand. The overall costs of both railroad construction and operation had to be balanced with the total costs of yarding and loading to produce the most economical logging plan.

Robert J. Filberg, manager of Comox Logging, quoted earlier, described some of his company's yarding and loading methods at the extensive railroad show based at Headquarters in the Comox Valley on Vancouver Island.

We have been logging almost exclusively with skidders since 1910. I'm nearly ashamed to admit that we produce all of our logs with skidders that were purchased 22 years ago.

Each year we just naturally couldn't help learning a little something about how to handle this equipment so now we operate these old skidders to greater advantage and more efficiently than we did when we got them. Though the equipment is old, I'll assure you it is in mighty good mechanical condition and we have from time to time made slight mechanical improvements. These six machines are thoroughly standardized which is a great help for maintenance. Each skidder and loader is mounted on a steel car with swivel trucks. The overall length is only 27 feet [8.2 m]. The loading engines are 10 by 10 [25 x 25 cm] with four drums. The skidding engines are 12 by 12 [30.5 x 30.5 cm] with four drums. The boiler is 66 inches [1.68 m] with a seven-foot [2.1-m] high firebox. Total weight of each machine about 150,000 pounds [68 tonnes].

Our loading engines were originally designed for single line loading. Anyone who has loaded logs with a single line knows plenty about trouble. For some years we have been loading with a boom and find it quite satisfactory. Our booms differ from any other I know of in that they are 80 feet long and we log entirely around the setting without moving the skidder.... We set the skidder at right angles to the track; our first road is usually straight out from the skidder, then we go right around the tree. Some of the roads come behind the boiler but the boom is long enough and hung high enough to swing over the boiler and pick the logs up. We use a block if the logs are large but usually a straight line with a crotch and two tongs, one drum swings the boom to the log and a counterbalance swings the boom to the load. This rig works well and has the advantage of permitting a full setting to be logged without moving the skidder around the tree. Frequently, we have averaged 300 logs per side per day for a month and our best day was 856 logs loaded by one side in eight hours.

In skidding, we try to make 1250-foot [380-m] roads our maximum and seldom go out further than that, usually 1100 to 1200 feet [335 to 365 m]. We have had a lot of grief with long spans and don't like them, although we are operating one skidder on a float with an A-frame where the roads are 2500 feet [760 m] up a steep sidehill.

We operate gas cold deckers in conjunction with our skidders and about 25 percent of the logs handled by the skidders are cold decked for them. We cold deck long corners, behind curves and parts of settings where the timber is either small or scattered.

You know, it's impossible to work with anything for 22 years without becoming quite attached to it and that probably explains our regard for these old skidders....[38]

A Victoria Lumber &
Manufacturing Company crew
moves a spar to a setting where no
appropriate tree was available.
—GEOFF ROWE COLLECTION

In the final years of the steam era,
hardhats, steel-toed boots and
other safety equipment were in use
but the work of the loading crew
and others at the landings was still
dangerous and just as hard. These
two scenes are of MacMillan &
Bloedel at Franklin River. The
crews were working near the tower
skidder shown on page 157.
—MACMILLAN BLOEDEL
COLLECTION

A fully-rigged spar tree required an
enormous maze of cables to
support the spar and operate a
yarding and loading system. This
was one of MacMillan & Bloedel's
at Franklin River. —JACK CASH,
MACMILLAN BLOEDEL COLLECTION

Caterpillar tractors were used extensively in the woods during the last years of steam operations. Often, they skidded the loads to the landings as in this Franklin River setting. —JACK CASH, MACMILLAN BLOEDEL COLLECTION

Tractors or "Cats" could even be employed to load logs or, in this case, poles, using an auxiliary winch. These poles were being loaded by Alberni Pacific near Camp 1 in 1938. —VPL, 5541

These were the machines of the steam era in the woods, big, heavy, tough, overtly mechanical, sometimes dangerous, always noisy and smelling of hot grease, hot oil, smoke and steam. Something to be fond of and take pride in; something to curse at. The special equipment of the logging railroads of the steam era and the associated steam-powered yarding and loading machinery gave the lines their unique character and fascination. This same technology was also a powerful tool for resource exploitation and at the same time an instrument of landscape change. It evolved over approximately a 50-year period from the 1880s until 1930 through practical inventiveness and innovation and then, with minor exceptions, its development came to a dramatic halt. The Depression of 1929 virtually ended the purchase of new steam equipment for both rail and yarding operations. In fact, the decline in the economy meant that there was a surplus of good, used equipment on the market that carried most operations through World War II into the era of dieselization and trucking.

Steam cranes were functional and versatile pieces of equipment that could be adapted for log loading, track and bridge work or salvaging a wreck. This one belonged to B.C. Forest Products on its Bear Creek Camp operation in 1950.
— CAM CHOUINARD

Loading equipment for the small logs of the interior forests could be much smaller and lighter in construction than the huge machines needed to wield the logs cut from the coastal forests. This is a Barnhart loader owned by the Columbia River Lumber Company based at Golden.
— W. F. MONTGOMERY, BCARS, 73492

163

Alberni Pacific Lumber's No. 7 takes on water at Camp 1 in the Alberni Valley on Vancouver Island. The big saddletank Baldwin survived the end of steam railroading in the district to continue hauling logs for MacMillan & Bloedel at Franklin River and finally at the Nanaimo River until 1969.—MACMILLAN BLOEDEL COLLECTION

164

DEPRESSION, HEYDAY AND DECLINE

The Depression Years

"We had no money. Because you had the crews out anyway, you had to keep them going. You wanted to give them work...," reflected Gerry Wellburn who, in the 1930s, was trying to keep the men at Wellburn Timber as busy as possible, even if for only a few days a week.[1] The Great Depression of the 1930s hit the forest industry and the logging camps as it hit most sectors of the economy in those hard times. Some camps closed while others made major cutbacks in their operations.

George Robertson was logging on the west coast of Vancouver Island. He recalled the impact of the Depression on the Island Logging Company (a subsidiary of the Canadian Puget Sound Lumber & Timber Company) which had a railroad operation south of Jordan River:

They built a main line right to Jordan River [from Point No Point], there were the old remains of trestles and bridges for a long time. They put a grade, and the bridges in, and they even put the bridge across Jordan River [but] they never laid steel on it. The Depression hit... and it was never logged on. And when they went back logging... they were truck logging.[2]

Jack Payne worked through the Depression as a contractor building trestles and bridges for the logging railroads. He managed to keep working but often there was far more labour than money in a job.

Well, we would sometimes get one bent* a day, sometimes two or three. Depending on what you ran into, you know. I got $1.35 a linear foot for the ordinary trestle, not span, up to 35 feet [10 m] high. After that you'd get an increase. That took care of all the labour. They paid for all the machinery that was used and the materials, like iron work or anything like that. That was in the thirties, dirty thirties. There wasn't much money in that.[3]

For many men, the Depression years were a time of finding work wherever they could. Sometimes, a man could work for a few months relieving someone else, or

---

* A trestle bent on a logging railway bridge was usually made up of five pilings or timbers with all the associated bracing, finishing timbers and the cap. In this case, the rate would have included the decking.

pick up a few more months if an order came through. There certainly was no security. Spike Carson's experiences are typical of many young men trying to work on the railroads.

I went to work on April 6, 1930 for the E&N Railway in Port Alberni. Then in '31 I couldn't hold a job. My dad was looking after the waterworks dam up at China Creek for Port Alberni and I used to ride the [Alberni Pacific] train up there and back. The superintendent... called me down off the tender and I thought I was going to get kicked off because I was smoking a cigarette. Instead of that, he asked me if I'd like a job firing.... That was on the little 2-Spot. I worked on it for about two and a half or three months in '31 then the fireman came back for work. His father had died and he had been away.... Then I went firing a cold decker and I stayed at that job until the following May. By that time I could hold a job on the E&N again. I stayed there wiping until 1933 [at Port Alberni].

Then I stayed in Courtenay, then down to Duncan, then I went back to Port Alberni—that was '36. Then... I left the E&N and I went to work at APL [Alberni Pacific Lumber] braking, but I was only just on a relief job. Then I went back to the E&N again. Then in '38, there was a chance to go braking again, so I left the E&N and I went to APL and I stayed there. I went through, first of all braking, then, I guess you would call it a hostler, and then I went firing, and I got my ticket and then I went running. I ran engines for quite a few years up there then. In fact I ran right up until about three weeks before they finished up [in 1953].[4]

The times were tough and the work fragmentary. But if you worked in the better camps, conditions could still be good. Jack Payne recalled living at a Hillcrest Lumber camp during the Depression years:

Everything was rock bottom then. We were paying 75 cents a day at Hillcrest for room and board and you just couldn't eat all the food. I mean, the table was laden. You could fill your plate two or three times if you wanted. And it was good clean food. One of the best camps I ever worked in was Hillcrest Lumber Company.

In the morning you could have eggs and bacon or pancakes. At noon, everybody packed a lunch. But at night was a big feed. There was roast beef, and generally three types of meat on the table and lots of vegetables. Everything a man could wish for. They didn't make five cents in the cookhouse. They didn't intend to; they would just break even.

The bunkhouses were 30 or 40 feet [9 or 12 m] long and they were situated so the doors opened into a little room. And you had one bunk bed in there, a single bed, and just room enough to turn around, that's all. Otherwise very comfortable. Clean linen once a week. Brought the men in every night on speeders.[5]

By the end of 1932, economic conditions were about as bad as they could get and the Department of Railways reported that 12 of 45 logging railways in the province were closed. Of 777 miles (1250 km) of logging trackage, 167 miles (267 km), about 22 percent, were inactive. Total closures idled 29 steam locomotives of the 103 owned by the logging companies in British Columbia and undoubtedly many others were out of service on the active or marginally operating lines.[6] These figures translated into many lost jobs and many men desperate for the remaining work. When compared to 1929, the year the Depression began, when 852 miles of

Kapoor Lumber Company, located on the Canadian National's Cowichan Subdivision on Vancouver Island, was a Depression-era mill typical of many smaller companies that struggled during the lean years before World War II. The photograph was taken on May 24, 1935.—DAVID SCHOLES

Small logging railroads like that of the Royston Lumber Company were less and less competitive with trucking during the 1930s. By the end of the decade trucking had clearly won out and the small railroads were gone.
—JOHN LOCKNER

The Depression saw many locomotives laid up or prematurely scrapped. This Heisler, originally worked for Heaps Timber and then Campbell River Mills as No. 3. It passed to three other companies before arriving at the Vancouver Machinery Depot as shown on April 10, 1939, to be scrapped.
— RAILWAY NEGATIVE EXCHANGE

Donovan Corkery Logging Co. No. 4 was acquired by Comox Logging for its Headquarters operations. The big Baldwin 2-8-2 was photographed at Auburn, Washington on May 15, 1937 en route to Vancouver Island. Reboilered, it became No. 11 on Comox Logging, taking the place of No. 3 on the main line late in 1937. — ALBERT FARROW

In an optimistic 1934 promotion, Beyer-Garratt locomotives were advertised in the *British Columbia Lumberman* as being ideal for logging service. None operated in B.C.

track and 125 locomotives were listed by the logging companies, the extent of the decline is even more apparent.[7] Moreover, in the pre-Depression years, new locomotives and equipment, not to mention used machines bought in the United States, were being added to many lines. For example, seven new Pacific Coast Shays, two smaller Shays, one large Willamette, three Climaxes, two big Baldwin 2-8-2Ts, and a Porter 2-8-2 were ordered between 1927 and 1930 for B.C. logging railways. During the early Depression years, no new locomotives or equipment were acquired. In fact, for the entire decade, as far as is known, only two additional new steam locomotives were purchased. These were a Pacific Coast Shay for Merrill Ring Wilson in 1936 and a 70-ton (63-tonne) Heisler for Malahat Logging in 1939. In addition, two other Pacific Coast Shays, two 2-8-2s and probably some other equipment were acquired second hand from lines in the U.S. as conditions began to ease in the mid to late 1930s.

The status of the logging railroads and the equipment orders were indicative of the decline in the industry. They did not, however, show the plummeting sales of lumber nor the marginal production of the camps and mills that were still working but at greatly reduced volumes. "The forest industries felt the effects of the economic conditions acutely, both in volume and price of lumber products, and from an industrial point of view the year was the worst experienced since 1914," commented the Forest Branch in its 1932 *Annual Report*. The value of products from the B.C. forest industry had dropped to just over $35,000,000 for the year. The figures for 1928 had been nearly $94,000,000 and 1929, the year of the beginning of the Depression, had been only slightly less.[8]

Fortunately, as the Depression ground on, the situation slowly improved in the logging industry and the camps came back to life. William Rae, the Department of Railways' Chief Inspector was able to report by the end of 1938 that, "during the first part of the year practically all logging railways were in operation." He went on to note that, "... for two months in the summer, owing to numerous fires, camps were closed down. During this shut down period no work was done and no repairs made to equipment. After the fire season was over operations were resumed and continued until the 20th. December." Moreover, "... a number of larger operations extended the trackage of their railways and added more equipment."[9] Nonetheless, the total mileage of logging lines had increased by only 10 miles (16 km) since 1932 and was still 65 miles (105 km) less than in 1929, reflecting the impact of the pre-Depression years.

Although logging made a gradual comeback, and activity on the logging railways increased, so too, did the competitive advantages of trucking. The story of the development of truck logging goes beyond the scope of this book but by the middle to late 1930s, this development was a major force in limiting the expansion of logging railroads. For small contract loggers, it was much simpler and easier to work with a few trucks than to try to maintain a small, independent railroad. Trucking equipment was developed and improved at the same time as public

Elk River Timber

One of the largest railroad shows in the Campbell River district belonged to Elk River Timber. Camp 8, shown at left, was one of the major camps. The large engine house is in the left distance while the rows of well-maintained camp buildings are clustered next to the main line. The largest locomotive used by ERT was No. 5, a Porter 2-8-2. The big machine, with drivers that looked too small to support it, worked on the main line to the log dump at Campbell River. It was photographed at the Quinsam water tank on June 29, 1952.—WILMER GOLD (left); ROBERT HANFT, W. C. WHITTAKER COLLECTION.

ERT's Shays 1 and 2 worked on the logging spurs and would sometimes even be used double-headed on the heavy grades. No. 1 was photographed in June 1952.
—ROBERT HANFT, W. C. WHITTAKER COLLECTION

"The largest train out of Camp 8 was 85 cars with the Five-Spot. The engineer was Andy Teck and Norm Tompkinson was fireman. I was headend brakeman. We had no room to run around such a long train at the dump so we had to break it into three cuts. We dumped cars with the Humdurgin. Freddy Hopkins timed a cut of 27 cars—12 seconds a car to put them in the water. I was tripping the blocks and he was pushing them in. I figured we got about 120 cars a day for four years straight—a lot of timber going down there at that time [in the late 1930s]."—JOHN BUCHANAN

The big Porter was certainly not immune from trouble; not a wheel was left on the tracks but at least the engine did not roll over. Nonetheless, the engine crew would have their hands full.
—BILL CHAMBERS COLLECTION, CAMPBELL RIVER MUSEUM 13059

The line's big speeder proved helpful in many jobs on the logging railroad including moving camp buildings. In 1933, it was assigned to relocating camp cars from Camp 7 to Camp 8.
—BILL CHAMBERS COLLECTION, CAMPBELL RIVER MUSEUM 13047

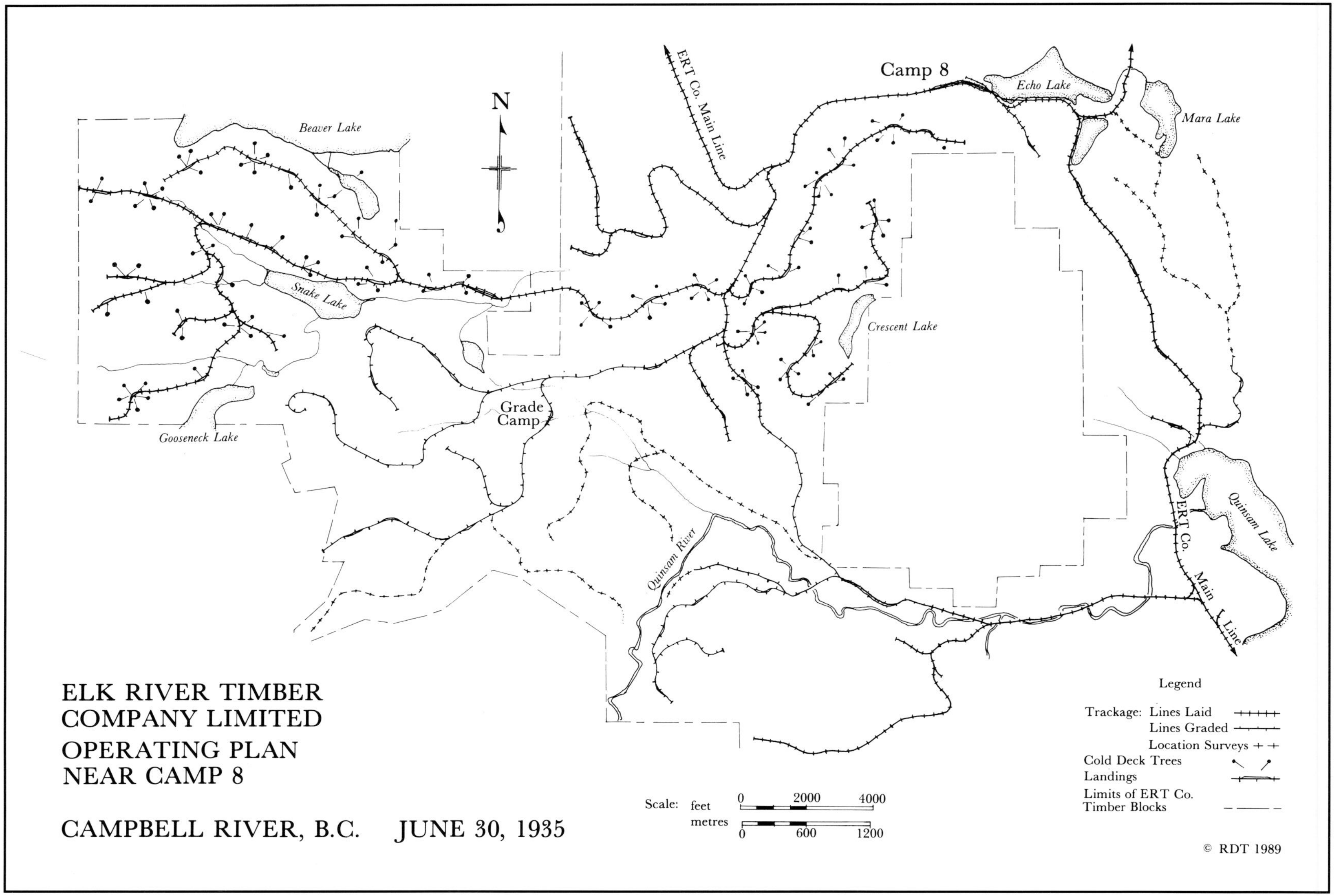

ELK RIVER TIMBER
COMPANY LIMITED
OPERATING PLAN
NEAR CAMP 8

CAMPBELL RIVER, B.C.   JUNE 30, 1935

Legend

Trackage: Lines Laid
           Lines Graded
           Location Surveys
Cold Deck Trees
Landings
Limits of ERT Co.
Timber Blocks

© RDT 1989

Scale: feet   0   2000   4000
        metres 0 600 1200

Camp 8

Mara Lake

Echo Lake

Quinsam Lake

ERT Co.   Main   Line

ERT Co. Main Line

Crescent Lake

Quinsam River

Beaver Lake

Snake Lake

Gooseneck Lake

Grade Camp

The railroad from Camp 8 extended east of Campbell River and Quinsam Lake as shown in the map. Later, a reload was built at Gooseneck Lake. The facility was photographed by G. M. Abernethy on July 26, 1944.
—BCFS, 2879-2

172

road systems were expanded and private logging roads were being constructed.[10] Even the larger operators found trucks an advantage. In fact, Comox Logging began its operations at Ladysmith in 1936 using trucks to haul all its timber to tidewater and was one of the pioneers in truck logging, its timber hauling records being in the top two or three companies in western North America.[11]

The use of trucks as feeders for the railroads in the west coast forests was only just beginning in the late 1930s. By this time, the trucks were big and powerful enough to carry the equivalent of a full carload of logs to the transfer points, making a quick and efficient shift from truck to train possible. Cost factors were swinging increasingly in favour of trucking. Not only was it cheaper to build roads instead of railways on a per mile basis, but usually the trucks could operate on grades twice as steep as the trains, making it possible to build much shorter, more direct roads.[12]

To speed up hauling, Comox Logging's main line truck road out of Ladysmith was hard-surfaced into the timber stands west of the town. Eight diesel-powered trucks were in use in the early 1940s and others were operated by contractors. Each truck was capable of handling 12,000 to 15,000 feet (28 to 35 m^3) of timber per trip.[13] Overall, the Ladysmith operation was capable of hauling 150,000,000 feet (354 000 m^3) of logs annually. By mid-1943, approximately 200 miles (320 km) of logging roads had been constructed in the area.[14] Impressed by the efficiency of these operations, Comox Logging expanded the use of trucks and introduced them to its Headquarters logging operations near Courtenay.[15] Contract trucks began feeding timber to the established railroad system in the Comox Valley; it was the beginning of a process of gradual conversion that would see the end of railroading in the area within another decade. However, the outbreak of World War II in 1939 disrupted the introduction of new equipment and ideas and gave the logging railroads a reprieve from competition.

Wartime Expansion

World War II finally brought Canada out of the Depression years of the 1930s and dramatically increased the demand for lumber and construction materials. At the same time the war brought shortages of equipment and skilled labour. Old equipment that had survived the Depression years had to be kept in use because new locomotives or motor vehicles were virtually impossible to acquire when alternatives existed. As a result, the use of trucks was slowed during the war years because of the military demands for heavy equipment, fuel and materials. At the same time, there were growing wartime requirements for timber. The railroads became indispensable and while most steam operations continued through the war, some camps had closed.[16]

On southern Vancouver Island, large stands of previously inaccessible timber remained in the Nanaimo River Valley. To exploit these forests, Comox Logging

Even during the Depression years, VL&M kept its stable of steam machinery in excellent condition. No. 9, a Pacific Coast Shay, was bought by the company in 1929.
—JACK CASH, MACMILLAN BLOEDEL COLLECTION

Brooks-Scanlon-O'Brien's 2-8-2 No. 2, a Baldwin built in 1923, was the largest logging rod locomotive to work on the mainland coast but it worked there only a few years before being sold to other related operations in the United States.
—ROOZEBOOM COLLECTION, BCARS, HP67888

and the Victoria Lumber & Manufacturing Company (which became the Victoria Lumber Company in 1944) embarked on a joint railroad development. It was to be one of the last major logging railroads built in British Columbia and it would be one of the last survivors. Ironically, however, the *West Coast Lumberman* commented that "... it is probable that were it not for the difficulties in getting trucks, tires, gasoline and roadbuilding machinery Comox Logging & Railway Co. would have built a truck road to Nanaimo Lakes rather than a railroad. But wartime conditions made the railroad more feasible and so, in April, 1942, construction began." The article also noted that, "Comox... has been one of the pioneers in the extensive use of trucks... and has been a model of that technique."[17] Both companies needed reliable supplies of logs for their mills, described as being able to produce about 300,000,000 feet (708 000 m³) of lumber annually.[18]

The new railroad ran north from Ladysmith, following the grade of the old Canadian Collieries (Dunsmuir) Ltd. line, to the north side of the Nanaimo River where the new line swung west.[19] From there, the tracks were laid following the river into the stands of new timber. VL&M tracks branched off near Jump Creek and crossed the Nanaimo River to their main camp while Comox Logging continued on west to the Nanaimo Lakes. The maximum grade on the line was about two percent and the gain in elevation from Ladysmith to the Nanaimo Lakes was approximately 700 feet (210 m) over the 22 miles (35 km) of line. Superintendent James "Jimmy" Sheasgreen, quoted in the *West Coast Lumberman*, noted:

The whole distance was graded between April, 1942, and November of the same year.... Speed was the idea, but it was a tough assignment in view of the shortage of labor and the difficulty of getting delivery of equipment and material. However, we managed to put 80 men to work and we gave them three gas electric shovels, a couple of Carco bulldozers and put them on double shift. The terrain was anything but easy, with rivers and creeks to cross and a lot of heavy boulder country to go through. But we kept things moving and finished on time.[20]

Comox Logging planned to use trucks as feeders to the main line logging railroad but some spur lines also were constructed, particularly in Deadwood Valley to the north. First Lake and Second Lake were used as holding and sorting areas for the logs brought in to the rail head. The sorting provided a standard load for each rail car. Normally, First Lake was used to hold saw logs while Second Lake held pulpwood.[21] More details of the operations are provided with the accompanying photographs.

The main line required 10 bridges including a 90-foot (28-m) pile trestle over Boulder Creek at Mile 13 and, on the Deadwood branch, a massive frame trestle over Berkeley Creek that was 125 feet (38 m) high and 600 feet (183 m) long with two 50-foot (15-m) log spans. Overall, it required 500,000 feet (1180 m³) of lumber and took two months to construct. Moreover, there was the major crossing of the Nanaimo River on the right-of-way of the old colliery line. For this

The most spectacular feature of the new railroad into the Nanaimo River valley
was the bridge over the Nanaimo River. No. 16 is southbound over the span.
— B.C. GOVERNMENT PHOTO

177

bridge it was possible to reuse the steel centre spans from the old railway.[22]

Another important feature of the new line was Comox's log dump at Ladysmith Harbour. This facility was carefully engineered and designed for both railroad and truck traffic. The dump was capable of handling 1,000,000 feet (2360 m³) of timber daily. A large, permanent A-frame structure was built for unloading trucks while an ingenious device was built at the Headquarters shops to dump the logs from the rail cars. Known as the "Humdurgin," the machine was built on the frame of a scrapped Shay locomotive and was a more refined version of a dumping machine used by the company at Royston on its Headquarters line in the Comox Valley. Self-propelled by a gas engine, it ran on a track parallel to the dump. With use of a drum and cable to raise a large steel arm, the loads could be rolled off the rail cars quickly and efficiently. In fact, with everything running smoothly, two cars could be unloaded in a minute, a 30-car train in 15 to 20 minutes. A chain drive powered the drive shaft to the locomotive trucks. The dump itself was 280 feet (85 m) long and heavily built on a solid fill behind a cribbing. The brow log was 20 x 20 inches (0.5 x 0.5 m) in cross-section, protected by sheets of steel boiler plate. The slope down to the water was constructed of 60-foot (18-m) long logs, each 30 inches (0.75 m) in diameter. The face of the logs was protected with old tractor treads.[23] The "Humdurgin" remained in operation for over 40 years and became a prized part of the collection of the Ladysmith Railway Historical Society when the operation closed in the mid-1980s.

Another interesting innovation known as a "Moby Dick" was used on the railway at the Nanaimo Lakes reload. It was described by the Railway Department as having ". . . a large opening similar to a whale's mouth which gathers the logs so that a load of logs can be picked up at one time and dropped on to specially constructed flatcars. The operation is very efficient, and the loading-works and railway operate twenty-four hours a day during certain seasons of the year."[24]

The new railroad logging show was unusual in several other respects. It crossed the main line of the E&N just north of Ladysmith which, for safety, required an interlocking signal system to be installed. This system was controlled by an operator stationed in a tower building at the crossing of the two lines.[25] Later, in 1949, so that the Victoria Lumber Company logs could be moved on directly to Chemainus for milling, a yard and interchange track with the E&N had to be constructed. From Ladysmith, E&N crews took the loaded trains south to Chemainus and returned with empty trains of log cars. Another feature of the new line was that it permitted the development, by Canadian Collieries (Dunsmuir) Ltd., of a mine at White Rapids on the Nanaimo River. Coal from the mine was hauled over the new line to the E&N and from there to the wharves of the colliery company at Nanaimo for shipment. The mine began shipping coal late in 1944 and reached full production in 1945.[26]

Living conditions were improving for the loggers. For the expanded operations

The development of the White
Rapids coal mine along the Comox
Logging line added traffic for the
new railway. Comox's No. 11 was at
the construction site of the tipple
on May 23, 1944. —BILL &
DOROTHY JOHNSTONE COLLECTION

Comox Logging's Heisler No. 10
was transferred from Headquarters
to the new Nanaimo Lakes railway.
—WILMER GOLD

Crossing the E&N just north of Ladysmith required the construction of an interlocking signal system to protect trains from collisions. In late afternoon winter sunshine, No. 11 works past the tower in this beautiful photograph from January 1956. The Ladysmith yards and shops (at left) were crowded with equipment in December 1955, including locomotives 11 and 16, usually used on the main line, and the 7 and the "Deuce." In July 1956, No. 16 was photographed pulling out of Ladysmith with a train of empties for the Nanaimo Lakes.
—ELWOOD WHITE

The log dump at Ladysmith was the destination for the Comox Logging trains from the Nanaimo Lakes. No. 11's train was being unloaded by the Humdurgin in the photograph above from September 4, 1958. At left, nearly 25 years later, the Humdurgin was still in operation. The origin of the name remains obscure but some other similar, but steam-powered, unloaders were also called Humdurgins on Vancouver Island. Comox Logging used one at Royston on its Headquarters show, as did ERT at Campbell River.
—DAVE WILKIE; ROBERT D. TURNER

The Seven-Spot was transferred from Headquarters to Ladysmith. It was still on the Headquarters line in July 1944 as shown at right. Later it was fitted with a tender.
—L. A. JOHNSON, JIM HOPE COLLECTION

Comox Logging shared the main line with Victoria Lumber Company trains. Victoria Lumber's No. 7, shown crossing the Nanaimo River in 1964 as MacMillan Bloedel & Powell River's 1077, worked for many years on the railroad.
—DAVE WILKIE

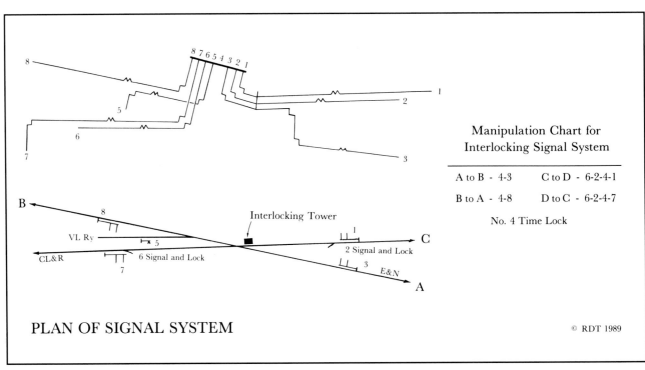

8 7 6 5 4 3 2 1

8

5

6

7

1

2

3

B

8

VL Ry

5

CL&R

6 Signal and Lock

7

Interlocking Tower

1

C

2 Signal and Lock

3

E&N

A

Manipulation Chart for Interlocking Signal System

A to B - 4-3	C to D - 6-2-4-1
B to A - 4-8	D to C - 6-2-4-7

No. 4 Time Lock

PLAN OF SIGNAL SYSTEM

© RDT 1989

Ladysmith

The interlocking signals and protective derails north of Ladysmith were a complex mechanical system controlled from the tower by the operator. Comox Logging, Victoria Lumber (later MacMillan & Bloedel) and CPR trains all passed regularly. John Auer knew the operation well as he pulled the heavy control levers to clear a log train in 1983. — ROBERT D. TURNER

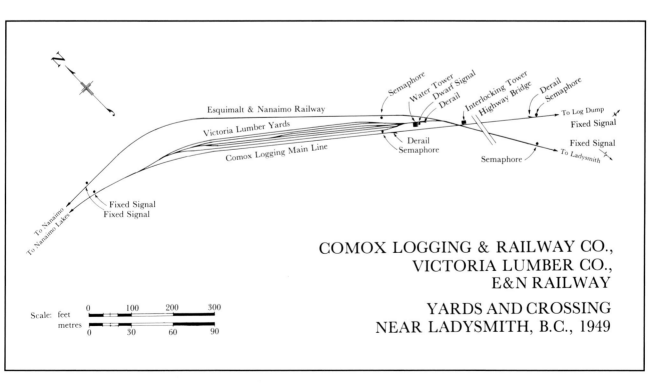

**COMOX LOGGING & RAILWAY CO.,
VICTORIA LUMBER CO.,
E&N RAILWAY**

**YARDS AND CROSSING
NEAR LADYSMITH, B.C., 1949**

185

in the Ladysmith area there were no plans to build logging camps in the woods at the end of the new railroad. Instead, the loggers were taken by train to the end of the line each day. "Loggers will continue to make their homes in Ladysmith and the surrounding community," noted Robert Filberg, general manager for Comox Logging. "This is one of the beneficial changes that has occurred in the logging industry. Men who work in the woods nowadays have their homes within easy reach of the logging operation. Many of them have families and have a permanent stake in the country where they work, owning their own homes and in some cases small farms."[27] It is interesting to note that Ladysmith was established in the early 1900s as the home for miners working at the Extension colliery to the north. The miners, like the later generation of loggers, rode by train from Ladysmith, over part of the same right-of-way, to their place of work. Pete McGovern ran the loggers' trains out to the woods:

All the crew came from Ladysmith. There was no road in then, everybody went by rail. You left at 6:30 in the morning with a crew train, it would be either the No. 7 or the "Deuce." Four box cars — four crummies — with benches. Stoves in all of them. The old "7" could get going at 30 miles [50 km] per hour with that. It was a straight roll through. It took two injectors to keep water in the boiler going up there with the crew train but you could take the little "Deuce" and go up there with one injector, no trouble with steam. It was just a straight roar!

Close to 200 men by the time you'd pick them up.

Then the No. 11, the main line engine, followed it and sometimes there'd be a couple of Shays or maybe a Heisler and the "Deuce." They'd all be up there; follow one another up.[28]

Ladysmith became a major logging centre on southern Vancouver Island. Comox Logging built its offices and a large shop facility to service the locomotives, rolling stock and trucks operating in the district. With the new railroad in full operation, the combination of Comox Logging, VLCo. and E&N trains made Ladysmith a busy place indeed.

Another area affected by the wartime needs for timber was the Queen Charlotte Islands. On Moresby Island, the isolated logging railroad operated by A. P. Allison (Allison Logging Co. Ltd.) on Cumshewa Inlet suddenly became strategically important because of the demand for light-weight Sitka spruce. "War-time conditions have again brought that giant of the Pacific Coast forests, Sitka Spruce," wrote R. S. Perry in the *British Columbia Lumberman*, "... into special prominence as the world's most valuable wood for aircraft manufacture."[29] The wood had many applications, but one of the most noteworthy was in the famous "Mosquito" twin-engined fighter-bomber.

The operation had been established in 1936-37, when a camp was built at tidewater near the head of Cumshewa Inlet and a standard gauge line constructed inland to Skidegate Lake, a distance of about 5.5 miles (8.9 km). Two coal-fired Climax locomotives, a Marion steam shovel and an assortment of rolling stock were used. Cumshewa Inlet was a particularly remote location for a

Logging on the Queen Charlottes

On Moresby Island, spruce, cedar and hemlock were carried by rail. A. P. Allison developed the railroad which became Aero Timber Products during World War II. Allison's Climax No. 2 is shown in 1938 at the log dump on Cumshewa Inlet. An Edwards gas car, called the "green hornet," was used to carry the loggers from camp to the woods. —BCFS, 5328; BILL ROBINSON COLLECTION

187

camp; coastal steamers and fledgling airline services provided the only reliable transportation to the outside world. Most of the logs from the camp were towed in huge rafts for 500 miles (800 km) or more to Powell River and other southern points for processing.

Constructing this line had presented unusual problems. A. P. Allison told the *West Coast Lumberman*:

The trouble with these islands [the Queen Charlottes] is there's nothing to give a foundation. We have had to snake in around mountains and in many spots the grade of the standard gauge logging track is 6 percent. And often the ground on which the railroad is built is little more than swamp. [30]

In several locations on the line, it was necessary to sink 25-foot (7.5-m) piles to establish a base for the tracks. "We have to use a steam shovel here owing to the nature of the ground. A bulldozer wouldn't be so effective in the muskeg," commented Allison. Logs from the operation, 40 percent Sitka spruce, 40 percent western hemlock and 20 percent western red-cedar, were towed in rafts to mills on the south coast. Hemlock was supplied to Pacific Mills Ltd. at Ocean Falls and large quantities of spruce and cedar were shipped to the Powell River Company at Powell River. Allison, by arrangement, was cutting logs from Powell River Company stands as well as his own. [31]

With the increased demands for logs, Allison Logging increased production, acquired another locomotive — a three-truck Heisler — and began to ship enormous quantities of timber to the south. In June 1941, for example, 3,500,000 feet (8260 m³) of prime cedar and 850,000 feet (2000 m³) of spruce were assembled into two large Davis rafts — each 800 feet (243 m) long, 80 feet (24.4 m) wide and 30 feet (9 m) in draught. The tug *St. Faith* towed the rafts separately across Hecate Strait where they were assembled into a single tow for the journey to Vancouver, which took nearly a month. [32]

In June 1942, Allison's operations were taken over by the Canadian government and continued on functioning as Aero Timber Products Ltd. Spruce production had become extremely critical to the war effort. Bob Swanson spent most of three years working on the Charlottes keeping the well-worn, temperamental, often obsolete machines running.

I went up there in 1943 by plane to test all the boilers at Cumshewa Inlet. When I got there, the five locomotives were all broke down; none of them was running.

Bob Filberg went up. "What am I going to do?" he says. "I'm bringing the timber controller up."

"All right, I'll get them going for you." Anyhow, I phoned down and got the stuff sent up on the next boat and some of it flown up.

Filberg was a very well-liked guy. He went to [Premier] John Hart and got me taken off [on leave from the Railway Department] and I went off to the Charlottes. When I was finished they put me back as Inspector.

The main camp and shop facilities were located on Cumshewa Inlet at Allison Camp, later called Aero Camp. Climax No. 1 and an unidentified Climax in the shops were both in need of work in this late-1940s photo. At right is Shay No. 6 which was purchased in 1947 from Merrill & Ring at Pysht, Washington. — MAURICE CHANDLER COLLECTION

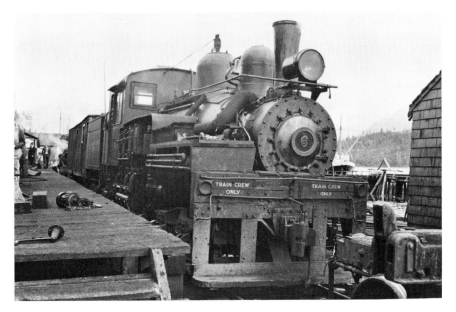

Allison's equipment, including the big unit photographed at left in 1940, burned coal. Oil was normally used in drier regions to reduce the danger of fires starting. Later, the steam engines on the Charlottes were converted to burn oil. Climax No. 3 is shown (above) at the log dump with the camp buildings in the background.

—H. W. WEATHERBY, BCFS, 2483-6 (left); MAURICE CHANDLER COLLECTION (above)

Timber from the Charlottes had to be moved across the open waters of Hecate Strait. Davis rafts were used to prevent the logs from being lost. This drawing is from the *ABC Lumber Trade Directory* for 1921.

Locomotives at Aero Camp

No.	Type	Builder/No.	Date	Dimensions	Tons	Notes
1	2T	Climax/1491	1918	12 × 14, 33″	45	1
1 (2nd)	3T	Lima (PC Shay)/3344	1930	13 × 15, 36″	90	2
2	2T	Climax/1511	1918	12 × 14, 33″	45	3
3	2T	Climax/1547	1920	12.5 × 14, 33″	50	4
4	2T	Climax/1539	1919	13.25 × 14, 33″	50	5
5	3T	Heisler/1487	1923	17.25 × 15, 38″	70	6
6	3T	Lima (Shay)/3285	1925	12 × 15, 36″	70	7
7	0-6-0	Plymouth/3365	1920			8
Gas Motorcar	Model 20	Edwards	1924	(41 passenger)	19.5	9

Notes: All references to A. P. Allison Logging (ALCo), Aero Timber Products Ltd. (ATP), the Powell River Co. (PRCo) and Kelley Logging (KLCo) were at Cumshewa Inlet. Other abbreviations: abandoned (ab.); scrapped (sc.); purchased (pur.). Dimensions shown are cylinder bore and stroke and driver diameter.

1 Pacific Mills Ltd. No. 1 (Ocean Falls); Owens Logging Co. No. 1 (Green Bay); ALCo No. 1; ATP No. 1; PRCo (KLCo) No. 1; Sold 1948 for stationary boiler.

2 Merrill-Ring-Wilson Ltd. No. 4 (Rock Bay); Salmon River Logging Co. No. 5 (Kelsey Bay); PRCo (KLCo) 2nd No. 1; Canadian Forest Products Ltd., for parts (Englewood), boiler to CFP No. 115.

3 Pacific Mills Ltd. No. 2 (Ocean Falls); lease — Owens Logging Co. No. 2 (Green Bay); ALCo No. 2; ATP No. 2; PRCo No. 2; Sold in 1952 for stationary boiler (Patterson Boiler Works).

4 Timberland Development Co. No. 3 (Ladysmith); Booth Logging Co. No. 1 (Goliath Bay); Vancouver Bay Logging Co. Ltd. No. 2; ATP No. 3; PRCo (KLCo) No. 3; ab. 1955, sc. 1961.

5 Vancouver Lumber Co. No. 2 (Port Neville); Mainland Cedar Co. No. 2 (Port Neville); Mainland Tbr. Co. No. 2 (Port Neville); Bernard Timber & Logging No. 4 (Oxford Bay); Fulmore Lake Logging No. 3; Gustavson Bros. Logging No. 2 (Jervis Inlet); ATP No. 4; PRCo (KLCo) No. 4; ab.

6 Miller Logging Co. No. 5 (Sultan, WA); ALCo No. 3; ATP No. 5 (Cumshewa Inlet); PRCo (KLCo) No. 5.

7 Merrill & Ring Lumber Co. No. 6, (Pysht, WA); PRCo (KLCo) No. 6.

8 Merrill & Ring Lumber Co. (either Squamish or Theodosia Arm); O'Brien Logging Co. No. 7 (Stillwater); PRCo (KLCo) No. 7; Western Forest Industries Ltd. No. 7, later No. 40 (Honeymoon Bay) (rebuilt with Cummins diesel); Westcan Terminals Ltd. (Ogden Point, Victoria); Ladysmith Railway Historical Society (Ladysmith).

9 Morrissey, Fernie & Michel Ry (Fernie, B.C.); ALCo; ATP. The car had two Buda 4-cylinder engines, one mounted on each truck, to provide extra power for steep grades on MF&M.

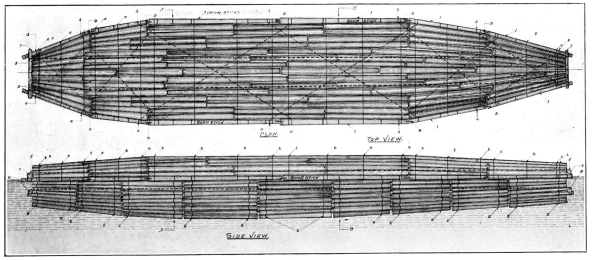

Robert J. Filberg, manager of Comox Logging at Headquarters, took on wartime duties and managed the critical spruce logging on the Queen Charlottes.
— *B.C. Lumberman*

Steamships such as the Canadian National's *Prince John* were often the only connection people living in the remote logging camps had with the rest of the world.
—ALBERT H. PAULL

By the early 1970s, all that remained of Aero Camp were abandoned buildings, pieces of machinery, a fast disappearing right-of-way into the woods and parts of Climax No. 4.
—ROBERT D. TURNER

Plymouth diesel No. 7, used by Kelley Logging at Aero Camp, survived the end of the railway to work for Western Forest Industries at Honeymoon Bay on Vancouver Island as No. 7 and later No. 40. It was sold again to Westcan Terminals in Victoria and was eventually donated to the Ladysmith Railway Historical Society.—ROBERT D. TURNER

I stayed wherever they needed me — at Cumshewa or at Juskatla. I took charge of all the shops. I was mechanical superintendent of the whole thing. I got the best men I could. I got into trouble over that for stealing men, but I had the best master mechanics I could get. We brought that thing up. We got them running and tested and put them to work. Before I left there, we had three of the five running. Then I had all the steam donkeys and all the boats to take care of.

Production continued at a high rate until early 1945 when the demand for timber began to fall off dramatically. The entire operation was offered for sale in September. It was acquired by the Powell River Company which reorganized the operation as part of its Kelley Logging Company subsidiary. Much of the equipment was worn out, some of it fit only for scrap. Over the next few years, two large Shays and other needed equipment was brought in. The railway continued to operate until August 31, 1955.[33]

The Post War Years: Merger and Abandonment

The end of World War II brought many changes to the forest industry in British Columbia and to the logging railroads. Military requirements for trucks and related equipment had lessened, and no longer limited the availability of new equipment for the logging companies and the period of "making do" with old or antiquated equipment passed. Alternatives to the surviving railroad operations were once again feasible. Moreover, developments during the war had improved truck technology, increasing the competitive advantages of truck logging. Expanding operations that might have used railroads a generation earlier, found expansion of truck hauling the most economical and practical approach to log transport.[34] Improved trailers, transmissions, brakes, tires and engines all increased the flexibility and hauling capacity of trucks during the 1940s. In addition, improvements to roads and bridges extended the operating range of truck hauling.[35] The economic recovery of the war years and the resulting profits provided the capital for the conversion to trucking. The more flexible truck systems opened up the logging of stands that previously would have been uneconomical because of low quality or density.[36]

Before logging railways in the years after the war are discussed, the importance to the forest industry of the CPR's E&N Railway and the Canadian National's branch lines on Vancouver Island need to be outlined. Soon after its opening in 1886, the E&N became active in transporting logs and with each expansion of its services, particularly to Port Alberni, Courtenay and Lake Cowichan in the years just before World War I, its connections with the forest industry grew. Large areas of timber were made accessible for logging, particularly in the Cowichan district. The same pattern was followed by the expansion of the CNR into largely unsettled areas of forest land until its construction ended in the Cowichan area in the 1920s. In many ways, the E&N and the CNR each acted as the main line routes for connecting logging railways. The E&N hauled tens of thousands of

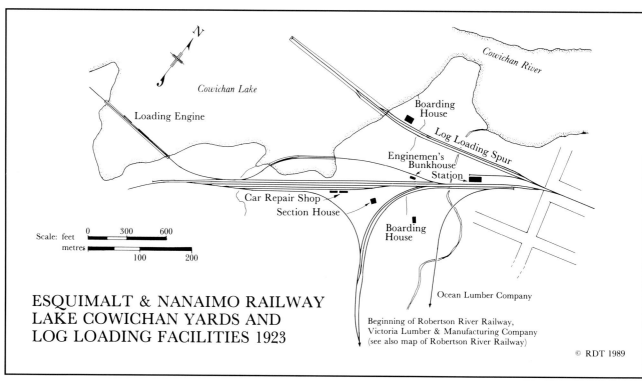

**ESQUIMALT & NANAIMO RAILWAY
LAKE COWICHAN YARDS AND
LOG LOADING FACILITIES 1923**

Log Hauling on the E&N

The E&N's Lake Cowichan branch line was a forest products railroad from its inception. It was built as part of an agreement with the Empire Lumber Company for the sale of timber from the railway's land grant. From its completion in 1913 until abandonment in 1984 it carried thousands of carloads of logs, lumber and shingles from the camps and mills in the district.

Logs were brought to the E&N either by rail or in booms down the lake. The loading facilities (left) were seldom idle. At right, a typical train of logs rolls past the station and in the middle photograph, down the valley. CPR 2-8-0s and 4-6-0s were used on the log trains. The 3200s (middle photo) and older 3100s (bottom right) were well-suited to these duties. The 3281 was photographed pulling through Lake Cowichan on August 15, 1940. Bob Brown is in the cab of 3186 at Crofton. Many of the logs were hauled to Crofton where a log dump was located. From there they were towed to mills or sold for export. Logs were also carried over the E&N to Chemainus and, later, Ladysmith.

—W. F. MONTGOMERY, BCARS, HP73647 (left); NAC, PA40919; TED ROBSON COLLECTION; ALBERT H. PAULL

195

Logs
on the CNR

The CNR on Vancouver Island
hauled thousands of carloads of
logs, poles and lumber on its
twisting route through the forests
of the Island. With logs from
Kapoor, CNR 2149 heads towards
Cowichan Bay over the huge
Koksilah River bridge at Mile 51.1
on April 16, 1958. Mills depended
on the CNR as their route to
market. Finished lumber moved to
Victoria's Ogden Point and other
Island ports for export.
—DAVE WILKIE

carloads of logs from the Cowichan Valley to Chemainus, Crofton and Ladysmith over the years, as well as serving numerous mills along the line. A 1944 article noted that more than 37,000 cars of logs had been hauled in the previous three years. High production did not overcome the backwoods qualities of the E&N line between Lake Cowichan and Crofton. Harry Guy, an engineer on the run was quoted joking that half his time was spent shooing cows off the track. Deer and cougars were also frequently encountered on the right-of-way.[37]

The daily routine of the crew working on this stretch of E&N line was as follows: the men left Duncan at 6:00 a.m., picked up a train at Hayward, 1.7 miles (2.7 km) away, and took it to Osborn Bay, a distance of 4.6 miles (7.4 km). From Osborn Bay, they went down to the dump at Crofton, 2.5 miles (4.0 km) distant. After the logs were dumped into the sea, a process taking about an hour and done by the logging companies with the assistance of the rail employees, they returned the empty log flats to Lake Cowichan, via Osborn Bay and Hayward, and did "a little switching" at the lake terminus. The line from Hayward to Lake Cowichan, dominated by logging trains, was 18 miles (29 km) long. At Lake Cowichan, they picked up 20 flats, already loaded by the logging companies, and took them to the siding at Hayward, before returning to Duncan.[38] In busy times, several crews might work the line on staggered shifts.

Like the E&N, the CNR hauled large volumes of logs from Kapoor and other camps to Cowichan Bay at the mouth of the Cowichan River. E&N and CNR trains also brought supplies and mail to the many isolated logging camps that became established along their routes. Further details of both major railways' operations are included with the accompanying photographs.[39]

The war years had been hard on the logging railroads. Pressures for efficiency and high production and shortages of both labour and materials took a toll on equipment. "In making inspections of steam locomotives serious defects were disclosed which necessitated very extensive repairs to the boilers and machinery to bring them up to a satisfactory condition," noted J. H. Short, Acting Chief Inspector of Railways. "Owing to the war the industrial companies were handicapped by being unable to secure mechanics and material to make the necessary repairs, and in several cases extensions had to be given over the five-year period for internal and external inspection of boilers to avoid reducing production of essential war materials."[40]

At the end of World War II there was still a substantial network of logging railroads operating in the province, with all but two located on Vancouver Island. One was on the Queen Charlottes and the other on the south coast of the mainland near Powell River.

At Cowichan Bay, the logs are unloaded beneath the maze of cables at the dump. This year, 1958, marked the last use of steam power on the Cowichan Subdivision.
—DAVE WILKIE

Logging Railroads in 1945

COMPANY	LOCATION	MILES	KILOMETRES
Alberni Pacific Lumber Co., Ltd.	Port Alberni	75.0	120.7
Aero Powell River Co., Ltd.	Cumshewa Inlet (Queen Charlotte Is.)	17.5	28.2
B. & D. Logging Co.	Hyde Creek, V.I.	2.0	3.2
Bloedel, Stewart & Welch, Ltd.	Great Central	16.0	25.7
	Menzies Bay	59.6	95.9
	Franklin River	48.0	77.3
Canadian Forest Products, Ltd.	Nimpkish Valley	28.5	45.9
Comox Logging & Railway Co.	Headquarters	29.0	46.7
	Ladysmith	41.1	66.2
Deep Bay Logging Co., Ltd.*	Fanny Bay	8.5	13.7
Elk River Timber Co., Ltd.	Campbell River	72.0	115.9
Hemmingsen-Cameron Co., Ltd.	Port Renfrew	19.5	31.4
Hillcrest Lumber Co., Ltd.	Cowichan Valley	17.5	28.1
Industrial Timber Mills, Ltd.	Youbou (Cowichan Lake)	36.0	57.9
Lake Logging Co., Ltd.	Honeymoon Bay Cowichan Lake)	43.8	70.5
Malahat Logging Co., Ltd.	Port Renfrew	34.1	54.9
Mayo Bros. Timber Co., Ltd.	Sahtlam and Seymour	10.0	16.1
O'Brien Logging Co., Ltd.	Stillwater (Powell River)	4.6	7.4
Pacific Logging Co., Ltd.	Cowichan Lake	5.0	8.0
Salmon River Logging Co., Ltd.	Kelsey Bay	37.0	59.5
Victoria Lumber Co., Ltd.	Fanny Bay	16.3	26.2
	Chemainus	39.2	63.1
	Total length of railroad:	660.2	1059.5

* operations suspended

Compiled from: Province of British Columbia, Railway Department, *Annual Report*, Year ended Dec. 31, 1945.

For the steam logging railroads, the mid-1940s period was an Indian summer; a developing momentum would make dramatic changes inevitable. Ten years later, the mileage had declined by nearly 60 percent to 284.7 miles (458.2 km) including some trackage which was restricted to mill yards and connecting mills to common carrier lines. These latter operations included Western Forest Industries and Hillcrest Lumber. There was only one area of expansion and that was in the Nimpkish Valley where Canadian Forest Products had increased its trackage to over 100 miles (160 km).[41]

The years immediately after World War II were also a time of dramatic corporate changes in the forest industry. In 1946, the holdings of Industrial Timber Mills, Malahat Logging, Hemmingsen-Cameron and other logging and milling operations were merged to form British Columbia Forest Products Ltd. Their major railroads in the Renfrew and Cowichan districts of Vancouver Island were consolidated, as well as their other operations. In 1951, the

The years after World War II brought together on Vancouver Island the greatest concentration of Pacific Coast Shays anywhere. The Victoria Lumber Company's 1088 was one of 17 that worked in the woods there. But the post-war years were also a time of change and decline. The 1088, like most others, was scrapped during the 1950s as trucks took over log hauling. — MACMILLAN BLOEDEL COLLECTION

Hillcrest Lumber

Hillcrest Lumber, owned by the Stone family, was a major lumber producer in the Cowichan Valley from the early 1920s until the late 1960s. The first mill (left), located west of Duncan, was replaced with a larger mill fed by logging railroads, as shown at right. In 1943, a large new mill (above) and company town was built at Mesachie Lake near Lake Cowichan. Hillcrest phased out logging railroads but retained two Climaxes as switchers.
—WILMER GOLD (above); GERRY WELLBURN COLLECTION (left); AUTHOR'S COLLECTION (right)

In the post-war years, the sawmills were modernized and many small mills were closed. Pulp and paper plants became increasingly important components of the forest industry. MacMillan & Bloedel's big mill at Port Alberni was representative of the major operations in the 1950s and 1960s. The mill originally belonged to the Alberni Pacific Lumber Company. —JACK CASH, MACMILLAN BLOEDEL COLLECTION

interests of Bloedel, Stewart & Welch merged with the H. R. MacMillan Export Company (which controlled Alberni Pacific Lumber and Victoria Lumber Company) to form MacMillan & Bloedel Limited (M&B). This brought all the railroad logging lines of the merging companies under one ownership. In 1959, the Powell River Company merged with MacMillan & Bloedel to form Mac-Millan, Bloedel and Powell River Limited, subsequently renamed MacMillan Bloedel Limited in 1966.*

Following the mergers, the railroads continued to be critical components in log transport, but the end of their use in most logging operations was clearly in sight. By the end of the 1950s, another 100 miles (160 km) of trackage had been abandoned, leaving just three surviving logging lines—Canadian Forest Products, Comox Logging, and MacMillan & Bloedel—and several small switching operations.[42] Truck logging was the way of the future and the 1950s was a decade of dramatic change.

The experience of Western Forest Industries (WFI) at Honeymoon Bay, on Lake Cowichan is probably representative of the conversion from steam railroad operations to the full use of trucks in moving logs to the mills. The antecedents of this operation in the Cowichan area, McDonald Murphy Logging and Lake Logging, had operated logging railroads since the 1920s. By the early 1950s, WFI was operating a well-established railroad from its mill at Honeymoon Bay to its major camp at Gordon River, a distance of 14 miles (22.5 km). When the line was in its heyday, five locomotives (including the only Willamette used in Canada) and as many as 135 log cars were in use with the railroad handling as much as 400,000 feet (945 m³) of timber daily. In 1942, trucks were introduced to the operation to feed logs to the railroad. On average, the truck haul was about five miles (8 km) from the landings to the reload points. As logging progressed up onto the steeper, higher elevations of the Gordon River and Sutton Creek watersheds, construction costs increasingly weighed against further expansion of the railway and for the extension of truck roads.[43]

By 1953, economics for WFI had swung in favour of a complete conversion to trucking. Although the combined rail and trucking system could deliver 45,000,000 board feet (106 200 m³) of timber to the mill, trucks alone could handle the loads more cheaply. A 10-mile (16-km) road replaced the rail line. Even though the trucks used at that time were not as large as the trucks of later decades, they had nearly twice the capacity of the light-weight rail cars. These were limited to 5,500 board feet (13 m³), whereas the trucks could handle 10,000 feet (24 m³) over much steeper grades. In fact, Gordon Dodds, logging superintendent, reported to *The Timberman* that, overall, trucking was at least 25 percent cheaper and, moreover, there was a reduced chance of forest fires. The truck fleet that replaced the

* Subsequent references to MacMillan & Bloedel reflect the corporate name appropriate to the time of the discussion.

The year 1953 brought an end to railroad logging at Western Forest Industries at Honeymoon Bay. Willamette No. 3 (above), Shay No. 4 (shown at left at Lake Cowichan on May 26, 1953) and most of the remaining locomotives and rolling stock were all sold for scrap. Pacific Coast Shay No. 5 was retained and a Plymouth diesel was purchased for use around the mill.
—NICHOLAS MORANT, CPCA, M277; ALBERT FARROW

railroad consisted of 13 Cummins-powered Kenworths with Columbia trailers and four Pacific trucks and trailers. All of the trailers carried 12-foot (3.7-m) bunks with 36-inch (0.9-m) high stakes.[44]

By the fall of 1953, the railroad into the woods had been eliminated, with large sections of the right-of-way converted to the truck road. However, WFI retained about seven miles (11.25 km) of trackage from the sawmill at Honeymoon Bay to Lake Cowichan where it met the E&N. Two locomotives, Pacific Coast Shay No. 5 and Plymouth No. 7, were kept to move lumber cars over the line but the rest of the railroad equipment was eventually sold or scrapped. Willamette No. 3 was not sold for scrap until July 1956 and was still more-or-less intact awaiting scrapping in Vancouver in 1958.[45] Eventually, both of the surviving locomotives were to be preserved. Robert E. Swanson purchased the Shay and put it to work at North Vancouver for Railway Appliance Research Ltd., switching the docks at Vancouver Wharves, before eventually selling it to the Cass Scenic Railroad in West Virginia.[46] The Plymouth was eventually preserved at Ladysmith. Its story is related in the next chapter.

At nearby Mesachie Lake, the Hillcrest Lumber Company, owned and operated by the Stone family, had also phased out its railroad woods operations but retained some equipment for switching the company's large mill. Hillcrest also shipped and received cars over the E&N at Lake Cowichan via the WFI trackage that ran from Lake Cowichan to Honeymoon Bay. Hillcrest's continued use of steam power — the last Climax locomotives working for the forest industry in North America — is portrayed in the next chapter.

Like WFI, the other strongholds of steam power crumbled in the 1950s. Kelley Logging's line, the only steam railway on the Queen Charlotte Islands, was abandoned in 1955 when trucks took over.[47] Its equipment was unceremoniously loaded onto a barge and towed away to the south or simply left behind at Aero Camp. British Columbia Forest Products ended railroading at all of its operations in the Cowichan Lake area at Nitinat Camp and to the west out of Port Renfrew. On northern Vancouver Island, the Salmon River Logging Company in the Sayward District closed down between 1949 and 1950 and the Elk River Timber Company at Campbell River ceased railroading by 1953. Moreover, Comox Logging's Headquarters line closed in 1953. Taking a different approach under different conditions, Canadian Forest Products, as we shall see later, expanded and modernized its rail operations while increasing the use of trucks. MacMillan & Bloedel began the wholesale conversion of its railroad system to truck haulage. The steam operations inherited from Alberni Pacific, Bloedel Stewart & Welch, and the Victoria Lumber Company were all targeted for rapid conversion.

MacMillan & Bloedel estimated the conversion of its Menzies Bay, Copper Canyon (Chemainus) and Nanaimo River operations to truck hauling would cost $2,300,000, with $1,600,000 of this total being required for new equipment. By the end of 1952 the plans had grown to include the former Alberni Pacific railroad

Comox Logging's No. 16 showed the evidence of over 30 years in the woods when photographed at Ladysmith in 1960. Comox Logging added a tender from the scrapped No. 3, cut down the side tanks and filled them with ballast.
—ALBERT FARROW

Salmon River Logging in the Sayward District closed its railroad show by 1950 and sold its equipment. No. 4 went to O'Brien Logging at Powell River but ended its days back on Vancouver Island with Canfor.—PERCY STACY, BCARS HP82115

Comox Logging closed its Headquarters railroad in 1953, ending over 40 years of rail logging in the Comox Valley. No. 2, shown at Headquarters, was transferred to Ladysmith. Heisler No. 8 was at Headquarters on May 26, 1953. Log trains passing through Courtenay were a familiar sight and residents collected free bark for firewood from the cars.
—TED ROBSON; RAILWAY NEGATIVE EXCHANGE; TED ROBSON

Comox Logging's Locomotives 1909-1984

Including equipment under Crown Zellerbach Canada Ltd., and Crown Forest Industries Ltd.

Steam, Gas and Diesel locomotives

No.	Type	Builder/No.	Date	Notes
1	2-6-2	Baldwin/33561	1909	1
2	2-6-2T	Baldwin/34921	1910	2
3	2-6-2	Baldwin/35871	1911	3
4	2T	Heisler/1233	1911	4
5	2T	Heisler/1244	1912	5
6	2T Shay	Lima/2657	1913	6
7	2-6-2T(T)	Baldwin/34270	1910	7
8	2T	Heisler/1232	1911	8
9	2T	Heisler/1243	1912	9
10	2T	Heisler/1242	1912	10
11	2-8-2	Baldwin/57409	1923	11
12	2T Shay	Lima/3311	1927	12
14	2T Shay	Lima/3243	1923	13
15	2T Shay	Lima/3289	1925	14
16	2-8-2T(T)	Baldwin/61159	1929	15
17	0-4-0Gas	Whitcomb/12675	1928	16
18	2-8-2T	Baldwin/60942	1929	17
—	0-4-0Gas	Westminster Iron Works?		18
20	0-4-0Gas	Vulcan/1352	1909	19
107	0-4-0Gas	Plymouth/1662	1924	20
7128	VO1000	Baldwin/64745	1943	21
4097	RS-3	Alco/80317	1952	22
8247	RS-3	MLW/80992	1954	23

Notes: Leased equipment, except No. 18, is not included. Locomotives were leased from other companies as well as the CPR on many occasions. Speeders not shown. Early equipment may have been ordered through CL&R's parent: the Canadian Western Lumber Co. Control passed to Crown Zellerbach in 1953. Crown Zellerbach Canada Ltd. was purchased by Fletcher Challenge Ltd. and operated as Crown Forest Industries (CFI) in 1983. Equipment acquired for parts or scrap is not listed.

[1] Originally lettered Comox & Campbell Lake Tramway Co.; sc. 1943.

[2] Display Courtenay 1960.

[3] Sc. Headquarters, *ca.* 1944, tender to No. 16.

[4] To Alberni Pacific Lbr., No. 4 wrecked 1936.

[5] Sc. 1955.

[6] To Pacific Coast Terminals, No. 9; sc.

[7] Ex Howe Sound, Pemberton Valley & Northern; Howe Sound & Northern; PGE No. 2; pur. 1920. Display Squamish 1965.

[8] Ex Columbia River Lbr. (Golden) No. 1; sc. 1950.

[9] Ex Columbia River Lbr. (Golden) No. 3; sc. 1949.

[10] Ex Columbia River Lbr. (Golden) No. 2; sc. 1952.

[11] Ex Donovan Corkery Lbr. Co. pur. 1937 and given new boiler; display Ladysmith 1962. Used at both Headquarters and Ladysmith.

[12] Ex Merrill & Ring Lbr. Co. No. 2; display Ladysmith 1962.

[13] Ex Merrill & Ring Lbr. Co. No. 3; sc. 1954.

[14] Ex Merrill & Ring Lbr. Co. No. 4; to Elk Falls Co. No. 1; to National Museum of Science & Technology, Ottawa.

[15] Ex Chas. R. McCormack Lbr. Co., later US Army 101; CL&R pur. 1944; used tender from No. 3 and in service March 1945; to West Coast Railway Assn. used briefly on Alaska RR and Victoria Pacific Ry.

[16] Originally not given a number; to Elk Falls Co. No. 2.

[17] M&B 1007, leased 1959; returned to M&B and renumbered 1055; remained in service until 1971; to B.C. Government for preservation.

[18] Details uncertain.

[19] Ex Gwilt Lumber Co. steam locomotive, rebuilt with gas engine. Called "Canary." 20 tons.

[20] Ex Alberni Pacific; to CFI 1983; donated to Ladysmith Railway Historical Society by CFI.

[21] Ex US Army, pur. 1960; 1973 to Elk Falls Co. (CFI in 1983); donated to Ladysmith Railway Historical Society by CFI.

[22] Ex Delaware & Hudson, pur. 1973; to CFI 1983 and transferred to Elk Falls pulp mill in 1986.

[23] Ex CPR, pur. 1980; to CFI 1983; donated to Ladysmith Railway Historical Society by CFI.

on the west coast of Vancouver Island. This was a 43-mile (69-km) main line haul from Deep Lake to the dump near Port Alberni. Of all of these operations, only Nanaimo River would retain rail equipment for the main line haul through to Ladysmith where the logs were carried by the CPR to Chemainus. Even here, however, all hauling to the end of track was to be by truck.[49]

These were large and diverse operations and the conversion to trucking was far from simple. The equipment roster of one of the logging lines gives some indication of the size of the operations being replaced. At Chemainus in 1951, MacMillan & Bloedel had 10 locomotives, 188 skeleton cars, 35 flatcars, and 98 auxiliary cars and speeders.[50] New roads were required, bridges had to be built, maintenance and repair facilities developed or expanded, equipment purchased and men trained. Moreover, the flow of logs could not be seriously disrupted during the reconstruction. By mid-1953, the end was in sight. On July 3, 1953, the crew of Val Dick, George Rolfe, Harry Eaton and Ray Chamberlain brought the last trainload of logs down to Chemainus from Copper Canyon. Just over two months later, on September 9, Don Moore, B. St. Johns, Al Vilms and J. Bona-gura worked the last carloads of logs on M&B's former Alberni Pacific line (the Ash River Division of M&B) to tidewater on Alberni Inlet.[51]

B. A. "Spike" Carson was an engineer with Alberni Pacific when the railway was abandoned.

When they finished with the railroad in '53, I went over to driving truck, you see. Of course they said that we all could put in for different jobs when the railroad was finished. . . . This was about three weeks to a month before they finished up with the railroad altogether.

They didn't even use them for parts. They went for scrap. In fact, this big Shay, the No. 9, she was the last one that ran up there. A fellow by the name of Don Moore was running her. He came into Bainbridge, at the interchange with the CPR, with a load of steel, and they just stopped her, tied her down, and the next morning they started cutting her up with a torch.[52]

By the end of 1953, Menzies Bay trains also had ceased operations. After the official end of log hauling, there were clean-up trains and scrapping trains, but there was no turning back. Some vestiges of the lines, particularly watertowers and bridges, remained for years.

Following the demise of the railroad at Menzies Bay, some of the surviving equipment was tranferred to Franklin River, notably the 2-6-6-2T Mallet (No. 6, later 1006); and the 2-8-2T (No. 4, later 1066) went to the Chemainus mill for continued operations as a yard switcher. Similarly, before the end of railroading at Alberni Pacific, Baldwin 2-8-2T No. 7 ("7-Spot"; later 1007 and finally MacMillan & Bloedel's second No. 1055) was moved to Franklin River for further service. "Spike" Carson described a tragedy that followed this move:

They loaded her on a scow and took her down to Camp A. That winter they had some pretty heavy rains at Franklin River. This morning [the engineer] came out to go to work. . . . He saw another fellow running the "7-Spot." Well, actually it was the 1007, because MacMillan put a

208

Alberni Pacific's 2-8-2T No. 7 came from the Campbell River Timber Company along with its twin the No. 8. In the photograph above, No. 7 arrived at the log dump on the Alberni Canal with 28 carloads of logs from Camp 1. In 1953, the railroad was abandoned and trucks took over the log hauling.
— MACMILLAN BLOEDEL
COLLECTION

Fireman Merton Blough in the cab of Alberni Pacific's No. 8 on the line between Deep Lake and Camp 1 in the Alberni Valley in 1951. — MACMILLAN BLOEDEL
COLLECTION

"10" in front of all their numbers, and made four-number engines. So he went in and raised hell and said he had enough seniority to take it so they gave it to him. So he took it, and that was his first trip on the "7-Spot" at Franklin River.

That was the day they went through the bridge at Camp A. The freshet had washed out from under the pilings, and apparently that was a little tricky spot coming into it. You use retainers going down into the yard, but you have to judge it so that your retainers are free when you are crossing the bridge. Apparently he held them on too long, and he was working steam real hard when he pulled the bridge underneath him, and down she went. He got drowned and the head brakeman got drowned. . . . All that happened to the locie was they bent the eccentric rod.[53]

The story of the 7-Spot was far from over. The machine was salvaged and repaired and later sent over to Ladysmith where it was leased to Comox Logging as their No. 18. Then, as Comox turned to diesel power for its line, the engine once again ran for MacMillan & Bloedel, this time as No. 1055. On the Nanaimo Lakes line it was an ideal main line locomotive and worked until the end of railroading a decade later as described in the next chapter.

The Franklin River Division did not survive the decade as a railroad operation. The conversion to trucking was completed in 1957 with the official last run taking place on May 29 in the presence of a party of 68 guests and company directors, including Prentice Bloedel and H. R. MacMillan.[54] The demise of railroad logging at Franklin River was reported in *The Truck Logger*, noting that the conversion to trucks ". . . will permit more complete utilization and protection by making accessible the timber at higher elevations beyond the reach of rail. It will also permit conversion of the whole area to patch logging, increasing effective natural regeneration and improving fire and insect protection by greater accessibility. It will also increase the economic recovery of logs, particularly pulp grades. . ."[55] The article also noted that the greater flexibility of trucks could be used to advantage to supply logs of different sizes and species to fill the changing needs of the mills.

Franklin River had modern steam equipment, including Pacific Coast Shays and M&B's 2-6-6-2T Mallet, which was transferred there from Menzies Bay in the early 1950s. However, these machines still represented 25-year-old ideas and designs and, as happened in other locations, the best rail-accessible timber was already logged. Trucks had made their appearance in the division's operations in 1946 in the China Creek area and trucking was expanded in 1953 in the Nitinat region. Logs from the Nitinat were transferred from trucks to the railroad for transport to the booming grounds on Alberni Inlet.[56] The joint rail and truck operation used 12 Hayes trucks with 12-foot (3.7-m) log bunks and it was estimated that the fleet would increase to about 20. Over the 14 miles (22.5 km) of railroad from Camp B to the log dump at Franklin River, there were 23 timber bridges, totalling in length about one mile (1.6 km) of expensive and troublesome maintenance problems. The elimination of these bridges by the 6.5-mile long (10.5-km) replacement road to a new dump at Coleman Creek was itself a important advantage in the conversion.[57] All of the surviving equipment at Franklin River including the Mallet and two Pacific Coast Shays, was cut up for scrap.

The net result of these many changes in the logging industry was that by the end of the 1950s, there were only three logging railroads left in British Columbia — Canadian Forest Products in the Nimpkish Valley, and Comox Logging and MacMillan & Bloedel's Nanaimo River lines — although the common carrier lines, including the E&N and the major lines on the mainland, still moved large quantities of logs by rail. Some steam also survived in mill-switcher service, but the days of steam power in the woods were rapidly drawing to a close.

Alberni Pacific's Alco 2-8-2 No. 6 was moved to Chemainus for work at Copper Canyon when the APL lines were phased out. It was renumbered 1055.

—NICHOLAS MORANT, CPCA M5481

Chemainus and Copper Canyon

Steam railroading was part of life in Chemainus on Vancouver Island for seven decades. These four pages capture some of the diversity and activity before the abandonment of the Copper Canyon railway. The last years of steam operations are illustrated in the next chapter.

The shops of the Victoria Lumber & Manufacturing Company were well equipped and staffed with a crew who could tackle just about any job on steam equipment. As Jack Howe, a 46-year veteran of shops remembered—if they needed it, they made it. In the late 1930s, Bob Swanson was master mechanic and he applied his great talents to the VL&M equipment. An example was the No. 3 Skidder, the first interlocking skidder on Vancouver Island. It was rebuilt in the Chemainus shops with air controls, extra engines and boiler, and a tender was added. Bob Swanson is fourth from right in the photo of the shop crew beside the skidder. At lower left is a large Marion shovel rebuilt by the shops.

Porter No. 4 (later 1044) emerged from the shops ready for the main line to Copper Canyon. Speeder No. 102, designed and built at Chemainus, had an air reverse, dual controls, and Westinghouse air brakes. No. 5, a veteran from 1906, was kept in immaculate condition. Climaxes No. 3 and No. 7 were ready for work in 1938 while Pacific Coast Shay No. 9 was recorded taking on water in 1937.—JACK M. HOWE

VL&M's No. 4 was a versatile engine that worked from the woods camps of the Copper Canyon line (at left) down to the log dump at Chemainus (at right). The engine originally came from the Timberland Development Company whose interests were acquired by VL&M in 1929.
—JACK CASH, MACMILLAN BLOEDEL COLLECTION

The change in VL&M's name, after its purchase by E. P. Taylor from the Humbird interests in 1944, shows on the huge lumber shed. Two years later, Victoria Lumber was bought by the H. R. MacMillan Export Company.

Train crews could stay together for years, forming an efficient team. Len Cary, engineer; Bill Cathcart, fireman; Gunner Jacobson, conductor; and Jim French, brakeman, worked together for over 20 years on Shay No. 6, the mill switcher.
—MACMILLAN BLOEDEL COLLECTION

Trailer No. 2 operated with
Speeder 103, doubling the capacity
of the powered speeder.
—JACK M. HOWE

Menzies Bay

Bloedel, Stewart & Welch's railway from Menzies Bay inland to the forest lands around Campbell Lake was a large and impressive operation. Camp 5, built in 1942 and located on the shore of Brewster Lake, housed about 500 people, including 40 families, during the last years of railroad logging. The beach camp was at Menzies Bay, or Bloedel as the Post Office was called. In 1950, before the all-out conversion to truck hauling began, 69 miles (110 km) of track were used as was a large stable of steam equipment, some of it illustrated on these pages.

BS&W No. 6, a Baldwin Mallet 2-6-6-2T, was acquired from the Saginaw Lumber Company of Brooklyn, Washington. Although a diesel might have been preferable, the low cost of the 20-year-old steamer made the difference. The Mallet was used on the main line.
—TED ROBSON

B

216

Scenes on the Camp 5 railway: No. 4 with crew cars and boomsticks crossing a low pile trestle; Shay No. 5 with a heavy train in 1948; No. 4 rounding a side hill at Mile 15 on the West Main with the rising waters of the newly-dammed Campbell Lake in the background; No. 4 returning to the woods at Mile 17 near Lower Campbell Lake; and Shay No. 15, near Camp 5. This engine was rebuilt at Menzies Bay after the wreck near Franklin River shown on page 80. — TED ROBSON

Menzies Bay Continued...

Bloedel, Stewart & Welch bought the first Pacific Coast Shay built and put it in service as No. 11. It served for 22 years at Menzies Bay. The locomotive came to an untimely end when it lost air pressure and went out of control on a steep grade. The runaway ended in the spectacular pileup recorded above on August 27, 1949. Beyond salvage, the engine was written off. There were too many good used locomotives available to justify rebuilding the wrecked Shay.

The lineup of equipment on the Camp 5 operation could be impressive and included Climax No. 7, which was later wrecked, Mallet No. 6. and several Shays.

Shay No. 15 , wrecked near Franklin River in 1939, was rebuilt and worked out of Menzies Bay until the line was shut down. It was photographed at Camp 5, between shifts, with crew cars waiting to take the loggers from camp out to the woods.
—ALL TED ROBSON

One Spot at Great Central

Bloedel Stewart & Welch's Shay No. 1, built in 1911, first worked at Myrtle Point and was transferred to Menzies Bay in 1928 for construction and log hauling. Later it was used as mill switcher, as shown, at Great Central Lake, north of Port Alberni. This was the site of a major mill and logging operation. After its retirement, the Shay was to be sold for export. However, Gerry Wellburn bought it and moved it to his property at Deerholme and eventually to the B.C. Forest Museum.

—MAURICE CHANDLER

Franklin River

At Franklin River, on the south shore of the Alberni Inlet, west of Port Alberni, Bloedel, Stewart & Welch developed a new logging operation in the mid-1930s. In 1933 only four miles (6.4 km) of track were used but by 1936 nearly 30 miles (48 km) were constructed. Franklin River remained a major railroad show through the demanding years of World War II until 1957 when trucks took over.

Jack Cash photographed the railroad in its last years: the log dump on the Alberni Inlet; Shay No. 19 bringing logs from Nitinat Camp B on May 7, 1957; unloading trucks next to some skeleton cars at the dump; and, from the Great Central–Sproat Lake area, a truck to rail transfer of the type used at Franklin River. — MACMILLAN BLOEDEL COLLECTION

A two-truck Shay, probably No. 9, winds down to the log dump at Franklin River. —LEONARD FRANK

After Alberni Pacific's railroads were scrapped, No. 7 (which was renumbered 1007) was transferred to Franklin River to work on the main line. Later, it was transferred to the Nanaimo River operations and was leased to Comox Logging at Ladysmith. It was photographed on July 28, 1960 at Nanaimo River Camp. It was renumbered as MacMillan & Bloedel's second 1055 and its later career is featured in the next chapter.
—ALBERT FARROW

M&B's Mallet 1006, photographed in May 1956, could handle 35 cars of logs from Camp B to Camp A on the main line at Franklin River. The compound locomotive had a very quiet exhaust, leading to its nickname "Whispering Jesus." Like Pacific Coast Shay 1027 (at right) it was scrapped after the conversion to trucking was completed in 1957. — ELWOOD WHITE; MACMILLAN BLOEDEL, COURTESY MAYNARD ATKINSON

B.C. Forest Products

In 1957, steam railroading ended on all of B.C. Forest Products' operations. These included the remaining lines at Nitinat (Cowichan Lake) and from Bear Creek Camp to Port Renfrew. BCFP's conversion to truck hauling began in 1950.

On April 10, 1956, a year before the railroad closed, Pacific Coast Shay No. 17 brought a long train of logs down to Nitinat Camp at the west end of Cowichan Lake. Note the speeders and other equipment.
—ELWOOD WHITE

Nitinat Camp was a base for extensive logging around the west end of Cowichan Lake and towards Alberni Inlet to the west.
—WILMER GOLD

Obsolete after 29 years of working in the woods, BCFP No. 17 rests at Nitinat Camp in July 1957. The locomotive was purchased in 1947 from Weyerhaeuser Timber at Headquarters, Washington. It was scrapped in 1959. —RAILWAY NEGATIVE EXCHANGE

BCFP inherited Climax No. 5 from Industrial Timber Mills. It was the largest Climax built and was originally sold to Timberland Development at Ladysmith. Out of service by the mid-1950s, it was scrapped. —WILMER GOLD

No. 19, another of BCFP's four Pacific Coast Shays, would not see service again. It was scrapped in 1959, a year after this photograph was taken. —RAILWAY NEGATIVE EXCHANGE

BCFP No. 6 rests in the sun at Bear Creek Camp a year before the end of rail service. The isolated communities such as Bear Creek depended on the speeders and the trains for their connections with the outside world.

The extension of roads with the expansion of truck logging gave the loggers and their families greater mobility and many people moved away from the remote camps. — ELWOOD WHITE

Steam at Canfor

Canadian Forest Products remained a stronghold of steam through the 1950s, although new diesels were certainly taking on their share of the log hauling. The largest locomotive working for Canfor was 2-6-6-2 No. 111, acquired from Weyerhaeuser in 1946, rebuilt in Vancouver, and placed in service in 1947. —LEONARD FRANK PHOTOS

No. 111 was an impressive machine and worked on the main line hauling
the trains of logs assembled from the branch lines by smaller locomotives.
As trucks increasingly took over moving the timber from the landings to
transfer points, the geared engines and smaller rod locomotives were
phased out. When diesel 303 arrived on the property in 1959, 111's days
were numbered and it was scrapped in 1961. — ELWOOD WHITE

Pacific Coast Shay No. 29 was one of two operated by Canfor. Purchased from Bloedel, Stewart & Welch in 1950, it was scrapped in 1961. In September 1956, it was working at Camp L at the north end of Nimpkish Lake.
—ELWOOD WHITE

No. 4 was a chunky Porter 2-6-2T that came to Canfor in the mid-1950s from Stillwater. It was also at Camp L in September 1956. At that time, the railway along Nimpkish Lake was incomplete and logs were towed down the lake and reloaded onto the railway.
—ELWOOD WHITE

A major lightning fire burned an extensive area near Vernon Camp in 1952 and salvage logging of the Maquilla burn was initiated. No. 112 was assigned to this work in 1956. —ELWOOD WHITE

The Log dumper at the Beaver Cove booming grounds was a large steam-powered mobile A-frame. —OWEN HENNIGAR

No. 11 (later 115) in the 1950s leaving camp at Englewood with a refrigerator car and freight for the isolated camps in the Nimpkish Valley. —ALAN KOLLMAN

No. 113 was the last active steam engine at Canfor. After diesels took over all regular service, it remained on standby and was used for company picnics and other special events. —DAVE WILKIE

Gas loco No. 253, photographed in 1959, was used as the switch engine at the Nimpkish shops. It came from the Capilano Timber Company. —ALAN KOLLMAN

The Three-Spot, a Shay dating to 1919, was used towards the end of its life as switcher at either Woss or Vernon camps. It was scrapped in 1959. —BCARS, HP81744

Good-natured pranks were part of life on the logging lines. Consider the time when someone stuffed empty milk cans down the stack of Climax 102. When the crew came on shift and started out, opening the throttle, the exhaust blew the cans up the stack and all over the yards.
—AS RECALLED BY GEORGE LUTZ

As trucks increasingly took over bringing the logs from the active logging areas to the main line railway, the geared locomotives were retired. They were too slow for main line service. Climax 101 was scrapped in 1959.
—STEVE STARK COLLECTION

Woss Camp remained the centre of operations for Canfor in the Nimpkish Valley. Crews worked from Woss to reloads and landings and early morning could be a busy time. In this photo, both 113 and 112 are steamed up and ready for the day's work. —J. REVEL, BCFS, 15384

The big 111 shuffles through Woss Camp in September 1956 with logs destined for the dump on Nimpkish Lake. —ELWOOD WHITE.

Camp L, at the north end of Nimpkish Lake, was where the logs from the southern parts of the Nimpkish Valley were reloaded from the lake back onto railcars for transfer to the booming grounds at Englewood. — BCARS, HP, 82132

When the new railway along Nimpkish Lake was completed in 1957, the line between Camp L and Englewood was no longer needed except to handle increased output from the salvage logging at the Maquilla burn. In September 1956, Camp L was still a busy place as Shay No. 29 steamed through. — ELWOOD WHITE

Snow is not uncommon on northern Vancouver Island and it could cause its share of problems for the logging railroad. Shay No. 5 and a Pacific Coast Shay are steamed up, about to leave camp in the 1950s. — STEVE STARK COLLECTION

Canadian Forest Products' Locomotives,
Northern Vancouver Island

Number+		Type	Builder/No.	Date	Notes
Steam Locomotives					
5		3T Shay	Lima/3280	1925	1
7		2T	Climax/1505	1920	2
101		3T	Climax/1577	1921	3
102		3T	Climax/1688	1924	4
111	—	2-6-6-2	Baldwin/60811	1929	5
112	—	2-6-2T	Baldwin/56323	1923	6
113	55	2-8-2	Alco/61859	1920	7
114	103	3T Shay	Lima/3269	1924	8
115	11	PC Shay	Lima/3350	1936	9
116	4	2-6-2T	Porter/6821	1923	10
117	3	3T Shay	Lima/2687	1913	11
118	29	PC Shay	Lima/3319	1928	12
Diesels and Gas Locomotives					
250	96	0-4-0/gas	Skagit/121	1929	13
251	98	Diesel/ Shay	Lima/Tyee	re:1951	14
252	7	Diesel/ Climax	Climax/CFP	re:1952	15
253	97	0-4-0/gas		1923	16
300	95	Diesel	GE/13166	1941	17
301	—	SW1200	GMD/A830	1956	18
302	—	SW1200	GMD/A831	1956	18
303	—	SW1200	GMD/A1715	1959	18
4804	—	SW1200	EMD/19663	1954	19

Notes: Speeders and other small powered equipment not listed.
+ Locomotives were renumbered into 100 series in 1957 as shown in first column; second column are original numbers.

1 Ex Wood & English No. 5; to CFP 1941; 110 tons; sc. 1954.

2 Ex Beaver Cove Lbr. & Pulp No. 1; ex Wood & English No. 7; to CFP 1941.

3 Ex Rat Portage Lbr. No. 1; ex Chehalis Logging No. 1; ex Vedder Logging No. 1; to CFP 1944; 70 tons; sc. after 1959.

4 Ex Nanaimo Timber No. 1; ex Vedder Logging No. 2; to CFP 1944; 70 tons; sc. 1959.

5 Simple articulated. Ex Weyerhaeuser Timber Co.; pur. 1946, sidetanks removed and rebuilt with tender at Vancouver Iron Works; to Englewood 1947; sc. 1961.

6 Ex Snoqualmie Falls Lbr. Co.; to CFP 1947. Display Beaver Cove.

7 Ex Portland, Astoria & Pacific; to Alberni Pacific 1928, No. 5; HR MacMillan Export Co. 1055; M&B 1055; to CFP 1953; 145 tons; maintained operational.

8 Ex Scott & Howe Lbr.; Howe-McGibbon Tbr.; Maywood Logging (all WA); to CFP 1946; sc. 1959.

9 Ex Merrill Ring Wilson No. 5; ex Hillcrest Lbr. No. 5 and No. 11; to CFP 1953; sold to Robert Swanson 1962 (Railway Appliance Research Ltd., North Vancouver, No. 115); then donated to Fort Steele Heritage Park, Cranbrook.

10 Ex Salmon River Logging, Kelsey Bay, (pur. used from WA), No. 4; O'Brien Logging No. 4; to CFP 1955; sc. 1961.

11 Ex St. Lawrence Pulp & Lbr., Pabos Mills, P.Q.; ex Nimpkish Timber Co.; to CFP; 70 tons; sc. 1961.

12 Ex Cascade Tbr. No. 109; ex St. Paul & Tacoma Lbr. No. 12; ex BS&W 29, Menzies Bay; to CFP 1956; sc. 1961.

13 Ex Weyerhaeuser Timber Co., Longview, WA; to Wood & English 1940; sc. Nimpkish Camp early 1970s.

14 Rebuilt from Shay (Lima 3163, built 1921) ex Pacific Mills No. 3; Export Lumber Co. No. 3; Bloedel, Stewart & Welch No. 3; Great Central Sawmills No. 3; BS&W No. 8; Deep Bay Logging No. 2; to CFP; 50 tons; sc. 1973.

15 Rebuilt from Climax No. 7 at Nimpkish Shops; sc. 1973 at Nimpkish Camp.

16 Ex Capilano Timber Co.; rebuilt from steam locomotive; to CFP 1945; sc. early 1970s at Nimpkish Camp.

17 Forty-five tons; ex US Army; ex Port of Olympia; sold 1960.

18 301-303 acquired new.

19 Ex Georgia Pacific 1203 (Coos Bay Lumber 1203), Powers, OR; purchased 1972.

Predecessor company Wood & English Timber Company (which acquired equipment from the Nimpkish Timber Company and Beaver Cove Lumber & Pulp) owned, in addition to those mentioned in the notes above, the following locomotives:

No. 1	2T Shay	Lima/2962	1918	a
No. 2	2T Shay	Lima/2345	1910	b
No. 4	2T	Climax/1279	1913	c
No. 6	3T Shay	Lima/1913	1907	d

a Purchased new, 55 tons; sc. 1940; boiler to stationary use, Woss Camp.

b Ex Blocom-Vanderhoof Logging, Acme, WA; to Nimpkish Tbr. in 1919; 55 tons; retired April 1935; fell from barge and left derelict near Beaver Cove.

c Ex Peninsular Railway, Shelton, WA; to Nimpkish Tbr., 1922; 45 tons; inspection expired 1931; remained derelict for many years.

d Ex Idaho & Washington Northern Railway, No. 6; ex Corbin Coke & Coal No. 6; Beaver Cove Lumber & Pulp No. 6; to Wood & English 1929; 70 tons; retired 1939; fell from barge and left derelict near Beaver Cove.

SOURCE: Roster developed primarily from: notes provided by Alan Kollman, Owen Hennigar and other employees; BCRHA *Canadian Forest Products*; Green, *British Columbia Industrial Locomotive*; Koch, *The Shay Locomotive*; Railway Department files; Taber and Casler, *Climax, An Unusual Locomotive*; and inspections of equipment.

Canfor's Last Steam Locomotive

Canfor's 113, the veteran Alco that first came to the Island in 1939 for Alberni Pacific, survived all steam equipment on the Englewood Logging Division. A favourite with the crews, 113 was kept on standby and cared for under the eye of George Lutz, railway superintendent. Retired in 1976, it looked as if it might never steam again. These August 1988 photos proved the contrary. Alex Matkoski had no trouble readjusting to the feel of the throttle.

—ROBERT D. TURNER

Hillcrest Lumber Company operated the last Climax locomotives working for the forest industry. No. 10, which was the second to last Climax built, ran until 1968.—ROBERT D. TURNER

No. 9, shown at Mesachie Lake in June 1957, was in logging and mill service for 50 years before being retired in 1965 and placed on display at the B.C. Forest Museum.
—DAVE WILKIE

5

STEAM'S FINALE

The Last Steam Show: MacMillan & Bloedel

By the late 1950s, steam railroad technology was at best an anachronism in North America. The main line railroads across the continent had long ago made the commitment to complete dieselization; steam's place would be in parks or at best in excursion service as a public relations gesture. By the end of 1958, there was not a single main line steam locomotive to be found in service on any of the major railways—the CPR, CNR and PGE—in British Columbia. Only a very few industrial or switching operations retained steam power and it was clear that for these too, time was limited.

Of the three logging railroads that survived in British Columbia into the 1960s, two major operations—Comox Logging and Canadian Forest Products—had switched to diesel locomotives and retained steam just as standby power. Only MacMillan & Bloedel continued to operate a logging railroad using steam power on a regular basis. In the end, it was the last of thousands of logging lines in North America using steam and, against all reasonable predictions, it continued until December 1969.

The log haul on MacMillan & Bloedel's operation on the east coast of Vancouver Island had four components. The first used trucks. Logs were moved from the cutting areas in the Nanaimo Lakes district to the end of the railroad where they were loaded onto CPR wooden skeleton log cars. From this transfer point, steam power took over. Running from the reload camp, the steam locomotives hauled the logs down to a yard and interchange with the CPR called Velco, just north of Ladysmith. There, the loaded log cars were spotted in the yard and the locomotives took on water for the return trip to the Nanaimo Lakes. From Ladysmith, the CPR hauled the logs to Chemainus, just over seven miles (11 km) to the south, where M&B operated one of its major sawmills, the former Victoria Lumber Company plant. At Chemainus, the CPR delivered the loaded log cars to a yard south of the mill and picked up empty cars for return to Ladysmith. From the yard at Chemainus M&B crews moved the cars down a steep, twisting switchback to the log dump on Chemainus harbour. Again, it was steam power that moved the logs. Diesel power never stepped in to replace these locomotives;

they worked right up until the end of the show when the inevitable logging trucks finally took over the entire log haul.

M&B maintained two steam locomotives during the last years of the Nanaimo River camp operation. These were No. 1077, a 2-6-2 built by Montreal Locomotive Works in 1923, and No. 1055, a Baldwin 2-8-2T of 1929. Both machines had spent their entire working lives on Vancouver Island. The 2-6-2 had been ordered by Cathels & Sorensen for their logging line out of Port Renfrew on the west coast of the Island. Later, it was traded for a Climax locomotive, to the Victoria Lumber Company of Chemainus.[1] The engine worked the main line west of Chemainus in the Copper Canyon logging areas and was eventually transferred north to the Nanaimo Lakes region where it continued to perform main line duties. The engine remained on the property until the railway was closed and it was then acquired by the provincial government for restoration and use on the Museum Train, a project of the British Columbia Provincial Museum (now the Royal British Columbia Museum). Restored to full working order, No. 1077 was a featured exhibit on the train during its tours of Vancouver Island and parts of the Lower Mainland. Later, it appeared in movies, including *The Grey Fox*. In 1989, it was moved to Fort Steele Heritage Park near Cranbrook for active service on the park's railway.

The 1055 had an even more varied career. It began service for Campbell River Timber Company in 1929 and was later sold to Alberni Pacific Lumber. APL became part of MacMillan & Bloedel in the early 1950s and with the decline in railroad operations in the next few years, the locomotive, then No. 1007, was transferred to Franklin River and later the east coast of the Island. For a short time it operated under lease to Comox Logging as No. 18 and then became M&B's second locomotive to be numbered 1055. Versatile and powerful, it took over from 1077 as the primary engine on the log haul from the Nanaimo River Camp to Ladysmith, and No. 1077 became the standby locomotive.

Keeping steam running in the 1960s still required hard work and ingenuity. Also, it took the interest of men like Pete McGovern, Spike Carson and Bob Swanson, who liked working with the steam equipment, ensuring that it was well maintained and efficient. MacMillan Bloedel carried out heavy repairs at the Chemainus mill's shops, which were well equipped for handling steam locomotives and machinery because the big mill itself was still steam-powered. Needing boiler work in the 1960s, No. 1055 was taken to the Chemainus mill where the old hands with steam had an opportunity to try their skills once again. Spike Carson worked on the overhaul.

They stripped her down, retubed her, did some boiler work on her and I went down and rebricked the firebox on her. I hadn't done one for years and years, but old Hap down there, he came to me and said: "How would you like to go down and put a firebox in the 55?" And I said, "Sure, I'd like to go." I didn't have to do any packing . . . they saw that all the bricks, the mortar

Comox Logging ran steam regularly on the Nanaimo Lakes line shared with MacMillan & Bloedel until 1960 when the company acquired a diesel (discussed in the next Chapter). No. 11 remained on standby and was called out for a brief return to service in 1962 when the diesel was being repaired. Afterwards, it was displayed near the company offices. — STEVE SVIATKO

All of the remaining steam locomotives on Comox Logging were preserved. No. 16, shown above at First Lake water tank in 1959, was sold to the West Coast Railway Association while No. 7, at left, was put on exhibit at Squamish because it had worked on the Pacific Great Eastern when new. —DAVE WILKIE; ALBERT FARROW

and everything was packed in there. But there's an awful lot of bricks in one of those things though. That's about a two-day job just laying bricks. Of course, there's a lot of fitting to be done too; arch and all that kind of stuff has to go in. However, two years later, that firebox was still in her, so it must have been a pretty good job at that.[2]

Not all repairs were done at Chemainus, and the crews took pride in looking after their equipment. Just as they had in years past, the men knew their machines well. In the early 1960s, when 1055 needed new tires on the driving wheels, they were changed right at the Nanaimo River camp. The heavy, awkward steel tires of a locomotive have to be heated so that they can be placed over the driving wheels' centres. When a tire cools, it shrinks to make a tight fit around the centre casting. Pete McGovern, 1055's regular engineer during its last years of service, described the process.

We had to get it [1055] jacked up, so the wheels were all clear of the rails, the side rods off — the rods all off. We just split the old tires with a torch because they were no good anymore and took them off. We got a wood fire going and heated sections of rail and put the new tires on top of the rails, and heated them up that way. So that way, they got the heat all through them. We had plenty of time to set them on the wheel and clamp them before they would start pinching [as they cooled off].

We'd carry them over with tongs and put them on, hang them on the top of the wheel, put a chain around the top, as they would slip onto the bottom themselves. Just tap them on and put a couple of clamps on them, then let them cool down. They'd put on a drop of cold water, enough to nip them so they'd stay in place. You didn't want to put too much cold water on them because that'd just harden the tire and make it too slippery after.

One day we got four on and the next day we did the same. Then we had to put the rods back on again and hang the brake arms and rigging. Jack Smith, Les McCannon, Fred Lawes, Dick Whisker and myself. A couple of them in the shop would give us a hand in between.[3]

In December 1969, 1055 made its last runs hauling logs to Ladysmith and was then stored at the Nanaimo River camp. Later, it was taken to Chemainus where it operated as a mill switcher before being acquired by the Provincial Government for preservation. After many years in storage at the Chemainus mill, it was moved to Ladysmith when the large, obsolete mill was demolished in the early 1980s. The huge mill had been built to handle the old-growth logs of the Douglas-fir forests of eastern Vancouver Island. Not only was the steam machinery obsolete, but the supply of large logs was gone. Smaller logs from second-growth stands could be handled more effectively with different machinery. A few years later, a more modern, smaller operation, with a considerably reduced labour force, opened at Chemainus.

The steam power at the Chemainus end of the M&B operation was equally interesting. The favoured locomotive was a Porter-built 2-6-2T, No. 1044, built in 1924. This chunky machine started its long career as Timberland Development Company's No. 4 and ran at first as a coal burner. When acquired by the Victoria

Lumber Company, it also ran as No. 4 and later 1044. The machine was rebuilt a number of times for different duties. While in main line service on the Copper Canyon line it pulled a tender, apparently from a retired CPR switcher. For a few years its side tanks were removed but later they were reinstalled. In its last assignment as a mill switcher, it ran without a tender and used the weight of its water tanks effectively for extra traction on the steep switchback that was a feature of the Chemainus operation.

The Chemainus switchback was the last one of many hundreds in use in the forest industry. The train crew would handle about 10 loaded skeleton cars, two idler cars (used to keep the locomotive clear of the log dump) and a small caboose down to the log dump. This meant backing down the first leg of the steep grade, stopping past the switch and then pushing the loads down a long, sweeping "S" curve on a steep gradient to the log dump. Coming back up was the reverse but the track was so steep that the engines had difficulty handling even the empty cars back up to the yard, particularly since they had to start up on the grade, pushing uphill from a standing start at the tail of the switchback. From both trackside and on the locomotive, the noise of the working engine could be overwhelming. Spike Carson worked on the switchback in the 1960s.

We backed down over the switch, picked up the little caboose. Then when you pull down over the tail track, I guess that's a good 2.2 percent anyhow... with 10 loads, and there's possibly three or more car lengths of rail behind you. You're sitting on some pretty rusty old rail too. Not only that, you have that fly ash coming in there all the time. That's the slipperiest piece of railroad that I ever worked on in my life. You could cover that rail with sand and still slip!

Coming up, you used to bat hell out of her when you came around from the flat, around the curve, and you'd just make it over, that was all. You only had 10 empties and two idlers, and you just made it, that's all. Mind you, the 44 is only about a 60-ton [54-tonne] engine anyhow. Then too, her tires were worn pretty bad and they were hollow, and of course that makes them slippery. That place, you're either going uphill or you're going downhill, one or the other.

There was one place [on the tail track of the switchback] about halfway back where there was a bit of flattening off. That was the only way to catch your feet. Otherwise you would have quite a struggle getting her started from there up.[4]

The badly worn tires on No. 1044, remembered so clearly by Spike Carson, led to its retirement before the shutdown of the log hauling operation. At the end of the railroad operation at Chemainus, 1044 was placed on display in the community.

The standby engine at Chemainus was M&B's No. 1066, which started its long career as Bloedel Stewart & Welch's No. 4. Like most rod engines, this heavy 2-8-2T was used on the main line and worked for many years out of BS&W's camp at Bloedel (Menzies Bay) north of Campbell River. When this line was abandoned to truck hauling in 1953, the locomotive was moved south. The big Baldwin ran occasionally to relieve 1044 until the Porter was taken out of service in 1968. Then 1066 carried on hauling the last logs down to the dump and was later used as a mill switcher for a short time. After MacMillan Bloedel brought

1055 down to Chemainus, 1066 remained in storage in the mill yard before being placed on display near Squamish on the Mainland. There, the engine languished until 1986 when it was moved to Qualicum where volunteers restored it and constructed a permanent shelter for its display.

Nanaimo Lakes

The last steam railroad show was MacMillan Bloedel's Nanaimo Lakes to Chemainus log haul. Through the 1960s, when every other logging railroad in North America either converted to diesels or was replaced by trucks, a small stable of steam locomotives continued to work in the woods of Vancouver Island. Time, it seemed, had stood still. The next few pages portray those last few years before steam's inevitable end came in December 1969. The album begins, above, with trucks bringing in the logs to the reload in the Nanaimo River Valley.—PETER ROBIN, BCFS, 16581

Start of the Day

The day started early at Railroad Camp at the western end of M&B's line up the Nanaimo River Valley. The locomotives were seldom shut down overnight but there were still the routine chores of oiling around the running gear, fuelling, taking on water and finally moving over to the log transfer before the first trip down to Ladysmith. There, the logs were taken on to Chemainus by the CPR. When there was a steady demand for logs, two shifts might work with each crew taking two loaded trains to the interchange with the CPR. Pete McGovern, shown above after retirement, was one of the veteran crew members.

—ROBERT D. TURNER

Towards the end of steam operations, 2-8-2T 1055 and 2-6-2 1077 were used on the line. The 1055 was the regular engine with the 1077 maintained on standby. The first order of the day was to do any switching at the transfer and pick up the loaded train. At right, 1077 is shown at the transfer. From the camp, the line rejoined the main line to Ladysmith, which was shared with Comox Logging. Sometimes, the M&B trains had to wait for Comox Logging's train to clear the junction, as shown below when 7128 passed 1077. Both scenes were photographed on April 3, 1964.—DAVE WILKIE

The railroad had many scenic locations including the spectacular steel bridge over the Nanaimo River. The 1055 eases downgrade during fire season with a track-sprinkling car leading the train. In February 1969, 1055 pulls into the yard at Ladysmith where the cars will be dropped off for the CPR to take to Chemainus. — DAVE WILKIE; ROBERT D. TURNER

At right, 1077 crosses the weathered pile trestle over Boulder Creek with a train of empties in September 1967. — DAVE WILKIE

Crown Zellerbach's ownership of Comox Logging became more evident when the equipment was painted bright orange. Baldwin 7128 winds downgrade through the second-growth forests on its way to Ladysmith in 1972.
—ROBERT D. TURNER

The second crossing of the Nanaimo River brought the tracks back to the south bank of the river and into the reload camp. The 1077 pulled into camp (below) on September 16, 1967.—DAVE WILKIE

Back to Camp

The Nanaimo River Camp marked both the beginning and the end of the day for the crews. The laminated span over the Nanaimo River is shown at right with 1055 bringing a fuel oil tank car ahead of the empty log cars.
—JOHN ILLMAN

The big water towers at camp supplied the steam locomotives and firefighting equipment as required. On standby, 1077 waited through 1969 but was not used in the last year of operation. On a summer weekend in 1964, above, 1055 sits quietly, ready for the routine of log hauling to begin on Monday morning.
—ROBERT D. TURNER

Steam at Chemainus

Esquimalt & Nanaimo crews brought the MacMillan Bloedel log trains from Ladysmith to Chemainus. John Mahy is riding the pilot of E&N Baldwin 8000 as the train eases its way over light trackage at the Chemainus yard on December 27, 1967. The loaded cars will be dropped off and the empties, shown in the background, will be picked up and returned to Ladysmith. —ROBERT D. TURNER

With loads ready to dump, the day began for 1044 and its crew. The line down to the log dump was short but spectacular with a switchback and a grade of about four percent. —ROBERT D. TURNER

Standby power at Chemainus was 2-8-2T 1066, which began service as Bloedel, Stewart & Welch's No. 4. In its last years at Chemainus, 1066 looked grim and business-like with no lettering or trim. The crews preferred the smaller 1044 on the steep grade; 1066 tended to slip when the rails were wet or frosty. —ROBERT D. TURNER

Enveloped in steam, 1044 backs past the water tower at Chemainus. After picking up the loads and backing down the grade towards the switchback, the conductor releases the brake on the transfer caboose and eases it onto the end of the train. — ROBERT D. TURNER

The transfer caboose was needed for the conductor to pilot the train through the switchback and onto the log dump. Signalling that the log dump was clear of trucks, the conductor waves to the engineer in 1044. With the log dump crew ready to handle the train, the 1044 could proceed.

—ROBERT D. TURNER

Engineer Bob Strang kept careful watch over 1044 and a constant eye on the work at the log dump on a cold December day in 1967. The last loads have just been dumped by the Jill poke (at right).

—ROBERT D. TURNER

Down at the dump, 1044 pushes
the last cars up to the unloader.
The idler cars in front of the
locomotive kept the weight of 1044
off most of the trestle work.
—ROBERT D. TURNER

256

End of the
Show

The climb back up to the yards over the switchback from the log dump presented a spectacular display of steam railroading. In December 1969, it all came to an end when trucks took over all the log hauling for MacMillan Bloedel from the Nanaimo Lakes to Chemainus. Some of the men who worked on the line in the last years were Alex Davis, Onni Parta, Dick Marty, Stan Piper, Bob Strang, Pete McGovern and Colin Rae. After the shutdown of the railway, 1055 was brought down to Chemainus to switch carloads of lumber to the E&N but in 1971 this too was terminated when the E&N began to switch the mill. The fire was dropped from 1055 and the steam railroad era at Chemainus came to an end. — ROBERT D. TURNER

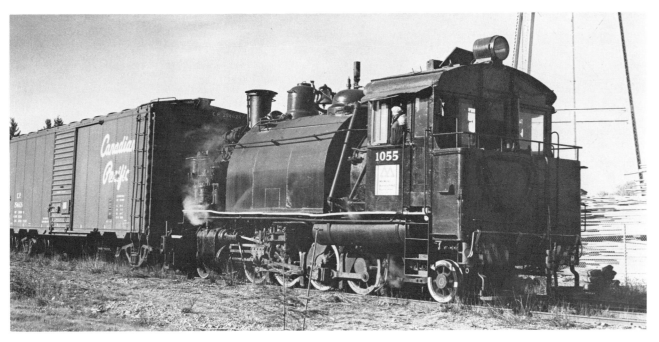

Hillcrest Lumber

Climax No. 10 of Hillcrest Lumber provided a lingering glimpse of steam operations through the 1960s. The locomotive was used to switch cars at Hillcrest's mill at Mesachie Lake and Western Forest Industries' mill at Honeymoon Bay. No. 10 is shown crossing the Robertson River with lumber from WFI destined for the CPR at Lake Cowichan and, at left, returning to Mesachie Lake.—DAVE WILKIE; ROBERT D. TURNER

The Last Geared Locomotives

Other than MacMillan & Bloedel's, there were only four steam shows left in British Columbia during the 1960s that were connected with the forest industry, and these were switching operations, not log hauling in the traditional sense. Hillcrest Lumber kept two beautifully-maintained Climax locomotives for switching at its mill at Mesachie Lake in the Cowichan district and the nearby operations of Western Forest Industries at Honeymoon Bay. The larger of the two machines, three-truck No. 10, was the regular engine while two-truck No. 9 remained on standby. The two Climaxes resided in an engine house beside the mill yard and were kept in spotless condition. The company, and several other lumber producers, owned a small 25-ton (22.7-tonne) Shay used as a dock switcher by the Osborn Bay Wharf Company near Crofton. The little Shay, a coal-burner, worked cars of lumber around the docks when ships came into port for loading cargo. Hillcrest had operated logging railroads in the Cowichan Valley for several decades; these were its last vestiges of railroading.

Hillcrest's two Climax locomotives were the last operating for the forest industry and in the 1960s, they also ran on a number of popular excursions which attracted people from all over the Pacific coast to see these unusual machines. Fortunately, all of Hillcrest's locomotives were preserved. Both Climax No. 9 and the little Shay from the Osborn Bay Wharf went to the British Columbia Forest Museum at Duncan. The Shay, rebuilt to three-foot gauge, is maintained in operation. The Climax was placed on permanent display in 1965.[5] The Stone family has continued to support the operations of the Forest Museum and has contributed a wing to one of the major buildings to house Shawnigan Lake Lumber Company's little Climax No. 2.[6]

No. 10 remained in use switching the Mesachie Lake and Honeymoon Bay mills until August 1968. Soon after, Hillcrest closed the mill and the entire plant was demolished. No. 10 was sold for tourist railway use in the hopes that the locomotive would see continued operation. It ran on several excursions on the switching line and in the early 1970s was on display as part of a short-lived tourist line, the Victoria Pacific Railway, using a section of abandoned CNR trackage north of Victoria. Eventually, the locomotive was moved to the Mount Rainier Scenic Railroad at Elbe, Washington, where it operated for several seasons.

When Hillcrest Lumber Company closed its mill and retired its two stalwart Climax locomotives, Western Forest Industries, located a few miles to the west, resurrected its small re-engined Plymouth switcher and operated the line to the CPR connection at Lake Cowichan until 1977. Later, WFI closed its mill and dismantled its large sawmill at Honeymoon Bay and the railroad was abandoned and soon scrapped. The Plymouth survived to be moved to Victoria's Ogden Point docks. There, under Westcan Terminals Limited ownership, the locomotive saw occasional use switching carloads of lumber at the docks formerly operated by Canadian National Railways.[7] Business declined and in 1987, the locomotive was donated to the Ladysmith Railway Historical Society, and was moved to Ladysmith to join the growing collection of vintage equipment around the old Comox Logging shops and yards.

Further north on Vancouver Island, on isolated trackage around the large pulp mill at Duncan Bay, a lone two-truck Shay, augmented by a small diesel, was retained by the Elk Falls Company. The Shay was used to switch cars around the mill and to unload railcar barges, usually carrying chemical tankcars, brought in from the Mainland. It was well suited to pulling cars off the barges, and during its brief sessions, the Shay put on a spectacular show of steam operation. However, when Crown Zellerbach acquired a newer diesel on its Nanaimo Lakes line in 1973, the company's old Baldwin switcher, described and illustrated in the next chapter, became available to replace the Shay. The Shay was then acquired by the National Museum of Science and Technology and moved to Ottawa in 1975 where it became an important addition to the national collection.

Two other Shays working in the 1960s cannot be excluded from this summary even though they were, not in the end, used in logging or lumbering. These were the property of Bob Swanson, who was then Chief Inspector of the province's Railways Branch of the Department of Commercial Transport (which included the responsibilities of the old Railway Department). Operating under the name Railway Appliance Research Ltd., they were used to switch the bulk loading terminal at Vancouver Wharf's North Vancouver operations. Both Shays — modern Pacific Coast types — were veterans of Vancouver Island logging operations and Bob Swanson, with a life-long interest in steam power, could not idly watch them being scrapped. Their service at North Vancouver bridged the gap between probable scrapping and eventual, more fitting, permanent preservation: one at Fort Steele Heritage Park in eastern British Columbia and the other at Cass, West Virginia, on the state-owned Cass Scenic Railroad which has a large and important collection of geared logging locomotives operating on some of the former trackage of the Mower Lumber Company.[8]

Not only did these last operations provide a lingering glimpse of steam power in operation but they also saved a diverse and important sample of locomotives and equipment from being scrapped. Survival of any steam power into the middle or late 1960s usually led to preservation and that is what happened to all of the locomotives operating or surviving in British Columbia during this period. They formed the nucleus of several worthy preservation efforts and the subsequent story of these locomotives is outlined in Appendix 1.

These pages present brief vignettes of steam's finale in the forest industry. Like all of the lines and equipment recorded earlier, the steam locomotive lasted, in regular service, only as long as it had an economically stable function to perform. Once either the forests were gone or an undeniably more economical and efficient technology arrived, change was inevitable and steam power passed into memory.

Switching at the Mesachie Lake Mill

Harry Wright eases his big Climax through the grass- and wildflower-covered tracks around the Hillcrest Mill in 1968. Switching the cars in the lumber loading sheds and through the tight clearances in the yards required care and attention to avoid accidents. Near the end of operations, No. 10 was fired up about once a week to interchange cars with the E&N. A locomotive became a home for the crews and a pot on the backhead of No. 10 made "the best damn coffee in the world."—ROBERT D. TURNER

Day's End

No. 10 shuffles into the shed; the
crew puts it to bed and goes home.
—ROBERT D. TURNER

Osborn Bay Wharf Company's beautiful little Shay No. 1 originally was built for Hillcrest Lumber in 1920. Until 1963 it worked the shipping wharfs at Crofton. Then it was rebuilt to narrow gauge for operation at the forest museum Gerry Wellburn was developing at Duncan.
—ROBERT D. TURNER; JOHN ILLMAN

The Last Shays

Shays were the most popular logging locomotives in British Columbia and it was appropriate that some should survive until the end of steam operations.

Elk Falls Company's No. 1, operating at the pulp mill north of Campbell River in 1968, became the last Shay working for the forest industry. After its retirement in 1973, it became part of the collection of the National Museum of Science and Technology in Ottawa. — ROBERT D. TURNER

Bob Swanson saved two Pacific Coast Shays from being scrapped and put them to work in North Vancouver until they found permanent homes for long term preservation. — ROBERT D. TURNER

Gerry Wellburn in the cab of Shay No. 1 at the B.C. Forest Museum. — ROBERT D. TURNER

Canadian Forest Products Ltd. operated the last surviving logging railroad in British Columbia in the 1980s. A modern railroad, using diesel power, it serves as a main line through the Nimpkish Valley. Trucks bring the timber to centrally located reload points where the logs are transferred onto the rail cars in full, bundled loads. In this 1984 scene, Canfor's 303, a General Motor's 1200 hp diesel, crosses the timber trestle and bridge over the Noomas River high above the shore of Nimpkish Lake in heavy winter rain. —ROBERT D. TURNER

 # THE DIESEL YEARS

Steam or Diesel? Testing the Options

Only two logging railroads followed the main line railways in switching to diesel power. Both were on Vancouver Island. These were the Comox Logging & Railway Company* at its Ladysmith operation on the southeast coast, and Canadian Forest Products (Canfor) in the Nimpkish Valley at the northern end of the Island. By the 1950s, when the ultimate retirement of steam power was clearly inevitable, so too was the demise of most logging railroads. Only operations that included a lengthy haul, directly from transfer points to a terminus, could compete effectively with trucks for moving logs.

There were many advantages to diesel power. The new diesels were significantly more fuel-efficient than steam locomotives and maintenance was greatly reduced. Overall, a great increase in reliability and decrease in costs resulted. Support facilities, particularly watertowers, were not required unless they were retained for fire-fighting purposes. Working with steam engines or machinery in the dry forests always presented a danger of forest fires and the diesels were less prone to throw sparks into the tinder-dry woods. Later, dynamic brakes, which could be applied to diesels, were another advantage in reducing the fire hazard of railroad operations. This system used the electric traction motors of the locomotives as generators on downgrades, creating resistance to the movement of the train. Using dynamics reduced the need for the application of train brakes as well as the possibility of sparks from over-heated brake shoes. Of course there were some drawbacks. Men had to be trained to operate and maintain the diesels and new servicing facilities were required. But the economics that applied to the major railroads also applied to the logging lines. Efficiency inevitably had a far greater impact than the romance of steam power.

Another factor in the demise of steam was the ageing of the equipment. Almost

* Comox Logging & Railway Company became a division of Crown Zellerbach Canada Ltd. as a result of an affiliation in 1950 of its parent company, the Canadian Western Lumber Company, with Crown Zellerbach. In 1956, the Canadian Western Lumber Company became a wholly-owned division of Crown Zellerbach Canada Ltd.

no new steam locomotives were built for logging service after the onset of the Depression of the 1930s. A decade of depression followed by World War II left the logging companies with an obsolete assortment of steam equipment in need of modernization and replacement. Moreover, advances in truck technology and the expansion of both public and private road systems contributed to the growing use of logging trucks. Complicating the equation, however, was the availability of some really good bargains on the used locomotive market, which could make diesels financially uncompetitive. As a result, despite the promising performance of diesels in many applications, most purchases of equipment were of used steam locomotives. The Railways Department inspected used locomotives before they were brought into the province. Bob Swanson, Chief Inspector, noted in 1948:

Considerable used railway equipment was imported subject to our prior inspection and approval. In many cases approval could not be granted, as much of the equipment did not come up to required standards; consequently such equipment was condemned and not imported. By taking full advantage of the service offered by this Department, the operators of the railways were not only saved considerable inconvenience but, as a result, obtained better and safer equipment to operate.[1]

Between 1946 and 1949, 16 used locomotives were imported.[2] The used locomotive market provided many excellent machines in the post-war years including at least six Pacific Coast Shays, and some large rod locomotives including BS&W's 2-6-6-2T and CFP's 2-6-6-2.[3] However, few of these locomotives were to see more than a decade of service.

The operators of the surviving logging railroads had an early example of successful dieselization in 1949 when the CPR's Esquimalt and Nanaimo subsidiary made a complete switch from steam to diesel power. The diesels took over everything from passenger service to log hauling on the E&N. The CPR's Baldwins turned in an impressive performance and the logging companies could not have helped being impressed.[4] But there was a difference between service conditions on a line like the E&N and those of the logging railroads. The diesel manufacturers were anxious to expand their markets and in October 1951, extensive tests were arranged on Vancouver Island logging railroads using a borrowed Great Northern, General Motors 1,200-hp diesel switcher, No. 15.

The tests were run on Comox Logging out of Ladysmith between October 8th and 12th. On the 15th and 16th, the tests were extended to the H. R. MacMillan Export Company's Victoria Lumber Company (soon to be part of MacMillan & Bloedel) operations in the Nanaimo River area, and between October 17th and 19th at the company's Copper Canyon line out of Chemainus. The operations were closely monitored by General Motors Diesel staff, Bob Swanson, Chief Inspector of the provincial Department of Railways, and C.M. Goodenberger of the Great Northern. Officials of other major logging railroad operators, notably Bloedel, Stewart & Welch, Alberni Pacific, B.C. Forest Products, Western Forest

The Competitors

The first test between steam and diesel power in logging railroad service came in October 1951 when the Great Northern's General Motor's switcher No. 15, shown at right, was brought to Vancouver Island. The diesel convincingly out-performed steam equipment. Neither Comox Logging's Baldwin 2-8-2 No. 11, photographed above by Dave Wilkie with an empty log train at Ladysmith, nor Victoria Lumber Company's 2-6-2, 1077 could match the diesel for power or fuel economy. Despite the results of the test, only two B.C. logging railroads made the conversion to diesel power. The 1077 was photographed at the Nanaimo River Camp on on March 27, 1953 while GN 15 was recorded at Vancouver where it was normally assigned. —ALBERT FARROW; NORMAN GIDNEY

Industries, Elk River Timber and Canadian Forest Products, were on hand to watch at least some of the demonstration runs, as was a representative of Canadian General Electric.

GN No. 15 demonstrated what diesels had been proving across the continent — that diesels were more powerful and more efficient than the steam locomotives they were built to replace. Undeniably, the tests were impressive. On the trials on the Comox Logging line the diesel could handle 38 loads from the Nanaimo Lakes loading area (against a grade of 0.75 percent uncompensated), whereas Comox's No. 11, a Baldwin 2-8-2, could handle only 24 loads. On the October 16th test, the diesel started 50 empty cars on the controlling grade from a standstill. It was later discovered that one of the cars had its brakes set, approximately equivalent to adding another five or six cars to the train. Later tests over the same trackage, but pulling Victoria Lumber Company trains, saw the diesel overtake Comox Logging's No. 11, assisted by No. 7, which was stalled on the controlling grade. Without uncoupling from its train, the diesel gave the steam locomotives a push over the hill. Overall, the speed and pulling capacity of the diesel was dramatically superior to the ageing steamers.

Savings in fuel, even allowing for the higher cost of diesel fuel compared to the heavy oil burned by the steam locomotives, were estimated at two-thirds. Moreover, steaming-up time was eliminated, water stops and frequent refuellings were unnecessary, and running times were significantly faster.[5]

However, despite these convincing tests there was no rush of orders. The capital costs for new diesels were still too high even with the substantial cost savings that would result. Good used steam locomotives still could be purchased for a fraction of the cost of new diesels and there were other complications relating to the long-term viability of the logging railroads. One example makes the point clearly. In 1946, Baldwin quoted to Bloedel, Stewart & Welch a price of $171,855 (including customs duty) for a 1,500-hp diesel roadswitcher (DRS-6-6-15-1) and $86,410 for a 660-hp switcher (DS-4-4-6-1); instead, BS&W purchased a large, used Baldwin 2-6-6-2T steam locomotive, originally built for the Saginaw Logging Company in 1928, (to become BS&W No. 6), had it fully reconditioned and in service, for a cost of $47,452. It is interesting to note that the quoted price on a new Baldwin 2-8-2 steam locomotive was $108,693 in 1946.[6] Diesels may have had their advantages, but they still were not cheap.

In many cases, the end of rail haulage was in sight. Some companies clearly had their eyes on the complete phase-out of the railroad lines in favour of truck hauling. With trucking on the horizon, the years that remained for the logging railways were insufficient to amortize the costs of a switch to diesel locomotives. So steam power remained on all of the lines on the Island for some years to come. However, the tests had certainly not been pointless because Canadian Forest Products on northern Vancouver Island was to acquire its first two of this type of locomotive just five years later.

In 1949, the CPR provided an early example of the successful use of diesel power when diesels replaced steam on the Esquimalt & Nanaimo Railway on Vancouver Island. Baldwin diesels were used on the E&N for all services including log hauling. The E&N moved logs for Comox Logging from Lake Cowichan to Ladysmith and also handled trains for Victoria Lumber (later MacMillan & Bloedel) between Ladysmith and Chemainus. In the photograph above at Mount Sicker, Baldwins 8012 and 8003 are returning to Lake Cowichan from Ladysmith with an empty log train on August 23, 1971. —ROBERT D. TURNER

271

On most of the other lines, including those of B.C. Forest Products, Elk River Timber, Western Forest Industries, and even the last stronghold of steam, MacMillan & Bloedel, dieselization would mean trucks not trains. The logging railways were scrapped and a complete switch was made to the highly flexible and versatile logging trucks. The story that remains to be told is of the only two railroad lines that switched to diesel power and ultimately became the last surviving logging railroads in Canada.

Comox Logging Turns to Diesel

Comox Logging had been impressed with the success of the early trials of Great Northern No. 15 on its Nanaimo Lakes operation, but the high price of the new power deterred the change from steam. Steam power continued in use at Ladysmith through the 1950s. Finally, the used locomotive market provided the solution. When it came, the change at Ladysmith was dramatic. In 1960, Comox Logging acquired a former United States War Department Baldwin VO-1000 model diesel switcher, numbered 7128, and retired all of its active steam power.

Only 2-8-2 No. 11 was retained in operational condition for standby service. Speeders and a small gas-engined switcher were available for shop switching and maintenance-of-way duties. The Baldwin diesel, built in April 1943, was a noisy, but powerful locomotive and it brought significant economies in fuel and maintenance to the line, albeit with a considerable loss in aesthetics. However, the old diesel was not without a certain rough charm or at least distinctive character. Each of its eight cylinders exhausted through a separate stack with sufficient vigour, when running hard, that the firing order of the diesel engine could be seen, felt and heard by anyone within a considerable distance of the tracks. The noise could be deafening; not quite the image of quiet efficiency that diesels were supposed to project.

The diesel worked the main line from the Nanaimo Lakes to the log dump at Ladysmith, picking up loaded log cars at truck transfer points en route. Comox Logging had been using trucks in its operations in the Nanaimo River Valley since the area was opened up during World War II, and few logging railroad spurs were built into the woods. Trucks were the feeder system for the railway and it was a partnership that worked effectively.

Steam returned only once to Comox Logging when, in 1962, the diesel broke down and No. 11 was fired up to work the log trains. It was a fine, but brief, last stand for Comox Logging steam and on the return of the diesel, No. 11 was retired permanently. This locomotive, along with No. 12, the last Shay on the property, was placed on display next to the company offices at Ladysmith. An arboretum, featuring many species of conifers, was developed on the property and other large artifacts from the steam era complemented the grounds. These included a skeleton log car and a massive donkey engine. Thereafter, if Comox Logging

Comox Logging's Diesel

In 1960, Comox Logging purchased a well-used Baldwin diesel switcher (a VO-1000 model) built in 1943. The 7128 was a powerful, tough locomotive and it replaced Baldwin 2-8-2s 11 and 16. It began service in a bright yellow (as shown on page 247) and then was repainted in grey and pink depicted in the scene above from February 1968 at Ladysmith. This photo also shows MacMillan Bloedel's 1055 in the distance and E&N's 8001. At right, 7128 is shown at the Ladysmith log dump in 1974. It had been repainted for Crown Zellerbach the year it was reassigned to work at the Elk Falls Company's pulp mill.
—ROBERT D. TURNER

Long loads could be difficult to handle; these were spanned across idler cars. —BCFS

Winter in the Nanaimo Lakes region. In the railroad's last years, the logs were handled at a dryland sorting area. —DAVE WILKIE

Alco RS-3 4097 replaced Baldwin 7128 in 1973. Ten years later, it rumbled over the crossing with the E&N and past the interlocking tower just north of Ladysmith. —ROBERT D. TURNER

Ladysmith Log Dump

Crown Zellerbach's 4097 rumbles downgrade to Ladysmith over Haslam Creek on October 14, 1977. —DAVE WILKIE

When the log trains arrived, the dump became a scene of great activity. These August 1983 photos show the logs being dumped, sorted and loaded onto a barge. —ROBERT D. TURNER

Humdurgin

The log dumping machine—the Humdurgin—at Ladysmith was an ingenious piece of equipment. Built on the frame of a Shay locomotive at the Headquarters shops, it was effective and efficient. Ed Yori ran the Humdurgin with a practiced hand. In November 1983, he started his 39th year with Comox Logging and its successors.
—ROBERT D. TURNER

The Humdurgin could unload a 30-car train in about 15 minutes. However, there were tricks to the trade. At low tide, the operator had to be careful to dump the loads sideways, not end on, or they might stick in the mud, blocking the dump, nor could the loads be piled on top of each other. The drop stakes on the log cars were released from the safe side of the cars by a cable. Joe Cliffe developed the spring-loaded "self-lift" stakes used by Comox which, after dumping, returned upright.
— ROBERT D. TURNER

Ladysmith Shops

The shops at Ladysmith, built during World War II, handled nearly all equipment maintenance. Experienced men kept the trains running safely and reliably. Art Dady, shown welding, started with Comox Logging in 1941 while Lou Pelter began in 1946. They were working in the main shop building in 1983 (lower left and above right). Bill Wright, shown in the carshop, lower right, where he was foreman, began working for Comox Logging on July 7, 1942. You can't replace the kind of knowledge that those years of experience bring to a job.

—ROBERT D. TURNER

The big shops were designed to handle railroad and truck maintenance. As General Manager Bob Filberg told the *West Coast Lumberman* in 1945, "When we hit on a new idea we put it down; whenever we made a mistake, we took note of it. And when finally we got around to building our new layout to handle under one roof all the complicated terminal operations . . . we consulted our record and drew our plans according to past experience, incorporating the new ideas we had gathered along the way." The main building was 84 x 203 feet (25 x 61.9m) with the railroad at the north end and trucks at the south. It had a 70-foot (21-m) locomotive pit, overhead crane and machine tools.

required relief motive power, it borrowed it either from MacMillan & Bloedel, which as noted in the previous chapter, was still using steam power, or from the CPR.

Even diesels need replacement and the weary Baldwin was relieved in 1973 by a well-used Alco RS-3 roadswitcher that originally came from the Delaware and Hudson Railway. No. 4097 actually included parts from two D&H units and, once in service, became a fixture on the line. With 1,600 hp available, the RS-3 had a decided edge over the 1,000-hp Baldwin and trips on the line were notably faster. The old Baldwin was far from dead however, and it was transferred to the Elk Falls Company's pulp mill, also a Crown Zellerbach operation, to replace Shay No. 1, still used at the mill to switch the railway barges which brought in chemical tank cars and other supply shipments from the mainland. The trackage down to the dock was steep, and at low tide, pulling the cuts of cars off the barge was a test for even the considerable hauling capacities of either the Shay or the Baldwin diesel. At least twice in its career, the Baldwin replaced steam power and perhaps strangely, because of its age and the relatively small numbers of Baldwin diesels to survive into the 1970s and beyond, it had become a curiosity and a vintage locomotive that was eventually to be preserved.

A second RS-3 (No. 8427) arrived on the property in September 1980 when the company acquired a former CPR locomotive amid rumours that the line was to be expanded deeper into the Nanaimo River Valley. During this period, other important improvements were made to the operation. Rolling stock was upgraded by the addition of more steel cars and a dry land sorting ground was established at the end of track in the Nanaimo Lakes area. The previous practice of dumping logs into the lakes, sorting them, and then reloading the timber onto the railcars was discontinued. At the other end of the line, a massive loading crane that could lift full carloads of bundled logs onto barges was installed at Ladysmith. This crane did not replace the log dump but was mounted just offshore in Ladysmith Harbour.

However, no extensions were made to the railway; the forest industry went into a severe recession in the early 1980s. Meanwhile, Crown Zellerbach Canada Ltd. had been acquired by the New Zealand-based forest products company Fletcher Challenge. Crown Zellerbach Canada Ltd. was renamed Crown Forest Industries and the operations in the Ladysmith area continued. Later, Fletcher Challenge also acquired a controlling interest in British Columbia Forest Products. In 1988, BCFP was renamed Fletcher Challenge Canada Limited, and the management structure of the two companies, although not the assets, was amalgamated.[7].

In the mid-1980s times were tough for the forest industry in British Columbia and the remaining timber available in the Nanaimo Lakes region was either too young or not in demand. In 1984 the end of rail logging was in sight and it was announced that the line would close. However, a fire caused extensive damage to

The Ladysmith shops remained the centre of the railroad for its entire history. The buildings were eventually preserved being donated to Ladysmith by Fletcher Challenge Canada Ltd.'s subsidiary Crown Forest Industries. At right, in a 1973 photograph, Baldwin 7128 is just outside the engine house. At right is the carshop.
—ROBERT D. TURNER

Comox's 107, with its well-polished locomotive bell, was the shop switcher. Speeders, such as No. 108 shown above, were used out on the line for track work.
—ROBERT D. TURNER

Track work was a tough, demanding and absolutely essential part of maintenance. Andy Piatkowaski (left), Andy Payne (centre) and Robin Morris (right) were repairing a switch near the dryland sorting area at the Nanaimo Lakes shortly before the line closed in 1984.
—ROBERT D. TURNER

283

Comox's little Whitcomb was transferred to the Elk Falls pulp mill. —ROBERT D. TURNER

Crown Forest Industries' railway ceased operations in 1984 and so too did log hauling from the Cowichan Lake region on the E&N. At left, two CPR GP9Rs lead a long train down the valley while below, an empty train pulls into Lake Cowichan. The station was preserved by the Kaatza Historical Society. The Lake Cowichan branch was abandoned soon after log hauling ceased. —ROBERT D.TURNER; DAVE WILKIE

the major bridge over the Nanaimo River and brought about a premature end of the line. Unexpectedly, the last logging railroad on southern Vancouver Island passed into history.

The shops and much of the equipment were donated by Crown Forest Industries to the City of Ladysmith and the Ladysmith Railway Historical Society. Included were locomotives No. 8427 and No. 107, a large speeder, several types of log cars, auxiliary rolling stock, the ingenious "Humdurgin" log unloader, and shop equipment. The historically rich site, with the original buildings (including the interlocking tower from the line's crossing with the E&N), steam and diesel locomotives and rolling stock, provided the basis for the development of a fine historical centre and a continuing asset to the community.

Crown's RS-3 No. 4097 was transferred to the Elk Falls mill where it once again replaced the old Baldwin switcher that had once ruled the line at Ladysmith. In the years that followed, the collection of equipment at Ladysmith has grown to include a fine representation of locomotives and rolling stock. Both steam locomotives No. 11 and No. 12, on display at the nearby arboretum, were moved back to the shops for restoration. In addition, locomotive No. 1055 (formerly owned by MacMillan Bloedel and for a time operated by Comox Logging as No. 18) was stored on the property for the provincial government. In the spring of 1989, Crown Forest Industries donated Baldwin diesel No. 7128 to the Society so that it, too, could become part of the collection. Dedicated volunteers and crews hired through various grant programs have restored equipment and made many improvements to the site.

With the closure of the former Comox Logging line only one logging railroad survived in Canada. The ranks were also dwindling in the western United States.

Log cars crowd the yard at Ladysmith. By the end of the show, the wooden cars at right had been replaced by all-steel cars.
—ROBERT D. TURNER

Pete McGovern and Gerry Wellburn pause for a moment as they share memories at Ladysmith in 1988.—ROBERT D. TURNER

The logging railroad story seems destined to end with the last operating logging railroad in Canada, Canfor's isolated and highly-efficient line on northern Vancouver Island. Logging by rail in the Nimpkish Valley began in the steam era and, as described earlier, expanded in the 1950s to become one of the largest operations on the Coast. A chronic problem of the logging operations in the Nimpkish Valley had been the need to raft logs down Nimpkish Lake. Rails connected the coast at Beaver Cove with the lake, but the shoreline presented a difficult and expensive route for railroad construction. The expedient had been to railroad logs down to the head of the lake, and from there to use tugs to tow the logs to a reload at the other end of the lake. There, trains could once again take over to transport them to the log dump. However, unloading, barging and reloading was a time-consuming and inefficient operation. CFP finally resolved the problem by embarking on a major expansion of the railway to bypass the lake. Construction of a 23-mile (37-km) line began in 1954 and three years later, on July 12, 1957, it was open for service. The introduction of diesels on the railroad and an increased use of heavy trucks operating to permanent reload facilities along the length of the line were further steps in the modernization of the operation.[8]

Canadian Forest Products' approach to dieselization was different from that of Comox Logging, and it predated the modernization of Comox's Ladysmith operation by nearly a decade. At first, rather than purchase new diesels, two steam locomotives were rebuilt with diesel engines. This was an unusual practice, but not unique to Canfor. However, the locomotives that resulted were certainly one-of-a-kind products. One was a two-truck Shay, stripped down and rebuilt into a diesel-hydraulic locomotive. This project was undertaken by the Tyee Machinery Company in Vancouver in 1951 and a well-proportioned centre-cab diesel emerged. "The product of engineering imagination and ingenuity," noted the *British Columbia Lumberman*. "Driven by a 400 hp. Cummins diesel engine, with a twin disc clutch torque converter and two speeds both forward and reverse, its tractive effort is 22,500 pounds [10 200 kg] at three miles [4.8 km] per hour, 8,100 pounds [3 675 kg] at 7.4 miles [12 km] per hour. Maximum speed in hydraulic drive is 20 miles [32 km] per hour; in direct drive about 25 miles [40 km] per hour."[9] The Railway Department noted that, "...this locomotive is being built as a pilot model under the supervision of the Department, with the idea in mind to convert other steam-operated geared locomotives over to diesel operation in the future."[10] The second conversion was no less imaginative. An elderly two-truck Climax was stripped completely down to its frame and running gear. A diesel engine was fitted (producing a diesel-mechanical locomotive rather than the usual diesel-electric arrangement) and a new cab and carbody (to enclose the engine) were built. Nothing else quite like it ever roamed

Canfor's Early Diesels

Canfor's 300, a 45-ton (40.8-tonne) General Electric, was powered by a 300 hp Cooper Bessemer diesel. Like other equipment that arrived before the completion of the railway between Beaver Cove and Nimpkish, it travelled over the line between Englewood and Camp L and was then barged up the lake. Alan Kollman recalled that for awhile it was used for hauling freight and switching, "but it didn't run long because of breakdowns." Alan worked on it in 1958-59 as fireman-brakeman and remembered its demise. "One of the mainline diesels had a wreck below Siding 2 and we were asked to go down and pull back about 12 loads into Siding 2, if we could, so they could get at the derailment. The 300's cooling shutters were hand operated and the engineer, concentrating on the Amps we were pulling, overlooked the temperature gauge. The engine overheated and a piston seized and threw a rod through the side of the block." Soon after, it was sold.
—RAILWAY NEGATIVE EXCHANGE

Canfor's two conversions of steam locomotives to diesel power were imaginative and functional. No. 251 was rebuilt from a Shay at the Tyee Machinery Company in Vancouver in 1951 while 252 was rebuilt from Climax No. 7 at Canfor's Nimpkish shops. The Railways Department worked closely with the company on the conversions and as Bob Swanson commented, "It was an age of experiment and growth of ideas. I was my happiest doing it. It was some fun."—ROBERT D. TURNER

Canfor
Bridges and Trestles

The Englewood Logging Division of Canfor features many spectacular wooden bridges and trestles. These pages highlight some of the larger spans. Two units (above) lead a long train of loads from Camp A reload to Beaver Cove over the Noomas River. At left, between log hauling runs, a crew takes a tank car out over the line from Beaver Cove to sprinkle the bridges. Here the train passes over the Kokish River.

—ROBERT D. TURNER

The East Fork trestle, south of Beaver Cove, is one of the finest surviving examples of timber trestle construction. The bridges along the line are expensive to maintain and also vulnerable to damage. A fire or an accident could put the railway out of service for some time, crippling production from the entire tree farm. Where possible, bridges and approaches are being filled but some spans are not practical to replace. The train is the same one shown on the opposite page, photographed in August, 1988.—ROBERT D. TURNER

The line to Vernon Lake crosses the Groves Creek on a spectacular laminated wooden span.
—ROBERT D. TURNER

High above the Noomas River, 4804 and 303 lead a long train of logs northwards up the Nimpkish Valley. The forested mountains in the distance are on the west side of Nimpkish Lake while the railway climbs high above the east side of the lake before turning east to follow the Kokish drainage to Beaver Cove. —ROBERT D. TURNER

the rails of the logging railroads; its high cab was perched off-centre, and on top was a muffler for the exhaust. It was a remarkable conversion that lived up to the innovative traditions of the logging railroads. The work was done by the company shop crews at Nimpkish in 1952. It was a true hybrid of technology; the photographs show the results of these conversions. These engines worked with steam power and did not represent a total shift to new technology. Both conversions were successful enough to keep the locomotives operational for another 20 years until they were scrapped in the early 1970s. However, the idea was not attractive enough to be adopted by other companies still operating steam equipment.

Canadian Forest Products then purchased three diesels. One was a used General Electric 45-ton (40.1 tonne) switcher acquired from the Port of Olympia in Washington. This machine, originally built in 1941 for the United States Army, became No. 95 and was later renumbered to 300 by Canadian Forest Products. Next, as part of an overall plan to extend and improve its logging railroad, Canfor bought two new diesel locomotives. General Motors Diesel Division supplied two SW1200 switchers (Nos. 301 and 302) specially modified for logging road service. These engines, built in 1956, featured dynamic brakes, enlarged fuel and water tanks, and top-mounted air reservoirs. In addition, they were fitted with Flexicoil trucks for better performance in main line service. The new diesels were a fine addition to the newly extended logging railroad. "These locomotives," noted Chief Inspector Bob Swanson in his Annual Report, "will ultimately replace some of the older steam locomotives in use, but at the present time, the operation is such that approximately seventeen locomotives are in service on this railway." He went on to comment that, "inasmuch as the Englewood operation is the largest railroad logging operation ever to exist in British Columbia, Inspectors have made a greater number of inspections at the Englewood operation than at other railway operations throughout the province."[11] In 1959, a third, virtually identical engine (No. 303) joined the roster. The new SW1200 diesel locomotives were more modern versions of Great Northern's No. 15 which had run trials on the Island in 1951.

As feeder operations were increasingly converted to trucking, the surviving steam power was retired. With the new diesels in full operation, the use of steam power rapidly dwindled. By the early 1960s, nearly all steam engines, including the geared locomotives and the massive 2-6-6-2 No. 111, had been scrapped; only two steam locomotives remained on the property. A third survivor, Pacific Coast Shay No. 115, was purchased by Robert E. Swanson in 1962 and moved to North Vancouver for continued operation as illustrated in the previous chapter. Of Canfor's two steam locomotives, 2-8-2 No. 113 was retained as standby power, which was prudent, but it was also brought out under steam for annual company picnics. The pride of the railroad crews and carefully tended by George Lutz, Railway Superintendent, and his men, No. 113 remained operational until 1975

Even Canfor's big 2-6-6-2 No. 111 succumbed to the competition from diesels. When the third new SW1200RS arrived from General Motors in 1959, the 111's days were near an end. After the completion of the railway along the lake, it had been used as far as Camp A reload. It was scrapped early in 1961.
—BCARS, HP82185

The diesel Climax switches a landing in the transition period when branch lines were still built into the timber.—J. REVEL, BCFS15397

293

when major work would have been required to keep it running. The veteran locomotive, after putting in revenue service hauling logs on June 5 and 6, 1975, was placed on display outside the company offices at Woss where it was to remain until 1988. This last log hauling service gave No. 113 the distinction of being the last steam-powered locomotive in Canada to haul timber on a logging railroad. The company's only other surviving steam locomotive, 2-6-2T No. 112, long neglected on the rip track behind the shops at Nimpkish, was cosmetically restored and placed on display, along with a wooden skeleton log car, at Beaver Cove.

Fortunately, the story of steam on Canfor's railroad was not over. The year 1988 marked the 50th anniversary of Canadian Forest Products and a company picnic and reunion was planned to be held at Woss in August. Thoughts turned to No. 113 again and a careful inspection followed. The 2-8-2 was moved to the shops at Nimpkish Camp and a restoration began. By the weekend of August 27, a remarkable transformation had occurred and the locomotive was under steam once again. Walter Infanti and his crew had done a beautiful job of bringing the locomotive back to life. The looks on the faces of the train crews and the passengers were all anyone needed to judge the happy results. The 113 was the hit of the celebrations.

Canfor's logging railroad did not remain static following dieselization and the retirement of steam power. The line has been systematically maintained and improved. Bridges have been replaced and modernized, while some have been replaced by fills. Rolling stock has been improved and upgraded. All log cars are steel and are equipped with heavy-duty roller bearings in all journals. In addition, and in keeping with the general movement in the industry to dry land sorting, all logs are now unloaded at a large sorting facility at Beaver Cove. This type of operation permits the use of high fixed stakes on the log cars improving their load capacity. Reloads are located along the line, their use depending on the demands for different types of timber and on the season — timber is cut at higher elevations in summer and in the valley bottoms in winter. In the mid-1980s, the diesels were fitted for multiple unit operation, further improving the efficiency of the railroad. Normally, a crew operates with a single unit, collecting loaded cars from the reloads and bringing them to a transfer point north of Woss. From there, a second crew works two units on the northern end of the line to the dry land sorting facility at Beaver Cove. The result is a highly efficient log hauling system. Overall, based on studies of the economics of continuing the rail operations, the railroad system still has a significant cost advantage over a switch to truck haulage.

Canadian Forest Products' railway in the Nimpkish Valley is the last survivor of the hundreds of logging lines that once ran on the British Columbia coast. Many decades have passed since the last logging railroad operated in the interior of the province, but there is a renewed interest in rail logging systems in the vast sub-boreal spruce forests of north central British Columbia. The large forest products companies operating at Prince George have been investigating the possibility of using the British Columbia Railway's inactive Dease Lake extension to expand their log supply for the 1990s. Should this develop, it would be a modern operation with a few similarities to the logging railways of the steam era.

No. 302 and a water car return to Woss Camp from Camp A over the timber trestle crossing Steele Creek. — ROBERT D. TURNER

Equipment and Operations

Hauling ore on a logging railway was unusual but from 1960-1963, Canfor hauled ore to Beaver Cove for the Nimpkish Iron Mines. They had 60 ore cars of 60-ton (54-tonne) capacity and from 15 to 45 cars per day were handled. The photo shows No. 303 spotting ore cars at the ship loading facility at Beaver Cove.—ALAN KOLLMAN

Canfor has used a variety of cabooses on its trains, including some former Northern Pacific wooden cars which lasted only a few years. The one at left was built by the company.
—ROBERT D. TURNER

A speeder, pulling a small trailer with supplies, heads south from Beaver Cove in 1979.
—ROBERT D. TURNER

Canfor has not hesitated to modernize and modify its speeders. This one was rebuilt with a crane.—ROBERT D. TURNER.

George Lutz spent many years with Canadian Forest Products. He started as a boomman in 1943 and retired as Railway Superintendent. He saw the transformation of the run down old Wood & English railroad into the expanded, dieselized operations of the 1970s.
—CANFOR

Heavy cranes have been very useful for bridge repairs or in replacing centre spans as shown here at Groves Creek on June 27, 1976. They are also useful in the unlikely event of a derailment.
—DAVE WILKIE

Tank cars, used for water, diesel fuel and gasoline, have an important place on the railway. These water cars are used for track sprinkling and fire fighting. Behind them, in the yard at Woss, are ballast cars and flat cars loaded with new yellow-cedar ties for the railway. The photo was taken on June 15, 1985.—ROBERT D. TURNER

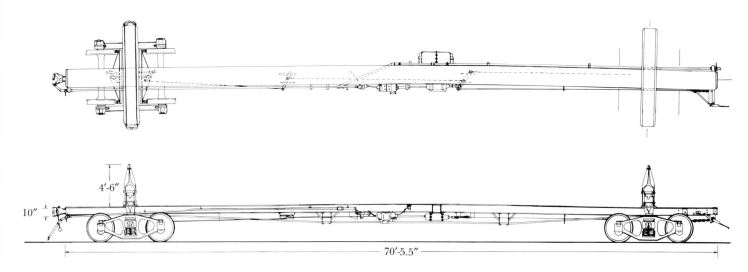

4'-6"

10"

70'-5.5"

CANADIAN FOREST PRODUCTS
70-foot (21-metre) Steel Log Car

Drawing based on company drawings and
photographs of cars *ca.* 1970.

Scale: ⅟₁₀"=1'- 0"

Canfor's log cars are all steel in construction. These photographs from the late
1960s show both a standard car and a 70-foot (21-m) car (similar to the car
shown above) used for carrying "boomsticks" and long loads. All cars were
subsequently modified to have higher fixed stakes when new loading and
unloading facilities were developed.—ROBERT D. TURNER

The train lineup at Woss on a wet weekend in 1974 included No. 4804, acquired in 1972 from Georgia Pacific in Oregon, and the 301. The caboose behind 4804 came from the Northern Pacific. The speeder shop at Woss is shown at right with a variety of equipment posed in front. Diesel Shay, No. 251, rests outside the shops at Nimpkish Camp in 1973. The large A-frame building housed an overhead crane. Most maintenance on railroad equipment is carried out at Nimpkish.

—ROBERT D. TURNER

Camp "A" Reload

Camp A, north of Woss Camp, is a major transfer point between trucking and rail operations. Similar facilities are located near Woss, Maquilla and at Vernon. The capacity of trucks and the rail cars are matched so that a single truck load is swung onto a rail car forming its complete load, top right. In the scenes to the left, diesels taking the loads to Beaver Cove are backing into the reload. Note that the tank car is being used to sprinkle the bridge and tracks.—ROBERT D. TURNER

"Send it to Woss..." George Lutz remembered this classic story of rivalry between the camps. When Vernon Camp found it had far too many cats, they were quietly loaded into an empty speeder trailer. Soon Martin Nielsen coupled his speeder onto the trailer and made a routine run to Woss. When the doors were opened, the cats poured out, instantly doubling the cat population of Woss. Thereafter, a common expression was, "Don't destroy it, send it to Woss."

Vernon

Vernon, in the southern end of the Nimpkish Valley, was a major woods camp, a remote community whose only connections with the outside world were long hard drives over gravel logging roads or by speeder on the railway. However, after improved roads reached the Nimpkish from Campbell River, the camp was closed and the residents moved either to Woss or to Campbell River. The transfer facility remained although operated on contract. In June 1988 Ian Compton, below, of Holbrook Dyson Logging handles the transfer from the big Hayes truck to the steel skelton car with ease.— ROBERT D. TURNER

Along the Line

Crews meet at Camp A. Multiple unit operations began in the early 1980s and usually two diesels are operated north of Camp A while one unit works south to Vernon and from Woss to Camp A.

In the dispatcher's office at Woss Camp, Bill Green keeps all the log trains, speeders and special movements running smoothly. All trains are equipped with radios to communicate with Woss and with each other. — ROBERT D. TURNER

Nearing the end of the line, two units ease across the Kokish River just south of the dryland sorting ground shown at right. In the 1970s this facility, with its huge front end loaders, replaced the log dump.—ROBERT D. TURNER

NIMPKISH CAMP	114		
ACCIDENT FREE DAYS			
0925	510	LOADING	742
0928	261	RELOAD	2202
0929	232	TRUCK HAUL	951
0932	169	CONSTRUCTION	431
0943	241	SHOP	649
0945	101	F & B	100
HAVE A SAFE PRODUCTIVE DAY			

Restored

The 113, Canfor's last active steam locomotive, was retired in 1976 to display outside the company offices at Woss. However, in 1988, Canfor celebrated its 50th anniversary and held a reunion and celebration at Woss. To everyone's delight, 113 was refurbished and powered several excursions. In subsequent years, 113 has also operated with great success. Some of the crew who worked on the restoration pose with 113 at the end of the day. From left, they are: Reggie Paul holding his son Robert, Al Kenny, Sam Hardy, Alan Kollman, Alex Matkoski, John Murray, Walter Infanti, and Paul Hawryluk. On

this page, Alan Kollman (left) and Sam Hardy (right) in the cab along with retired superintendent Owen Hennigar and his grandson Troy Neale. At right, 113 crosses Gold Creek with a carload of passengers while below Alex and Sam supervise visits to the cab for a generation who may never have seen a working steam locomotive. And that is a happy note to end on.

—ROBERT D. TURNER

Steam operations in winter were spectacular. Comox Logging's No. 11, one of the last steam locomotives in use in British Columbia, is shown working upgrade with a train of log flats from the log dump at Ladysmith through a dusting of snow. In the background is the booming grounds for sorting the logs before they were towed to the mill for processing.
—ELWOOD WHITE

EPILOGUE

The story of the logging railways in British Columbia spans a little over one lifetime. Yet, from the building of the first logging lines in the late 1880s until the demise of all but one operation less than 100 years later, dramatic changes occurred. The steam logging railroads were a key technology that enabled a developing British Columbia to make enormous economic advances and at the same time caused profound changes in the landscape of the province.

It was railroading and related logging technologies — and the highly-skilled hard-labouring individuals who ran the machines and equipment — that brought about the elimination of vast areas of old-growth forests. Over virtually the entire Coastal Douglas-fir Zone on Vancouver Island and many adjacent areas of the Coastal Western Hemlock Zone on the Island, in the Fraser Valley and in nearby lowlands along the coast, the timber was cut. Almost every valley and the lower slopes of most ridges in this region were once logged by steam equipment, most of it operating in connection with a steam railway. In these areas, only meagre remnants of mature forest remain.

Landscape change on this scale does not happen overnight; the process took many decades. Throughout most of the steam era, nearly all of the leading politicians, businessmen, foresters, and the general public supported the over-riding philosophy of resource use that resulted in the depletion of the forests, and were responsible, directly or indirectly, for its implementation. Logging was a way of life, the backbone of the economy, and there always seemed to be more trees. The early development of a forest service in British Columbia, improved fire fighting equipment, growing public awareness of the value of the forests and insightful work like the landmark studies of Chief Justice Gordon Sloan gradually led to improved forest management and hastened regeneration of the second-growth forests. However, few thought to save any old-growth stands out of a sense of history or for ecosystem research and preservation. It is understandable but nonetheless tragic that so few areas of mature forest were saved to remind us of what this part of British Columbia was like such a short time ago and to provide areas for forestry research.

Fortunately there are a few residual stands and individual trees in parks and remote areas within the forest regions once logged by rail. Perhaps the best known is Cathedral Grove in MacMillan Provincial Park on Vancouver Island. In this small stand, donated by H. R. MacMillan, 800-year-old Douglas-firs have been preserved.

In contrast, our preservation record of the technology of logging railways has been very good. Perhaps technological change is easier to appreciate than landscape change. Machines are sidelined and scrapped. If work remains to be done, newer, more efficient machines are bought as replacements. In this way the steam machines slipped into history. Fortunately, farsighted individuals, notably Gerry Wellburn, Bob Swanson and others in industry and government, began to save some of the historically important machines before they were scrapped. And Gerry, it should be added, also saw the need to preserve representative areas of forest for their value as natural and historical resources. The presence of a small stand of old-growth Douglas-fir near Duncan led to the selection of the site for the British Columbia Forest Museum, founded by him.

Steam technology disappeared from the forests of British Columbia primarily for two reasons. Developments in diesel yarding and loading equipment and the advent of high-capacity, sophisticated trucks left steam machinery unable to compete economically by the 1950s. The other factor, which led to the abandonment of many logging railroads along the coast, was the disappearance of the lower elevation old-growth forests that the railroads were built and maintained to exploit. Even highly-evolved equipment like the Pacific Coast Shay was of no use without a resource base.

Steam machinery has an undeniable attraction for many people and the locomotives of the logging lines have a special appeal. In no small measure, the interest they evoke accounts for the substantial number that have been preserved. Twenty-four steam locomotives, two large diesels, and several smaller gas locomotives and speeders that saw service in the British Columbia logging industry have been set aside as part our historical record. This is a substantial collection, and one that will give future generations an opportunity to understand something from the formative years of the province and of life in an era when a steel machine, fire and water could be brought together to carry out enormous labours and bring tremendous change.

The steam era in the woods carries with it an aura of romance and excitement. But it was not an easy time in our history, marked as it was by two World Wars, the Great Depression and times of serious labour unrest. Yet, in the woods at least perhaps it is best remembered as a time of hard work, long hours, danger, comradeship and ingenuity. The crew on a logging train grew to depend on each other and on their equipment; mistakes were dangerous. A quiet self-reliance and humour were usually the marks of experienced men.

The whistle of a distant steam locomotive echoing through the forests and from far off mountains was a sound that few who have heard it will ever forget. The machines were fascinating to watch and most of the old-timers will agree that the engines took on individual characteristics and qualities with the passing of the years. The locomotives were tough and robust — like the men who worked on them. On both the men and machines the passage of the years left many signs of hard labour and history. None of them passed lightly over the land.

The crews took pride in their equipment. Even in the rugged conditions of working in the woods, where dust, mud, smoke and grease were a part of daily life, the machines were usually well cared for. Victoria Lumber & Manufacturing's No. 4, shown with a crew car at Copper Canyon in 1942, was a spotless example of a well-maintained logging locomotive.
—DAVE WILKIE COLLECTION

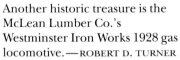

Another historic treasure is the McLean Lumber Co.'s Westminster Iron Works 1928 gas locomotive. —ROBERT D. TURNER

Preservation requires the dedication and hard work of many people. Bob Swanson and Dave Lowe (above) and Ken Rutherford (left) inspect Port Alberni's Two-Spot in 1981 as work began to restore it to operation.
—ALBERNI VALLEY MUSEUM

Type	Builder/Number	Date	B.C. Owners/Road No.	Notes
1) Steam Locomotives				
Geared Locomotives				
2T Shay	Lima/2305	5/1910	East Kootenay Logging, No.3	1
2T Shay	Lima/2475	9/1911	Bloedel, Stewart & Welch, No.1	2
2T Shay	Lima/2548	6/1912	Alberni Pacific Lumber, No.2	3
2T Shay	Lima/3147	12/1920	Hillcrest Lumber, No.1	4
2T Shay	Lima/3262	4/1924	Mayo Lumber, No.3	5
2T Shay	Lima/3289	10/1925	Elk Falls Co., No.1	6
2T Shay	Lima/3311	6/1927	Comox Logging, No.12	7
3T Shay	Lima/3320	7/1928	Western Forest Industries, No.5/RAR, No.114	8
3T Shay	Lima/3350	4/1940	Canadian Forest Products, No.115/RAR, No. 115	9
2T	Climax/1057	1910	Shawnigan Lake Lbr. No.2	10
2T	Climax/1359	6/1915	Hillcrest Lbr. No.9	11
3T	Climax/1693	3/1928	Hillcrest Lbr. No.10	12
Rod locomotives				
2-8-2	Alco/61859	1920	Canadian Forest Products, No. 113	13
4-4-0	Bald/2660	1872	Columbia River Lbr. No.1	14
2-6-2T	Bald/34270	2/1910	Comox Logging, No.7	15
2-6-2T	Bald/34921	7/1910	Comox Logging, No.2	16
2-6-2T	Bald/56323	1923	Canadian Forest Products No.112	17
2-8-2	Bald/57409	11/1923	Comox Logging, No.11	18
2-8-2T	Bald/58687	9/1925	MacMillan Bloedel, No.1066	19
2-8-2T	Bald/60942	8/1929	MacMillan Bloedel, No.1055	20
2-8-2	Bald/61159	12/1929	Comox Logging, No. 16	21
0-4-4T	Daven/1768	3/1920	M. B. King Lbr. / King Farris Lbr.	22
0-4-4T	Mar&Cant.	1879	B.C. Mills, Timber & Trading, "Curly"	23
2-6-2	MLW/65337	12/1923	MacMillan Bloedel, No.1077	24
2-6-2T	Port/6877	5/1924	MacMillan Bloedel, No.1044	25

2) Diesel-electric and Gas or Diesel-mechanical

Type	Builder/Number	Date	B.C. Owners/Road No.	Notes
0-4-0	Gas Plymouth/1662	1924	Comox Logging No.107	26
Tugaway	Gas West.IWks.	1928(?)	J. H. Baxter Pole Co.	27
0-4-0	Gas West.IWks.	1928	R. B. McLean Lumber Co.	28
0-6-0	Gas Plymouth/3365	1929	Western Forest Industries No.7/40	29
VO1000	Bald/64745	1943	Comox Logging/Crown Zellerbach No. 7128	30
RS-3	MLW/80992	1952	Crown Zellerbach/Crown Forest 8427	31

Abbreviations: Bald (Baldwin); Daven (Davenport); d. (dealer); Port (Porter); MLW (Montreal Locomotive Works); Mar&Cant. (Marschuetts & Cantrell); sc. (Scrapped); West. IWks. (Westminster Iron Works).

Notes:
Owners listed in order of acquisition. Not all dealers, camps or operating locations are shown. Company and other abbreviations: BS&W (Bloedel, Stewart & Welch); CL&R (Comox Logging & Railway Co.); CFP (Canadian Forest Products); CPR (Canadian Pacific Railway); d (dealer); M&B (MacMillan & Bloedel, also MacMillan Bloedel); RAR (Railway Appliances Research Ltd.); sc. (Scrapped); VL&M (Victoria Lumber & Manufacturing Co.); VLCo. (Victoria Lumber Co.).

[1] East Kootenay Logging, No.3 (Cranbrook); Polson Logging, No.3 (Hoquiam, WA); Rayonier Inc., No.3 (Hoquiam); display near Hoquiam. 24 tons.

[2] BS&W, No.1 (Myrtle Point); Great Central Sawmills, No.1 (Great Central); BS&W No. 1 (Great Central); MacMillan & Bloedel No. 1; G. E. Wellburn (1953) then to B.C. Forest Museum (Duncan). 42 tons.

[3] Weist Logging, No.1 (Port Alberni); Alberni Pacific, No.2 (Port Alberni); MacMillan & Bloedel, No.2 (Port Alberni); display Alberni, restored to operation by Alberni Valley Museum 1980s. 42 tons.

[4] Hillcrest Lbr., No.1 (Cowichan Valley); Export Lumber, No.1; Mayo Lumber (dealer); Osborn Bay Wharf Co. No.1 (Crofton); B.C. Forest Museum (rebuilt to 3-foot gauge for operation). 25 tons.

[5] Mayo Lumber, No.3 (Paldi); display Paldi then to B.C. Forest Museum (Duncan). First superheated Shay in B.C. 50 tons.

[6] Merrill & Ring Lumber, No.4 (Theodosia Arm); CL&R, No.15 (Headquarters & Ladysmith); Elk Falls Co., No.1 (Duncan Bay); National Mus. Science & Tech. (Ottawa). 50 tons.

[7] Merrill & Ring Lumber, No.2 (Squamish); CL&R, No.12 (Ladysmith); CL&R display (Ladysmith), 1962; Ladysmith Railway Historical Soc. 50 tons.

[8] Mayo Lumber, No.4 (Paldi); Lake Logging, No.5 (Honeymoon Bay), 1943; Western Forest Industries, No. 5 (Honeymoon Bay), 1946; Railway Appliance Research Ltd., No.114 (North Vancouver), 1964; Cass Scenic Railroad No.114 (Cass, West VA), 1970. Pacific Coast Shay. 90 tons.

[9] Merrill Ring Wilson, No.5 (Rock Bay); Mayo Lumber (d); Hillcrest Lbr., No.5 (Mesachie Lake), 1945; CFP, No. 11, later 115 (Englewood), 1953; Railway Appliance Research Ltd., No.115 (North Vancouver), 1962; Fort Steele Heritage Park, No.115 "Robert E. Swanson" (Fort Steele), 1970. Pacific Coast Shay. 90 tons.

[10] Shawnigan Lake Lbr., No.2 (Shawnigan Lake); Saltham Lbr.; Channel Logging, No.2, abandoned ca. 1930; salvaged G. Taylor, 1971; B.C. Prov. Museum (Museum Train) 1975-79; B.C. Forest Museum (Duncan) display. 23 tons.

[11] M.D.Olds, No.1 (Birch, MN); Alberta Lbr.; Canadian Robert Dollar Co.; Abernethy Lougheed, No.44 (Haney); Hillcrest Lbr., No.2 later 9 (Mesachie Lake); B.C. Forest Museum (Duncan), 1965. 50 tons.

[12] Hillcrest Lbr., No.3 later 10 (Mesachie Lake), retired 1968; excursions, then Victoria Pacific Ry, No.10 display (Victoria), 1971-72; stored; to Mount Rainier Scenic RR (Elbe, WA), 1980. 70 tons.

[13] Portland, Astoria & Pacific; Alberni Pacific, No.6 (Port Alberni), 1937; H. R. MacMillan Export Co. (VLCo/M&B), No.1055 (Chemainus) 1951; CFP, No.55 later 113 (Englewood/Woss), 1953-1976; display 1976-1988 then restored for operation. 135 tons.

[14] Northern Pacific, No. 56; Joseph Whitehead "Countess of Dufferin," 1887; CPR, No. 151, 1882; Columbia River Lbr. No. 1 (Golden), 1891; City of Winnipeg for display, 1910.

[15] Howe Sound Pemberton Valley & Northern, No.2 (Squamish); Howe Sound & Northern, No.2 (Squamish); Pacific Great Eastern, No. 2 (Squamish); CL&R, No. 7 (Headquarters/Ladysmith), 1920; display Squamish 1965.

[16] CL&R (Headquarters/Ladysmith); display Courtenay 1960.

[17] Snoqualmie Falls Lbr. No.6 (Snoqualmie, WA); CFP No.112 (Englewood/Woss); display Beaver Cove. 90 tons.

[18] Donovan Corkery Lbr. No. 4; CL&R No. 11 (Headquarters/Ladysmith), 1937; display Ladysmith 1962, Ladysmith Railway Museum, 1988. 72 tons.

[19] BS&W No. 4 (Bloedel); M&B No. 4 later 1066 (Bloedel/Chemainus); retired 1970; display Squamish 1978-1985; display Qualicum 1985.

[20] Campbell River Tbr., No.2 (Campbell River); Alberni Pacific Lbr., No.7 (Port Alberni); M&B No.1007 (leased to CL&R as No.18, 1959) later 1055; last operated 1971; to B.C. Government 1975, storage Chemainus and Ladysmith. 90 tons.

[21] Chas. R. McCormick Lbr.; CL&R No.16 (Headquarters/Ladysmith), 1944; retired 1960; to West Coast Railway Assoc. (Vancouver) 1964, leased to Alaska RR in 1967, and to Victoria Pacific Railway 1971-80.

[22] Vancouver Machinery Depot (VMD) (d); M. B. King Lbr./King-Farris Lbr., (Surrey/Newton, B.C.) No. 2, 1920-29; VMD (d); Canadian Sugar Factory Inc. (Raymond, Alta.) No. 9, 1933-58; John Poulsen, (Cranbrook, B.C.) 1958-71; Paul Fischer (Thorp, WA) 1971-1980; Monty Holm (Moses Lake, WA), 1980-present.

[23] Contractor's locomotive used San Francisco Seawall; Andrew Onderdonk contracts, CPR, 1881; Royal City Planing Mills (B.C. Mills, Timber & Trading) 1887 (various camps), retired 1927; display Hastings Park (Burnaby) 1931, to Heritage Village (Burnaby) 1973, at B.C. Prov. Museum (Victoria) 1986 on loan.

[24] Cathels & Sorensen No.1 (Port Renfrew); Renfrew Logging (Port Renfrew); Hemmingsen-Cameron Co. (Port Renfrew); Victoria Lumber & Manufacturing, No. 7 (Chemainus); Victoria Lbr. 7 later 1077 (Nanaimo Lakes); M&B 1077; to B.C. Government for Museum Train (1975-79), to Fort Steele Heritage Park (Cranbrook), 1989.

[25] Timberland Development No. 4 (Ladysmith); Victoria Lumber & Manufacturing, No. 4 (Chemainus); Victoria Lbr. 4 later 1044; M&B No. 1044; display Chemainus 1970. 67 tons.

[26] Alberni Pacific Lbr.; CL&R 107 (Crown Forest Industries); to Ladysmith Railway Historical Soc.

[27] J. H. Baxter Pole Co., near Port Clements, QCI, 1928-33; salvaged for restoration Port Clements Historical Society, 1988.

[28] R. B. McLean Lumber Co.; to Alberni Valley Museum. 14 tons.

[29] Merrill & Ring Lbr. Co (Squamish/Theodosia Arm); O'Brien Logging Co. (Stillwater); Powell River Co. No.7 (Kelley Logging) 1948; Western Forest Industries, No.7, 1956, in 1973 No. 40 (Honeymoon Bay); Westcan Terminals (Victoria) 1978; display Ladysmith Railway Museum, 1989. Rebuilt with 600 hp. Cummins diesel, 1948?

[30] U.S. Army No.7128; CL&R No.7128 (Ladysmith), 1960; Elk Falls Co./Crown Zellerbach (Duncan Bay), 1973; Ladysmith Railway Historical Soc. 1989. 120 tons.

[31] Canadian Pacific Railway No.8427; Crown Zellerbach Canada No. 8427, 1980; Crown Forest Industries No. 8427, 1983; donated to Ladysmith Railway Historical Soc. 1985.

REFERENCE NOTES

Prologue

1 Whitford and Craig, *Forests of British Columbia*, pp. 323-24.

2 *Ibid.*, pp. 1-2.

3 Douglas Cole and Bradley Lockner (eds.), *The Journals of George M. Dawson, 1875-1878*, p. 119.

4 See for example, Thomas A. Cox, *Mills and Markets. A History of the Pacific Coast Lumber Industry to 1900*.

5 Pacific Lumber Inspection Bureau, *Grading Rules and Basic Schedule of Douglas Fir, Pacific Hemlock, Sitka Spruce and Western Red Cedar Lumber for Export Shipment*. (Adopted by West Coast Lumbermen's Association and British Columbia Lumber and Shingle Manufacturers Ltd.) 1929, p. 8.

6 *Ibid.*, p. 31.

7 *Ibid.*, p. 25.

8 *Ibid.*, p. 23.

9 Hosie, *Native Trees of Canada*, p. 44.

10 *Ibid.*, p. 52.

11 *Ibid.*, p. 66.

12 "Life on a Logging Railroad," *The Timberman*, October 1944, pp. 52-53.

Chapter 1
The First Logging
Lines in B.C.

1 MacLachlan, *The Esquimalt & Nanaimo Railway, The Dunsmuir Years: 1884-1905*, p. 95.

2 Turner, *Vancouver Island Railroads*, Chapter 1.

3 Flynn, *Early Lumbering on Burrard Inlet*, pp. 41-43.

4 Claude Harvie, quoted in Darryl White ms. *Old Curly*, Heritage Park, Burnaby, from notes by Major Matthews, Vancouver City Archives.

5 J. S. Matthews papers, VCA "Memorandum of conservation with Mr. Percy Des Brisay, April 18, 1934."

6 Gerry Wellburn, notes on early logging railroads, RBCM and Lang, *Along the Way...*, pp. 17-19, which is the story of the Harvie family.

7 Darryl White, *Old Curly* ms. and Lavallée, *Canadian Pacific Steam Locomotives*, pp. 374-75.

8 Golden & District Historical Society, *Kinbasket Country*, pp. 25-29.

9 Lavallée, *Canadian Pacific Steam Locomotives*, pp. 367-68.

10 The machine, with a different boiler, is preserved at the British Columbia Forest Museum at Duncan. It was salvaged by Gerry Wellburn from the scrap heap at Chemainus.

11 "The Lumber Industry," *Victoria Daily Colonist*, January 2, 1899, p. 7.

12 Hardwick, "Geography of the Forest Industry of Coastal British Columbia," p. 50.

13 Gerry Wellburn notes, citing a Victoria Lumber Co. document seen in October 1945 but later missing.

14 Based on a roster compiled by W. H. Olsen, June 18, 1975; general locomotive roster information in Koch, *The Shay Locomotive*, and in Taber and Casler, *Climax—An Unusual Locomotive*; and Hearn and Wilkie, *The Cordwood Limited*, p. 35.

15 "Logging Methods in British Columbia," *The Canada Lumberman*, November 1902, pp. 8-9. The description of the locomotives notes the company having one Climax, one Shay and one Consolidation. However, builders lists suggest that the company may have had other equipment at that time. The Consolidation is presumably the former Pennsylvania Railroad 2-8-0 (No. 248) used at Chemainus. VL&M's smaller Climax is described in Taber and Casler as 35-ton and a 50-ton Climax is also noted as being on the roster at this time. W. H. Olsen also noted this second Climax in a company roster, photocopy, RBCM.

16 See Robert Griffin, *The Shawnigan Lake Lumber Co.*

17 Gerry Wellburn recorded the story of "Dudley" in "Walking Dudley... Shawnigan Lake's First Locie," in *Harmac News*, 2(3): pp. 14-15, in 1948. The article was based on interviews and research he carried out during the mid-1940s. The notes are now in the Wellburn Collection, RBCM.

18 *Ibid.*

19 Quoted in Robert Griffin, *The Shawnigan Lake Lumber Company*, p. 38.

20 This quote and the following description are from Gerry Wellburn's "Betsy... Hauling Logs at Shawnigan Lake in 1902," *Harmac News*, August 1947, pp. 8-9. Gerry's first sight of "Betsy" was recounted to RDT in an interview in 1988.

21 *Ibid.*

22 Canadian Willamette Company, *Willamette Logging Engines* (Catalog), Vancouver, B.C. ca. 1915.

23 E. S. Pretious, P.Eng., "The 'Walking Dudley,'" Industrial Age, 3(3): pp. 5-8. (Originally published in *The British Columbia Professional Engineer*, December, 1979.) Further details of this operation are provided in the photo caption notes by Major Matthews at the Vancouver City Archives.

24 *Op cit.*

25 Labbe and Goe, *Railroads in the Woods*, pp. 114-18; Koch, *Steam and Thunder in the Timber*, pp. 80-81; and John Labbe, "The Cable Locomotive," *Timberbeast*, Fall/Winter, 1985, pp. 6-9.

26 Turner, *West of the Great Divide*, Chapter 2.

27 Mercer, *Growth of Ghost Towns*, prepared for the Royal Commission on Forestry, provides an overview of the development of the forest industry in the East Kootenays. The discussion of logging railroad locations in 1908 is based on an untitled ca. 1908 directory of the Pacific Coast forest industry (photocopy, RBCM). Further expansion of the logging railroads is developed from: Green, *British Columbia Industrial Locomotives*; Ramsey, *PGE, Railway to the North*, pp. 60-65; Turner, *Vancouver Island Railroads*, Chapter 5; and "The British Columbia Logger in his Shirt," (originally published in *Man to Man* magazine in 1910, describing logging in the Squamish-Cheakamus area), *Whistle Punk*, Vol. 1, No. 2, pp. 16-23.

28 Gibbons, *Logging in the Douglas Fir Region*, pp. 60-74, 114-30.

29 Patrick Hind, "Incline railways tug tall timbers," *The Citizen*, May 31, 1989.

30 The major equipment suppliers including Washington Iron Works produced special engines for this type of operation. See *Washington Iron Works Catalog No. 20*, pp. 52-58.

31 Articles in the trade press include: H. G. Cowling, "Logging Inclines," *The Timberman*, August 1926, pp. 37-40; S. A. Stamm, "Incline vs. Long, Circuitous Railroad Spurs," *The Timberman*, September 1927, pp. 44, 62; and Russell Mills, "Use and Abuse of Logging Railroad Inclines," *The Timberman*, November 1930, pp. 52, 55.

32 See Turner, *Vancouver Island Railroads*, Chapter 1 and White and Wilkie, *Shays on the Switchbacks*.

33 Robert E. Swanson, interview with RDT November 10, 1989; White and Wilkie, *ibid.*; and Green, *British Columbia Industrial Locomotives, An All-Time Listing, Including Short Lines*.

34 Department of Railways, *Annual Report*, 1923 and 1924, Appendix D.

35 Robert E. Swanson, interview with RDT November 10, 1989. Bob Swanson remembered the narrow gauge operations in the Nanaimo area from some of his first work in the woods as a young man.

36 Based on: Burrows, *Railway Mileposts: British Columbia, Volume II*; an undated but ca. 1908 directory of the Pacific Coast forest industry (photocopy, RBCM); and Department of Railways, *Annual Reports*, 1917-1924 and trade directories.

37 Compiled from Department of Railways, *Annual Report*, 1918, p. R 15.

38 Department of Railways, *Annual Report*, 1924, Appendix D. See also, The Timberman, *Directory of the Lumber Industry Pacific Coast*, 1924, Portland, OR, for further details. The listings in these two sources differ slightly in the number of operations noted and often provide complementary information. The Department of Railways, as the government regulatory body, is probably the most accurate and up to date.

39 See Turner, *The Pacific Princesses*; Hacking and Lamb, *The Princess Story*; and Rushton, *Whistle Up the Inlet*. The Canadian National took over the steamship operations of the Grand Trunk Pacific in 1923.

40 Jim Wolverton, interview with RDT November 8, 1978 (PABC 3356).

41 Jack Payne, interview with RDT, September 21, 1988.

42 Gerry Wellburn, interview with RDT 1988.

Chapter 2
Steam in the Woods

1 See Koch, *The Shay Locomotive* and Ranger, *Pacific Coast Shay* for more details on the development of these machines.

2 See Ranger. 1965. *Pacific Coast Shay*; "Specifications of New Pacific Coast Shay," *The Timberman*, March, 1928, pp. 146, 148; "B.C. Secures First New Type Locomotive," *British Columbia Lumberman*, January 1928, p. 70; and "New Design Pacific Coast Shay Logging Locomotive" *British Columbia Lumberman* (Special Annual Logging Number), April 1928, pp. 102, 104.

3 Turner, "Logging Railroads and Locomotives in British Columbia: A Background Summary and the Preservation Record," *Material History Bulletin*, No. 13, pp. 3-20.

4 Ranger, *Pacific Coast Shay*, pp. 104-06.

5 Pete McGovern, interview with RDT September 20, 1988.

6 George Robertson, interview with RDT and Bob Griffin, 1980.

7 Taber and Casler, *Climax — An Unusual Steam Locomotive* and *The Climax Patent Geared Locomotives (Catalogue "L")*, Climax Manufacturing Company, 1924. Roster information also came from Department of Railways files (e.g., DR77 for Climax 214 on p. 64) and Green, *British Columbia Industrial Locomotives*.

8 Anon, *The Heisler Locomotive; Why you can haul at least 30% more per ton of locomotive with the modern Heisler*, Heisler Locomotive Works (undated but ca. 1925); and *Heisler Geared locomotives (Descriptive Folder 7090)*, Heisler Locomotive Works, ca. 1928.

9 "Getting Three Train Loads of Logs a Day, Instead of Two, Thirty Cars Each," *West Coast Lumberman*, June, 1924, p. 50.

10 Pete McGovern, interview with RDT, September 20, 1988.

11 For descriptions see "Heisler Introduces Three New 'West Coast Special' Locomotives," *West Coast Lumberman*, July 1, 1928, pp. 58-59; "The New 'West Coast Special'" *The Timberman*, July 1928, pp. 62-63; and "Specifications of New West Coast Heislers," *The Timberman*, July 1928, pp. 146, 148, 150.

12 Anon, *The Heisler Locomotive*.

13 Hauff and Gertz, *The Willamette Locomotive*.

14 The locomotive is noted in Koch, *Steam & Thunder in the Timber*, pp. 45, 50, as being built in 1920. Koch described the machine as "... a rather crude two-cylinder geared locomotive, a frank and outright copy that avoided infringing on any existing Lima patents and was delivered to a British Columbia Logging Company." In a reprint of *Washington Iron Works Catalog No. 20* by Northwest Shortline in Seattle, a reproduction of a microfilmed drawing of a two-truck locomotive is included as a supplement. In the notes it states that this particular locomotive, "apparently was never built."

15 George Robertson, interview with RDT and Bob Griffin, 1980.

16 Gibbons, *Logging in the Douglas Fir Region*, pp. 204-07.

17 Beauter, A. J. "Advantages of Rod Locomotives in Logging Service," *The Timberman*, November 1926, p. 70.

18 Kittle, G. Bruce, "Tractive Power of

Geared Engines," *The Timberman*, November 1926, pp. 68-69.

19 Freydig, Paul E. "Co-ordinating Geared and Rod Engine Service," *The Timberman*, November 1926, p. 70.

20 George Robertson, interview with RDT and Bob Griffin, 1980.

21 Pete McGovern, interview with RDT, September 20, 1988.

22 George Robertson, interview with RDT and Bob Griffin, 1980.

23 Compiled from Railways Department, *Annual Report*, 1924.

24 Pete McGovern, interview with RDT, September 20, 1988.

25 *Ibid.*

26 Richard V. James, interview with RDT, January 1989.

27 Tom Coates, interview with RDT and Bob Griffin, April 10, 1980. Bob Swanson provided details of maintenance pp. 83 and 85 on Nov. 10, 1989 in an interview with RDT.

28 Department of Railways, *Annual Report*, particularly 1925. The letter is from Railways Department Correspondence, BCARS, Box 8/20.

29 Tom Coates, interview with RDT and Bob Griffin, April 10, 1980.

30 See, for example, "Speeders Don't Speed," *Harmac News*, July 1948, p. 7 and Edna Slater, "Where have speeders gone?", *The Lake News*, April 16, 1986, p. 9. Bob Swanson in an interview with RDT Nov. 10, 1989 and in other conversations provided many details helpful to this discussion and the description of speeder development on page 92.

31 "Improved Speeders," *The Timberman*, July 1938, p. 77.

32 "Loggers' Railcar Has Many New Features," *British Columbia Lumberman*, April 1939, p. 84.

33 Railway Department, *Annual Report*, 1945, p. 8.

34 Railway Department, *Annual Reports*, 1946, p. LL8; 1947, p. BB9; 1948. For a detailed example see L. A. Rounding, "Rail Car Innovations at Franklin River," *British Columbia Lumberman*, June 1948, pp. 148, 150 and 152.

35 See Railways Branch, Department of Commercial Transport, Part IV, *Railway Safety-Appliance Standards*. Rules and Regulations Made Pursuant to the *Railway Act*, Chapter 285, R.S.B.C.

1948 as approved by *Order In Council* No. 2886, December 17, 1959.

36 George Geddes, "Travelling Fire Hall, Modern Fire Speeder Built in A.P.L. Shops," *Harmac News*, September 1948, p. 13, and "New Rail Speeder Adds Fire Fighting Power," *British Columbia Lumberman*, September 1948, p. 130.

37 "Modern Speeders," *The Timberman*, June 1937, p. 119.

38 Department of Railways, *Annual Report*, 1924.

39 Fred Hall, "Cedar Pole Making and Handling in 1929," *The Charlottes*, Vol. 1, pp. 19-20.

40 "New Gasoline Locomotive," *The Timberman*, April 1917, p. 54. I am indebted to the research by Richard Rajala on logging technology for the B.C. Provincial Museum (now RBCM) for references to several obscure pieces of equipment and developments.

41 "Gasoline Locomotives," *The Timberman*, September 1920, p. 46.

42 "Gas Logging Locomotives," *The Timberman*, July 1926, p. 237.

43 "Gasoline Logging Loco Does Heavy Work," *British Columbia Lumberman*, April 1925, p. 98.

44 *British Columbia Lumberman*, February 1924, p. 53.

45 On its seventieth anniversary in 1944, the company published an expanded catalogue including details of corporate history titled *Westminster Iron Works, Steel Products*. The catalogue illustrates a range of small locomotives some of which are specifically noted as having been built in New Westminster while others are not. It is not known how many logging locomotives the company produced.

46 The Alberni Valley Museum also preserved MacMillan & Bloedel two-truck Shay No. 2, which it maintains in operating condition, and a donkey engine from the McLean Lumber Company.

Chapter 3
Rolling Stock, Camps, Trestles and Skidders

1 From an interview with Jim Wolverton by RDT quoted in *Railroaders. Recollections from the Steam Era in British Columbia*, pp. 70-72.

2 The story of the life of Chief Charlie Jones is told in Bosustow, 1981, *Queesto, Pacheenaht Chief by Birthright*.

3 George Robertson, interview with RDT and Bob Griffin, 1980. See also *Queesto, Pacheenaht Chief by Birthright*, the autobiography of Chief Charles Jones written with Stephen Bosustow.

4 Robert J. Filberg, "Yarding and Loading," *The Timberman*, November 1932, p. 32.

5 Department of Railways, *Annual Report*, 1925.

6 Wellburn Collection, RBCM.

7 "V.E.W. Specialise in Heavy Logging Cars," *British Columbia Lumberman*, March 1929, p. 80.

8 "E&N Has Built 200 Log Cars at Russels," *Canadian Railway & Marine World*, June 1931, p. 368, and also July 1931, p. 443.

9 From a directory of the Pacific Coast forest industry, ca. 1908 (title and publisher uncertain; photocopy, RBCM).

10 Department of Railways, *Annual Report*, 1924.

11 Preserved in the collection of the Ladysmith Railway Historical Society.

12 George Robertson, interview with RDT and Bob Griffin, 1980.

13 Tom Coates, interview with RDT and Bob Griffin, April 10, 1980.

14 "Fire Fighting by Rail," *Harmac News*, August 1947, pp. 2-3.

15 *Ibid.*

16 The discussion of the Bear Creek Bridge is based on: "Malahat's Spectacular Railroad," *West Coast Lumberman*, October 1939, p. 53; A. K. G. Blakeney, "A Unique Railway Logging Bridge," *British Columbia Lumberman*, August 1940, pp. 53, 56; original plans and photos of the bridge provided by Eric Bernard; and visits to the site by RDT.

17 Gibbon, *Logging in the Douglas Fir Region*, pp. 226-39.

18 *Ibid.*, p. 230.

19 *Ibid.*, pp. 227-29.

20 *Ibid.*, pp. 232-33.

21 *Ibid.*, p. 233.

22 *Ibid.*, pp. 235-36.

23 Gibbons, *Logging in the Douglas Fir Region*, pp. 13-15.

24 Tom Coates, interview with RDT and Bob Griffin, April 10, 1980.

25 "Camp Cars De Luxe for B.C. Operation," *The Timberman*, May 1918, p. 39.

26 Tom Coates interview with RDT and Bob Griffin, April 10, 1980.

27 *Ibid.*

28 Gerald E. Wellburn, *Catalogue Information on Major Artifacts at the British Columbia Forest Museum*, sections C1-C4.

29 Canadian Willamette Company, Ltd., *Willamette Logging Engines* (Catalogue), ca. 1915.

30 "Yarding and Loading," by R. J. Filberg, *The Timberman*, November 1932, p. 32.

31 Gibbons, *Logging in the Douglas Fir Region*, p. 57 and Brown, *Logging*, pp. 192-93.

32 *Op cit.*, p. 194. See also Bill Roy, "The Evolution of the Donkey Engine," *Timberbeast*, Spring 1986, pp. 8-18.

33 Brown, *Logging*, p. 194. Logging equipment catalogues, such as those published by Willamette Iron and Steel Works, include detailed descriptions and diagrams of many loading and yarding systems.

34 See Brown, *Logging*, pp. 210-26.

35 Gibbons, *Logging in the Douglas Fir Region*, p. 127.

36 *Ibid.*, p. 127. See also "Lidgerwood Tower Skidder of the Early 1920's," *Tall Timber—Short Lines*, Winter 1988, pp. 18-21. A large Willamette tower skidder is preserved at Camp 6 in Tacoma, WA.

37 Tom Coates, interview with RDT and Bob Griffin, April 10, 1980.

38 R. J. Filberg, "Yarding and Loading," *The Timberman*, November 1932, p. 32.

Chapter 4
Depression,
Heyday and Decline

1 Gerry Wellburn, conversation with RDT and Peter Corley-Smith, June 21, 1989.

2 Gordon Robertson, interview with RDT and Bob Griffin, 1980. See also, Patrick O. Hind, *Point No Point and its Railway*.

3 Jack Payne, interview with RDT, September 21, 1988.

4 B. A. Carson, interview with RDT, January 16, 1978 (PABC 3355).

5 Jack Payne, interview with RDT, September 21, 1988.

6 Statistics compiled from Department of Railways, *Annual Report*, 1932.

7 Department of Railways, *Annual Report*, 1929.

8 Forest Branch, *Annual Report*, 1932, p. T19 and 1928, p. B19.

9 Department of Railways, *Annual Report*, 1938.

10 cf. "Logging Trailer Builders Have Kept Pace with Rapid Growth of Truck Logging," *West Coast Lumberman*, October 1940, p. 48; "Use of Private Roads Growing," *West Coast Lumberman*, April 1941, p. 37; E. F. Rapraegar, "How Motor Trucks are used in Douglas Fir Logging," *Timberperson*, Fall, 1983, pp. 16-19, (originally published in *Journal of Forestry* Vol. 33, No. 1, Jan. 1934); and Patrick O. Hind, "Caterpillar Logging in British Columbia," *Tall Timber—Short Lines*, Nov.-Dec. 1984, pp. 14-15.

11 "Some Results of 1939 Log Truck Movement," *West Coast Lumberman*, March, 1940, pp. 30, 32 and "Survey of Western Log Transportation in 1940 by Truck," *West Coast Lumberman*, April 1941, pp. 16, 18, and 21.

12 "Logging Trucks as Railroad Feeders," *West Coast Lumberman*, April 1939, pp. 12, 13, 76.

13 "Comox Expanding its Ladysmith Operations," *West Coast Lumberman*, August 1943, pp. 28, 31, 32 and 88 and "Comox Now Using Trucks in Headquarters Operation," *West Coast Lumberman*, December 1943, p. 40.

14 "Comox Expanding its Ladysmith Operations," *West Coast Lumberman*, August 1943, p. 28.

15 "Comox Now Using Trucks in Headquarters Operation," *West Coast Lumberman*, December 1943, p. 40.

16 Department of Railways, *Annual Reports*, 1939-1945.

17 "New Joint Railroad Taps Vast Timber Area," *West Coast Lumberman*, November 1943, pp. 16, 18, 20 and 96.

18 *Ibid.* For details of the corporate changes involving VL&M during this period, including its sale by the Humbird interests and eventual acquisition by H. R. MacMillan, see MacKay, *Empire of Wood*, pp. 150-157.

19 Turner, *Vancouver Island Railroads*, Chapter 1.

20 *Op cit.*

21 "Railroad Logging Survives on the Island," *The Truck Logger*, November 1959, p. 16.

22 *Ibid.*

23 This description is based on "New Unloader Set-up. The Realization of a Tidewater Rail and Truck Logger's Dream," *West Coast Lumberman*, June 1945, pp. 50-60, and numerous visits to the site between 1960 and 1989 by RDT. Detailed scale drawings by Chuck Yungkurth, based on measurements by RDT, further photos and information on the "Humdurgin" appear in Turner, "Pacific Coast Logging: Comox Log Unloader," *Railroad Model Craftsman*, January 1988, pp. 88-93.

24 Railway Department, *Annual Report*, 1958, p. 11.

25 After the end of service on the logging line, the tower was moved to the yards at Ladysmith by the Ladysmith Railroad Historical Society. Plans, based on measurements and photos by RDT, appear in "Building a Frame Interlocking Tower," by Julian Cavalier in *Railroad Model Craftsman*, August 1986, pp. 80-85.

26 Minister of Mines, *Annual Report*, 1944, pp. A115-16.

27 Quoted in "Building 25-mile Logging Railroad," *West Coast Lumberman*, March 1943, p. 54.

28 Pete McGovern, interview with RDT, September 20, 1988.

29 R. S. Perry, "War Restores Sitka Spruce to Prominence," *British Columbia Lumberman*, 1941, p. 54-55.

30 "Large Railroad Operation," *West Coast Lumberman*, July 1937, p. 58.

31 *Ibid.*

32 "4,350,000 Ft. of Logs in Single Tow," *British Columbia Lumberman*, July 1941, p. 63. Further use of Davis rafts is described by Patrick O. Hind, "Davis Log Rafts of Vancouver Is.," *Tall Timber—Short Lines*, Jan.-Feb. 1986, pp. 10-13.

33 The story of the logging railway at Aero Camp is based on Turner, "Logging in the Queen Charlottes," *Pacific News*, January 1973, 13(1) pp. 2-7. Additional sources included Department of Commercial Transport files on "Scrapped locomotives" made available to RDT in 1972, Department of Railways *Annual Reports*, interviews in 1971 with Stan Unsworth and Mr. and Mrs. Sonny Toleman, and two visits to the site in

1970 and 1971 by RDT. D. S. Richter contributed locomotive data for the roster. See also Powell River Products *Triangle* 4(9) p. 4 and *British Columbia Lumberman*, June 1942, and September 1945, pp. 4 and 35.

34 Gerry Wellburn, 1988, personal communication.

35 See Wentz, *Bringing Out the Big Ones*, and Brown, *Logging*, pp. 295-328.

36 Hardwick, Walter G. "Geography of the Forest Industry of Coastal British Columbia," p. 56.

37 "Life on a Logging Railroad," *The Timberman*, October 1944, pp. 52-53.

38 *Ibid.*, p. 53.

39 See also Turner, *Vancouver Island Railroads*, Chapters 2 and 4 and Turner, *West of the Great Divide*, pp. 221-29. For background on the development of the E&N in the Cowichan Valley see Darryl Muralt "Cowichan Lumber Boom," *Whistle Punk*, Spring 1984, pp. 3-9. Subsequent articles in *Whistle Punk* detail the history of several logging operations: Fall 1984, pp. 9-23; Summer 1985, pp. 13-20; Spring 1986, pp. 22-29.

40 Railway Department, *Annual Report*, 1945, p. 8.

41 Compiled from Railway Department, *Annual Report*, 1955.

42 Based on, Railway Department, *Annual Report*, 1958, and abandonment dates for the individual lines.

43 "Railroad Logging Gives Way to Trucks," *The Timberman*, November 1953, p. 98; Hauff and Gertz, *The Willamette Locomotive*, pp. 154-55; and Railway Department, *Annual Reports*.

44 *Ibid.*, and "Trucks Oust Railroad at Gordon River Operation," *The Truck Logger*, June 1953, p. 32.

45 Hauff and Gertz, *The Willamette Locomotive*, pp. 154-55.

46 Robert E. Swanson, personal communication, and see also Koch, *The Shay Locomotive*, pp. 124-34.

47 Turner, "Logging on the Queen Charlottes," *Pacific News*, January 1973, 13(1) pp. 3-7, and Railway Department, *Annual Report*, 1955, p. 26.

48 Last noted in Railway Department, *Annual Report*, 1949, p. JJ19, and 1952, p. II17. See also Harding and Duncan, *Sayward for Kelsey Bay*, pp. 76-77. The last logs hauled from Headquarters by CL&R were moved on December 24, 1953. See *B.C. Lumberman*, January

1954, p. 14. Comox Logging roster (p. 207) compiled primarily from: Anon, *The Heisler Locomotive*; Comox Logging & Railway Co., "Data on Steam Locomotives," D. Cummings, "Comox Logging & Railway Company," *The Steam Chest*, August 1962, pp. 1-8, 1, 2; Green, *British Columbia Industrial Locomotives*; Koch, *The Shay Locomotive*; and Railway Department files.

49 "Rail to Rubber," *Harmac News*, December 1952, p. 11.

50 "The Age of Steam in the Chemainus Forest Industry," notes by W. H. Olsen. Wellburn Collection, RBCM.

51 "The Iron Horse Retires," *Harmac News*, October 1953.

52 B. A. Carson, interview with RDT January 16, 1979 (PABC 3355).

53 *Ibid.*

54 "Sic Transit Gloria, M&B Retires its Last Locie," *British Columbia Lumberman*, July 1957, pp. 22-23, 100 and Gerry Wellburn, personal communication, 1987.

55 "It's 'Last of Locies' for M.& B. as Truck Logging Takes Over," *The Truck Logger*, June, 1957, pp. 11, 12.

56 *Ibid.* Alberni Inlet is often called the Alberni Canal.

57 "Trucks: Changeover," *The Truck Logger*, October 1956, p. 12.

Chapter 5
Steam's Finale

1 Detailed plans and photos of this locomotive were published in Turner, "Pacific Coast Logging: Cathels & Sorensen's Prairie," *Railroad Model Craftsman*, 52(9): pp. 87-90.

2 B. C. Carson, interview with RDT, January 16, 1979 (PABC 3355).

3 Pete McGovern, interview with RDT, September 20, 1988.

4 B. A. Carson, interview with RDT, January 16, 1979 (PABC 3355).

5 Details of acquisitions for the British Columbia Forest Museum are based on the Museum's catalogue records and conversations with Gerry Wellburn.

6 The Stone Wing opened in 1989.

7 Ken Perry, "Western Forest Industries Ceases Vancouver Island Rail Operation," *Pacific News*, August 1978, 18(8): p. 5.

8 See Koch, *The Shay Locomotive* and *Steam and Thunder in the Timber*.

Chapter 6
The Diesel Years

1 Railway Department, *Annual Report*, 1948, p. GG8.

2 Railway Department, *Annual Reports*, 1946-1949.

3 Ranger, *Pacific Coast Shay*, pp. 104-07.

4 Turner, *West of the Great Divide*, pp. 246-50 and Hanna and Dean, *Canadian Pacific Diesel Locomotives*, pp. 20-25.

5 T. F. Daily, *Report on the Demonstration and Test of a Standard 1200 H.P. General Motors Diesel-Electric Locomotive in Logging Railway Service*, October, 1951, General Motors Diesel Limited, Toronto, Ont.

6 Based on price quotations and specifications from Baldwin to BS&W and "Summary of Cost on Locomotive No. 6" in the Wellburn Collection, RBCM.

7 Fletcher Challenge Canada Limited, *1988 Annual Report*, pp. 4-8.

8 Canadian Forest Products Ltd., *The Englewood Logging Division*. (A booklet prepared for the opening ceremonies, June 12, 1957 from the Wellburn Collection, RBCM.) See also Railway Department, *Annual Reports*, 1954-1957 and *Canadian Forest Products*, British Columbia Railway Historical Association, (Bulletin No. 2), June 1960. Alan Kollman related details of No. 300 (p. 287) to RDT, 1990.

9 "Tyee Machinery Turns Out Railway Unit for Englewood," *British Columbia Lumberman*, August 1951, p. 140.

10 Railway Department, *Annual Report*, 1950, p. LL10.

11 Railway Department, *Annual Report*, 1956, p. HH16.

ᗷIBLIOGRAPHY

NOTE: The references included in the Bibliography are major published sources and related titles. Individual articles and other shorter works are cited fully in the footnotes for each chapter. Additional archival sources include the papers of the British Columbia Department of Railways, now held at the BCARS. These papers include correspondence of the Department's inspectors with the logging railway operators regarding the inspection and maintenance of equipment. Other holdings include the MacMillan Bloedel collection at Special Collections of the University of British Columbia Library, Vancouver, and the Wellburn Collection at the Royal British Columbia Museum, Victoria. In addition, the Royal British Columbia Museum has an extensive collection of industrial catalogues incorporating material from logging suppliers.

The logging and lumbering trade journals and magazines, particularly *The Timberman, The Truck Logger,* the *British Columbia Lumberman,* the *West Coast Lumberman, Harmac News,* and related journals such as *Canadian Railway & Marine World,* were consulted extensively. Trade and business directories including the *Directory of the Lumber Industry Pacific Coast,* published by *The Timberman,* the *Statistical Review and Directory of the Western Timber Industries,* published by the *West Coast Lumberman* and *The 'ABC' British Columbia Lumber Trade Directory and Year Book,* and the *British Columbia Directory* from various years were used throughout. I have also referred to the extensive rosters of locomotives and builders lists prepared by the Railway and Locomotive Historical Society. In addition, valuable information is contained in model building and historical magazines which often focus on logging railroads. Specific citations are included in the footnotes. In the footnotes, references to the author (other than in publications) are cited as RDT.

Adams, Kramer. 1961. *Logging Railroads of the West.* Bonanza Books, New York, NY.

Anon. ca. 1931. *Lumbermen's Atlas of British Columbia.* Gordon Black Publications Ltd., Vancouver, B.C.

Anon. 1982. *The Heisler Locomotive 1891-1941.* Benjamin F. Fline, Jr., Lancaster, PA.

Baptie, Sue. 1975. *First Growth. The Story of British Columbia Forest Products Limited.* British Columbia Forest Products Limited, J.J. Douglas, Ltd., Vancouver, B.C.

Bergen, Myrtle. 1979. *Tough Timber. The Loggers of British Columbia.* Elgin Publications, Vancouver, B.C.

Bohn, Dave and Rodolfo Petschek. 1984. *Kinsey Photographer. A Half Century of Negatives by Darius and Tabitha May Kinsey.* Volume Three. *The Locomotive Portraits.* Chronicle Books, San Francisco, CA.

Bradley, R. Ken. 1982. *Historic Railways of the Powell River Area.* The British Columbia Railway Historical Association, Victoria, B.C.

British Columbia Railway Historical Association. 1960. *Canadian Forest Products Limited. Nimpkish Valley Railway.* B.C.R.H.A. Bulletin No. 2, June 1960.

Brown, Nelson G. 1949. *Logging, the Principles and Methods of Harvesting Timber in the United States and Canada.* John Wiley & Sons, New York, NY.

Burrows, Roger G. 1984. *Railway Mileposts (Volume II): British Columbia. The Southern Routes from the Crowsnest to the Coquihalla.* Railway Milepost Books, Vancouver, B.C.

Carranco, Lynwood. 1982. *Redwood Lumber Industry.* Golden West Books, San Marino, CA.

Casselman, Verdun. 1988. *Ties to Water. The History of Bull River in the East Kootenay.* Published by the Author, Fort Steele, B.C.

Chambers, Edith D. 1973. *History of Port Coquitlam.* Web Press, Burnaby, B.C.

Cole, Douglas and Bradley Lockner (eds.)

1989. *The Journals of George M. Dawson: British Columbia, 1875-1878.* Vol. 1, 1875-1876. University of British Columbia Press, Vancouver, B.C.

Cox, Thomas R. 1974. *Mills and Markets. A History of the Pacific Coast Lumber Industry to 1900.* University of Washington Press, Seattle, WA.

Dean, Murray W. and David B. Hanna. 1981. *Canadian Pacific Diesel Locomotives.* Fitzhenry & Whiteside, Don Mills, Ont.

Drushka, Ken. 1985. *Stumped. The Forest Industry in Transition.* Douglas & McIntyre, Vancouver, B.C.

Esquimalt & Nanaimo Railway. ca. 1922. *Timber Lands and the Lumber Industry in the Esquimalt & Nanaimo Railway Company's Land Grant.* Land Department, Victoria, B.C.

Flynn, James E. 1942. *Early Lumbering on Burrard Inlet, 1862-1891.* Unpublished BASc Thesis in Forest Engineering, University of British Columbia, Vancouver, B.C.

Gibbons, William H. 1918. *Logging in the Douglas Fir Region.* Bulletin 711, United States Department of Agriculture, Washington, D.C.

Gold, Wilmer. 1985. *Logging as it Was.* Morriss Publishing Co., Victoria, B.C.

Golden & District Historical Society. 1972. *Kinbasket Country. The Story of Golden and the Columbia Valley.* Golden & District Historical Society, Golden, B.C.

Gould, Ed. 1975. *Logging; British Columbia's Logging History.* Hancock House Publishers, Saanichton, B.C.

Green, Mervyn T. 1986. *British Columbia Industrial Locomotives. An All-Time Listing, Including Short Lines.* Published by the Author, Richmond, B.C. Also second edition, 1987.

Griffin, Robert G. 1979. *The Shawnigan Lake Lumber Company.* Unpublished M.A. Thesis, University of Victoria, Victoria, B.C.

Hacking, Norman R. and W. Kaye Lamb. 1974. *The Princess Story. A Century of West Coast Shipping.* Mitchell Press, Ltd., Vancouver, B.C.

Harding, Rene and Frances Duncan. 1979. *Sayward for Kelsey Bay.* Published by the Authors, Sayward, B.C.

Hardwick, Walter G. 1963. "Geography of the Forest Industry of Coastal British Columbia," *Occasional Papers in Geography,* No. 5, Canadian Association of Geographers, B.C. Division, Vancouver, B.C.

Hauff, Steve and Jim Gertz. 1977. *The Willamette Locomotive.* Binfort and Mort, Portland, OR.

Hearn, George and David Wilkie. 1966. *The Cordwood Limited. A History of the Victoria & Sidney Railway.* British Columbia Railway Historical Association, Victoria, B.C.

Hind, Patrick O. 1984. *Pacific Great Eastern Steam Locomotives.* British Columbia Railway Historical Association, Victoria, B.C.

———. 1984. *Point No Point and its Railway.* Published by the Author, Victoria, B.C.

Hosie, R. C. 1975. *Native Trees of Canada.* Canadian Forestry Service, Department of the Environment, Ottawa, Ont.

Jones, Chief Charles, with Stephen Bosustow. 1981. *Queesto. Pacheenaht Chief by Birthright.* Theytus Books, Nanaimo, B.C.

Koch, Michael. 1971. *The Shay Locomotive. Titan of the Timber.* World Press, Denver, CO.

———. 1980. *Steam and Thunder in the Timber. The Saga of the Forest Railroads.* World Press, Denver, CO.

Krajina, V. J., K. Klinka and J. Worrall. 1982. *Distribution and Ecological Characteristics of Trees and Shrubs of British Columbia.* Faculty of Forestry, University of British Columbia, Vancouver, B.C.

Labbe, John and Vernon Goe. 1961. *Railroads in the Woods.* Howell-North Books, Berkeley, CA.

Lamb, W. Kaye. 1938. "Early Lumbering on Vancouver Island, 1844-1855," *British Columbia Historical Quarterly,* Vol. 2, No. 1, pp. 33-53; Vol. 2, No. 2, pp. 95-121.

———. 1977. *History of the Canadian Pacific Railway.* Collier Macmillan Publishing Co., New York, NY.

Lang, Margaret. 1967. *Along the Way.... An Historical Account of Pioneering White Rock and Surrounding District in British Columbia.* Published by the Author, White Rock, B.C.

Lavallée, Omer. 1985. *Canadian Pacific Steam Locomotives.* Railfare, Montreal, P.Q.

Le Masenna, Robert. 1979. *Articulated Locomotives of North America.* Sundance Publications, Silverton, CO.

Lewis, John E. 1980. *Reservation Narrow Gauge. A Chronicle of Biles-Coleman Lumber Company's Narrow Gauge Omak Creek Railroad (Bow & Arrow Short Line).* Published by the Author, York, PA.

MacKay, Donald. 1978. *The Lumberjacks.* McGraw-Hill Ryerson, Toronto, Ont.

———. 1982. *Empire of Wood. The MacMillan Bloedel Story.* Douglas & McIntyre, Vancouver, B.C.

MacLachlan, Donald F. 1986. *The Esquimalt & Nanaimo Railway. The Dunsmuir Years: 1884-1905.* British Columbia Railway Historical Association, Victoria, B.C.

McComb, Arnold M. and Wilfred W. Chittenden. 1988. *The Harrison-Chehalis Challenge. A Brief History of the Forest Industry Around Harrison Lake and the Chehalis Valley.* Treeline Publishing, Harrison Hot Springs, B.C.

McCulloch, Walter F. 1977. *Woods Words. A Comprehensive Dictionary of Logging Terms.* The Oregon Historical Society, (O.S.U. Book Stores, Inc.), Corvallis, OR.

Mitchell, Helen A. 1966. *Diamond in the Rough. A History of Campbell River.* Published by the Author, Campbell River, B.C.

Muralt, Darryl E. 1985. *Steel Rails & Silver Dreams. A History of the Dolly Varden Mines and the Narrow Gauge Dolly Varden Mines Railway.* Benchmark Publications, Ltd., Los Altos, CA.

———. 1982. "The Canadian Robert Dollar Company." *Callboard* (publication of the British Columbia Railway Historical Association), Vol. 5, No. 1, May 1982, pp. 11-20.

Pacific Inspection Bureau, Inc. 1929. *Grading Rules and Basic Schedule of Douglas Fir, Pacific Hemlock, Sitka Spruce and Western Red Cedar Lumber for Export Shipment.* Seattle, WA.

Powell River News Ltd., The. 1960. *Powell River's First 50 Years.* Powell River, B.C.

Prouty, Andrew Mason. 1985. *More Deadly Than War! Pacific Coast Logging 1827-1981.* Garland Publishing, Inc., New York, NY.

Ramsey, Gordon S. 1984. *The Shay Geared Locomotive. Alphabetical List of All*

Known Owners in the U.S. and Canada. Published by the Author, Pasadena, CA.

Ranger, Dan (Jr.). 1964. *Pacific Coast Shay.* Golden West Books, San Marino, CA.

Rees-Thomas, David M. 1979. *Timber Down the Capilano. A History of the Capilano Timber Company of Vancouver's North Shore.* The British Columbia Railway Historical Association, Victoria, B.C.

Rushton, Gerald. 1974. *Whistle Up the Inlet. The Union Steamship Story.* J. J. Douglas Ltd., Vancouver, B.C.

Sanford, Barrie. 1977. *McCulloch's Wonder. The Story of the Kettle Valley Railway.* Whitecap Books, Ltd., Vancouver, B.C.

———. 1981. *The Pictorial History of Railroading in British Columbia.* Whitecap Books, Ltd., Vancouver, B.C.

Seattle Car and Foundry Co. (Designers and Builders of Railroad and Logging Equipment). 1913. *Catalogue No. 503.* Seattle, WA.

Sloan, Chief Justice Gordon McG. 1945. *Report of the Commissioner Relating to the Forest Industries of British Columbia.* King's Printer, Victoria, B.C.

———. 1956. *The Forest Resources of British Columbia.* Queen's Printer, Victoria, B.C.

———. 1957. *Report of the Commissioner Relating to the Forest Industries of British Columbia.* Queen's Printer, Victoria, B.C.

Swanson, Robert E. 1960. *A History of Railroad Logging.* Dept. of Commercial Transport, Railways Branch, Victoria, B.C.

Taber, Thomas T. and Walter Casler. 1960. *Climax: An Unusual Locomotive.* Railroadians of America, Morristown, NJ.

Taylor, Geoffrey W. 1975. *Timber.* J. J. Douglas Ltd., North Vancouver, B.C.

Treleaven, G. Fern. 1969. *The Surrey Story.* Surrey Museum and Historical Society, Surrey, B.C.

Turner, Robert D. 1973. *Vancouver Island Railroads.* Golden West Books, San Marino, CA.

———. 1977. *The Pacific Princesses. An Illustrated History of the Canadian Pacific's Princess Fleet on the Northwest Coast.* Sono Nis Press, Victoria, B.C.

———. 1981. *Railroaders. Recollections from the Steam Era in British Columbia.* Sound Heritage Series No. 31, Provincial Archives of British Columbia, Victoria, B.C.

———. 1981. "Logging Railroads and Locomotives in British Columbia: A Background Summary and the Preservation Record," *Material History,* No. 13. History Division, National Museums of Canada, Ottawa, Ont.

———. 1987. *West of the Great Divide. An Illustrated History of the Canadian Pacific Railway in British Columbia 1880-1986.* Sono Nis Press, Victoria, B.C.

Washington Iron Works ("Pioneer Manufacturers, Originators and Specialists in Logging Engines and Equipment"). n.d. *Catalog No. 20.* Seattle, WA.

———. 1932. *Catalogue No. 32.* ("A Selected List of the Finest Modern Logging Equipment"). Seattle, WA.

Wentz, Walt. 1983. *Bringing Out the Big Ones. Log Trucks in Oregon 1912-1983.* Oregon Forest Products Transportation Association, Salem, OR.

Westminster Iron Works Company Limited. 1944. *Westminster Iron Works, Steel Products, 70th Anniversary.* New Westminster, B.C.

White, Elwood and David Wilkie. 1963. *Shays on the Switchbacks. A History of the Lenora, Mt. Sicker Railway.* British Columbia Railway Historical Association, Victoria, B.C.

Whitford, H. H. and R. D. Craig. 1918. *Forests of British Columbia.* Commission of Conservation, Canada, Ottawa, Ont.

Willamette Iron and Steel Works. n.d. *Canadian Willamette Company, Ltd., Builders in Canada of Willamette Logging Engines, Vancouver, B.C.* (Catalogue of Equipment). Portland, OR.

Wren, James A. and Genevieve J. Wren. 1979. *Motor Trucks of America.* University of Michigan Press, Ann Arbor, MI.

Young, Cameron. 1985. *The Forests of British Columbia.* Whitecap Books, North Vancouver, B.C.

Note on Metric Conversion of Board Feet: During the railroad logging era, the board foot was the standard unit of measure for lumber and timber. Metric conversions in the text are a simple conversion of the standard board foot (1 ft × 1 ft × 1 in). This is accurate for unfinished lumber. While subject to great variation, the scaling of logs usually took into account wastage in processing logs to lumber. This wastage could equal the amount of lumber produced. Modern metric measures of timber are not equivalent to those shown as they are based on different standards and measuring procedures and indicate the volume of fibre in the log. See: Austin Cary. 1932. *Woodsman's Manual.* Harvard University Press, Cambridge, Mass.; Nelson C. Brown. 1937. *Timber Products & Industries.* John Wiley & Sons, Inc., New York; and B.C. Lumber Manufacturers Association. 1948. *Lumber Tallying & Shipping.* Vancouver, B.C.

Island Logging Company's No. 2 Shay, built in 1923, featured a substantial spark arrester on its stack. Ads in the *B.C. Lumberman* featured the engine as one of the "latest" Shays in British Columbia. Tyee Machinery Co. of Vancouver was the agent for the Hofius Steel Equipment Co. of Seattle which was the Lima Locomotive Works Shay representative in Washington.

—*B.C. LUMBERMAN*

Page number references in italics indicate an illustration. Locomotives are individually indexed for larger companies only.

INDEX

323

325